100 Questions & Answers About Kidney Dialysis

Lawrence E. Stam, MD
New York Methodist Hospital
The Rogosin Institute

JONES AND BARTLETT PUBLISHERS
Sudbury, Massachusetts
BOSTON   TORONTO   LONDON   SINGAPORE

World Headquarters

Jones and Bartlett Publishers
40 Tall Pine Drive
Sudbury, MA 01776
978-443-5000
info@jbpub.com
www.jbpub.com

Jones and Bartlett Publishers
Canada
6339 Ormindale Way
Mississauga, Ontario L5V 1J2
Canada

Jones and Bartlett Publishers
International
Barb House, Barb Mews
London W6 7PA
United Kingdom

Jones and Bartlett's books and products are available through most bookstores and online booksellers. To contact Jones and Bartlett Publishers directly, call 800-832-0034, fax 978-443-8000, or visit our website, www.jbpub.com.

Substantial discounts on bulk quantities of Jones and Bartlett's publications are available to corporations, professional associations, and other qualified organizations. For details and specific discount information, contact the special sales department at Jones and Bartlett via the above contact information or send an email to specialsales@jbpub.com.

The authors, editor, and publisher have made every effort to provide accurate information. However, they are not responsible for errors, omissions, or for any outcomes related to the use of the contents of this book and take no responsibility for the use of the products and procedures described. Treatments and side effects described in this book may not be applicable to all people; likewise, some people may require a dose or experience a side effect that is not described herein. Drugs and medical devices are discussed that may have limited availability controlled by the Food and Drug Administration (FDA) for use only in a research study or clinical trial. Research, clinical practice, and government regulations often change the accepted standard in this field. When consideration is being given to use of any drug in the clinical setting, the healthcare provider or reader is responsible for determining FDA status of the drug, reading the package insert, and reviewing prescribing information for the most up-to-date recommendations on dose, precautions, and contraindications, and determining the appropriate usage for the product. This is especially important in the case of drugs that are new or seldom used.

Production Credits
Executive Publisher: Christopher Davis
Senior Editorial Assistant: Jessica Acox
Production Director: Amy Rose
Production Editors: Rachel Rossi/Laura Almozara
Manufacturing and Inventory Supervisor: Amy Bacus
Composition: Paw Print Media
Cover Design: Carolyn Downer
Cover Images: Top left photo: © Carme Balcells/ShutterStock, Inc.; Top right photo: © Monkey Business Images/ShutterStock, Inc.; Middle photo: © Daniel Mirer/New York Methodist Hospital; Bottom photo: © iofotopub/ShutterStock, Inc.
Printing and Binding: Malloy, Inc.
Cover Printing: Malloy, Inc.

Library of Congress Cataloging-in-Publication Data
Stam, Lawrence E.
    100 questions and answers about kidney dialysis / Lawrence E. Stam.
        p. cm.
    Includes bibliographical references.
    ISBN-13: 978-0-7637-5417-4 (alk. paper)
    ISBN-10: 0-7637-5417-X
    1. Hemodialysis—Popular works. I. Title. II. Title: One hundred questions and answers about kidney dialysis.
    RC901.7.H45S67 2010
    617.4'61059—dc22

                                        2008052442

6048

Printed in the United States of America
13 12 11 10 09   10 9 8 7 6 5 4 3 2

To my wife Claudia, the great love of my life now and always.

Contents

All of us know someone with kidney disease. Many of us have a friend or a family member on dialysis. This is because the number of people in the United States and the developing world with kidney disease is growing rapidly. In 2006 in the United States, 500,000 patients received some form of end-stage renal disease therapy. The Medicare cost to treat kidney disease was $23 billion.

Patients with kidney disease get a great deal of advice from well-meaning friends and family members. They are encouraged to drink more fluids to flush out the kidneys or to drink cranberry juice. Much of this advice is wrong.

The most common reaction to learning that one has kidney disease is fear. Patients are afraid of dying, of suffering pain and disability, and of the unknown impact that kidney disease and dialysis will have on their lives.

100 Questions & Answers About Kidney Dialysis is a user-friendly guide to kidney disease and dialysis. It gives basic information about kidney disease in language that is comprehensible to people without a scientific or healthcare background. It will help patients who are facing dialysis treatments learn what to expect and help prepare them for beginning dialysis treatments. The book's candid treatment of difficult questions such as "How long can I live on dialysis?" is designed to encourage patients to discuss important and difficult issues with their doctors and families. The more knowledge a patient has about kidney disease, the less fear he or she will have about starting treatment.

Dialysis was one of the most significant medical achievements of the twentieth century. Dialysis is life sustaining and improves the quality of patients' lives. It is important to remember that dialysis treatments have only been available to large numbers of patients for the past 40 years. The forces of globalization and economic development are bringing dialysis treatments to more patients and to areas of the world where dialysis has not been available before. The continued improvement in dialysis machines, dialysis membranes, new medications, and our understanding of kidney failure will result in significant improvement in dialysis treatments during the twenty-first century.

Acknowledgments

The process of writing *100 Questions & Answers About Kidney Dialysis* involved continuing conversations with several patients receiving dialysis treatments at the Rogosin Brooklyn Dialysis Unit, located at the New York Methodist Hospital in Brooklyn, New York. These conversations were invaluable in looking at kidney disease in new ways and developing creative strategies to face dialysis treatments. I would especially like to thank Erick Lucero, Henry Spellman, George Garcia, and Yoshi Reynolds for their hard work on this book. Staff members at the Rogosin Brooklyn Dialysis Unit helped provide expert information in their fields. Robin Grande, LMSW; Lisa Modica, RD, CDN; Ellen DeMarco, RN, MSN, MBA; Vera Auerbach; and Kotresha Neelakantappa, MD, all worked hard to make this book possible. Thank you Roxanna Bologa, MD, for your guidance on peritoneal dialysis. My wife Claudia S. Plottel, MD, gave me constant support, encouragement, and technical assistance.

PART ONE

The Basics

What do the kidneys do?

Where are the kidneys located?

Can kidney disease be inherited?

More . . .

1. What do the kidneys do?

Kidneys

Two fist-sized organs located in the posterior upper abdomen that maintain fluid and salt balance and detoxify the blood by eliminating toxins and poisons from the body in the urine.

The **kidneys** are a pair of internal organs that are each the size of a fist. They are composed of several different types of tissues including blood vessels, tubules, and supporting structures. The purpose of the large blood vessels is to carry blood to and from the kidney. Smaller blood vessels, called capillaries, filter the blood of water, salts, toxins, and medications. Once the blood is filtered, kidney tubules can reabsorb or secrete water, salts, or other substances based upon the needs of our body. On a very hot day, we can reabsorb much of the filtered water and salt to prevent dehydration. If we overeat and drink at a holiday party, our kidneys can eliminate extra water and salt to prevent us from becoming overloaded. Fluid and salt in the urine are carried by a collecting system resembling a funnel to tubes called the ureters. The ureters carry the urine to the bladder where it can be stored until a convenient time for us to urinate.

Erythropoietin

A hormone produced by the kidneys that signals the bone marrow to produce more red blood cells. In kidney disease, less erythropoietin is produced and anemia can occur. Erythropoietin can be given by injection to treat anemia.

In addition to the elimination process, there are cells in the kidney that make protein messengers called hormones. One of these hormones, **erythropoietin**, tells our bone marrow to make more red blood cells. Other cells store energy from the carbohydrates in the food we eat in the form of a polysaccharide called **glycogen**. Some kidney cells break down medications we take such as antibiotics and insulin to remove them from our bodies, which prevents us from accumulating too much medication. Many of the jobs our kidneys perform for us are unknown and are just now being discovered by scientists.

Glycogen

A polysaccharide composed of glucose, which is the principal storage unit of carbohydrates in the body.

2. Where are the kidneys located?

Most people have two functioning kidneys. They are located in the abdomen in the lumbar region of the back, right under the lungs (**Figure 1**). They are partially protected by the rib cage. Occasionally a person can be born with one kidney or one normal kidney and another that is small and not working. Another condition, known as **horseshoe kidney**, occurs when a person is born with a single large kidney. Most of the time people with one kidney or a horseshoe kidney have no symptoms. Patients who have a horseshoe kidney or a single kidney are often discovered when **ultrasound** or **computed axial tomography (CT)** scans are done for

Horseshoe kidney
A medical condition in which the right and left kidneys are fused at the upper or lower pole. Ninety percent of horseshoe kidneys are fused at the lower pole. The horseshoe kidney is capable of normal kidney function and is usually found when a CT scan or ultrasound (sonogram) is performed for abdominal pain or other symptoms. Patients with a horseshoe kidney are not predisposed to kidney disease.

Ultrasound
An ultrasound, also known as a sonogram, is a diagnostic test that bounces sound waves off internal organs, such as the kidneys, to obtain a picture of them.

Computed axial tomography (CT)
A computer generated three-dimensional x-ray picture of part of the body used for the diagnosis of disease. It is sometimes called a CT scan.

Figure 1   Kidney location

Source: Robert K. Clark, *Anatomy and Physiology: Understanding the Human Body.* ©2005, Jones and Bartlett LLC.

other reasons. Many times when we have pain in our back, we think it is due to a kidney problem. More likely, back pain is caused by muscle strain or spasm, or a vertebral disc problem. Pain in the back that radiates to the side or into the groin can be due to a kidney stone.

3. What is the glomerulus?

The kidneys are composed of about two million functional units called nephrons. A nephron is composed of a glomerulus, kidney tubules, and blood vessels. A **glomerulus** can be thought of as a small filter. It is made up of small blood vessels called capillaries. Blood comes to the glomerulus from larger blood vessels

Glomerulus

The part of the kidney composed of small blood vessels that filters the blood to produce urine.

Renal pyramid

Renal cortex

Renal medulla

Renal pelvis (collects urine)

Renal capsule (peeled back)

Ureter (carries urine to bladder)

Figure 1 cont'd.

Source: Robert K. Clark, *Anatomy and Physiology: Understanding the Human Body.* ©2005, Jones and Bartlett LLC.

called the renal arteries, which then branch into smaller and smaller blood vessels until they meet the glomeruli, which are one cell thick (**Figure 2**). Fluid, salts, sugars, and small substances can pass through the thin wall of the glomerulus, but larger substances such as proteins, red blood cells, and white blood cells are too big to be filtered. If the glomerulus is damaged, proteins or blood cells can find their way through the glomerulus and into the urine. This problem can be discovered by having a test called a urine analysis, which can be done at any medical laboratory. Often the first sign of kidney problems is discovered because a routine urine analysis done for a yearly physical, an application for life insurance, or for an employment physical contains protein or blood.

We can live a normal life with a reduced number of glomeruli. People who have a kidney removed surgi-

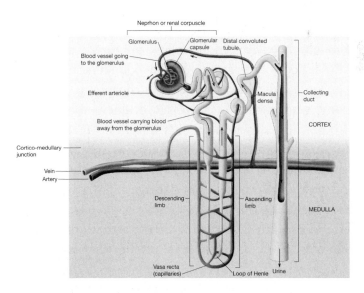

Figure 2   The functioning units of the kidney

Source: Robert K. Clark, *Anatomy and Physiology: Understanding the Human Body.* ©2005, Jones and Bartlett LLC.

Hypertrophy

An increase in the size of the kidney.

Diabetes

A disease characterized by an elevation of the glucose level in the blood. This can be caused by a decrease in insulin production by the pancreas or a defect in the insulin receptor.

Lupus erythematosus

A disease in which the body's immune system attacks its own organs. Also called systemic lupus erythematosus (SLE).

Sickle cell anemia

An inherited anemia that results in red blood cells forming a crescent shape. Sickle cells block small vessels and can result in injury to the bones, heart, lungs, and kidneys.

Atherosclerosis

A disease process that involves deposition of cholesterol in the walls of arteries, causing narrowing of the arteries. This can cause blood to clot, further reducing blood flow.

cally to donate for kidney transplantation have half the number of glomeruli. Over a period of time, the remaining glomeruli enlarge or **hypertrophy** and are able to increase their function.

As we age, out glomeruli normally decrease in number due to scarring. This is a silent process without symptoms and signs, and is often overlooked even by doctors.

4. What can damage the kidneys?

Hundreds of things can damage the kidneys. The most common medical problem that causes damage to the kidneys is uncontrolled **diabetes**. When a diabetic has a high blood glucose, this causes an enlargement of a part of the cell wall of the glomerular capillary filter called the basement membrane. Capillaries and other cells begin to enlarge. This leads to scarring or sclerosis of the glomerulus and results in the glomerulus becoming a damaged filter. Proteins from the blood can leak through the damaged filter and appear in the urine. This leakage can lead to further kidney scarring and damage. High blood pressure can contribute to further glomerular scarring and damage. Kidney problems can also be caused by urinary tract infections, medications, surgical procedures, kidney stones, as well as certain types of cancer. Diseases such as **lupus erythematosus** and **sickle cell anemia** can damage many parts of the body including the kidneys. Smoking and elevated cholesterol can cause hardening of the arteries or **atherosclerosis** to occur in the renal arteries that supply the kidneys with blood. **HIV** infection causes kidney problems in some patients. In many patients, multiple problems have contributed to kidney damage. The earlier we are aware of these problems, the better chance we will have of preventing kidney damage.

5. Can kidney disease be inherited?

Our parents have a tremendous influence upon our future health. We inherit one copy of each of our genes from each parent. The most common form of inherited kidney disease is **autosomal dominant polycystic kidney disease (ADPKD)**. In this disease, we only have to inherit one defective gene from either our father or mother. Most, but not all, people who inherit the gene develop some form of renal disease, which can be mild or severe. The gene causes our kidneys to form multiple cysts that increase in number and size over time. Scientists have found the location of two genes for polycystic kidney disease, one of which is on chromosome 16 called the *APCKD1* gene. This gene accounts for 90% of all cases of ADPKD. It can be diagnosed before birth. Another gene, *APCKD2*, has been found on chromosome 4. Screening for cysts is best done after 30 years of age with a kidney sonogram test, which can detect the cysts. An example of a disease where we need defective genes from both our parents is sickle cell anemia. This genetic disorder is most common in black patients, but can be seen in people of Italian, Indian, Hispanic, and other origins. About 5% of patients with sickle cell anemia will develop severe kidney problems. Diseases such as diabetes, hypertension, systemic lupus erythematosus, and kidney stones are more common in patients with parents who have these disorders. Most importantly, our parents are role models for our own lifestyles and behaviors. If our parents smoke cigarettes, we are much more likely to smoke ourselves. An overweight parent is more likely

HIV

The etiologic virus in HIV/AIDS infection. HIV can be transmitted through blood transfusion, intravenous drug use, sexual activity, and through a needle stick. HIV cannot be transmitted during dialysis treatments.

Autosomal dominant polycystic kidney disease (ADPKD)

The most common form of inherited kidney disease. Patients inherit the gene from either parent and many cysts form in the kidneys.

to have overweight children. This being said, we are not our parents. Many people are not affected by their genetic heritage. As medical science improves, new medications for diseases make the prognosis for young people with inherited diseases much better than that of their parents.

6. How do I know I have kidney disease?

Kidney disease sneaks up on us. If we develop chest pain, we immediately think of the heart. Cough, fever, and shortness of breath would cause many of us to seek medical attention for pneumonia. Most patients with kidney disease are asymptomatic in the early stages. Swelling of the legs, high blood pressure, blood in the urine, foaming of the urine, or a family history of kidney disease cause some people to be tested for kidney problems. The search for kidney disease begins with a visit to your doctor. He or she may be a family practitioner, internist, pediatrician, or gynecologist. A detailed history will be taken and a complete physical examination performed. The initial tests to screen for kidney disease include a complete blood count, a **blood urea nitrogen (BUN)**, **serum creatinine**, and **urine analysis**. If all these tests are normal, probably no significant renal disease is present. In diabetic patients, a urine test for **microalbumin** can detect very small amounts of albumen. A positive test can predict who has a high chance of developing kidney disease and who would benefit from early aggressive treatment. Other tests include a 24-hour urine collection for protein and creatinine clearance to accurately measure renal function. A kidney sonogram or sound-wave test is a safe way of looking for blockages of the

---

Blood urea nitrogen (BUN)

A common blood test used to screen patients for kidney disease. An elevated BUN can indicate decreased kidney function.

Serum creatinine

A blood test used to screen patients for kidney disease. Creatinine is a breakdown product of muscle. When the kidney function is decreased, the kidneys filter less creatinine and the serum creatinine level rises.

Urine analysis

A common screening test that looks for the presence of protein, glucose, and cells in the urine. It can help determine if further tests for kidney disease are indicated.

Microalbumin

A test designed to detect very small elevated amounts of the protein albumin in the urine that are not able to be detected by a routine urine analysis.

kidney due to kidney stones, prostate problems, or cysts of the kidney. If these tests are positive, your doctor may refer you to a kidney specialist. This specialist may be a medical kidney doctor, called a nephrologist, or a urologist, who is a surgeon who specializes in diseases of the kidneys, bladder, and prostate. The specialist has seen many different kinds of kidney problems. He or she can answer many of your questions and may want to obtain further testing to give you a specific diagnosis of the cause of your problem.

Kidney disease sneaks up on us. Most patients with kidney disease are asymptomatic in the early stages.

7. How common is kidney disease?

Kidney disease is becoming more and more common. This is in part due to our increased lifespan. Due to many advances is public health measures as well as medical treatments for heart disease, hypertension, and diabetes, we are living longer and more productive lives. When I began my education in medical school in the 1970s, it was very special to see a patient in the hospital who was 100 years old. Now it is much more common. As we live longer, the chance that we will develop disease processes that will affect our kidneys goes up. It is estimated that in patients in the Medicare system in 2004 over the age of 75 years, one million people had chronic kidney disease. In the 65- to 74-year-old age range, 600,000 people suffered from chronic kidney disease. In 2004 an additional 335,963 people were receiving **dialysis** treatments. The numbers are much higher today (about 500,000 patients) because kidney disease is growing at a rapid rate. This is partly due to the rapid increase of new patients with diabetes. As we become more affluent, we have more choices of both type and quantity of food. We are less likely to walk or to engage in physical

Dialysis

A scientific term for the movement of substances across a membrane by a process called diffusion.

activity. We are getting larger. As our weight increases, we increase our chance of developing diabetes. As a result, the number of diabetics in the population has soared. It is estimated that there are over 21 million diabetics in the United States. Because diabetes is the number one cause of kidney disease in industrialized societies, the number of people with kidney disease is increasing rapidly.

Our awareness of kidney disease is also growing. We are more likely to go to the doctor for a routine checkup than our parents. Once we are at the doctor, there is a good chance that blood and urine tests will be ordered. We are targeting those at high risk for kidney disease for screening. Finally, well-known personalities in the media or sports fields, such as Art Buchwald and Alonzo Mourning, have publicly discussed receiving dialysis treatments and a kidney transplant. We have become more knowledgeable about kidney disease and more willing to discuss it with our family and friends. This communication has led us to a better understanding of kidney disease and the need to take it seriously.

8. Can kidney disease be prevented by diet?

Special diets for the treatment of kidney disease have been available for many years. Before dialysis and modern medications were available, the only available treatment for kidney disease was a special diet. People with kidney disease were placed on low-protein diets in the hope that the progression of kidney disease would be slowed. In addition, intake of salt, potassium, phosphorus, and fluid was restricted. People on these diets could live longer, but the quality of their life was poor. They often became malnourished. In the 1980s, studies were conducted on rats with renal disease. Rats placed on low-protein diets showed a dramatic improvement in their survival compared to rats on high-protein diets. This resulted in a great deal of enthusiasm for protein restriction in the diet. Our normal diet in the United States is heavily weighted toward high-protein foods such as meat, fish, poultry, and milk products. Unfortunately, studies in people on low-protein diets were not as conclusive as the studies in rats. Many doctors still recommend a modest restriction in protein intake in patients with kidney disease.

Many patients believe that cranberry juice can be helpful for kidney disease. This idea comes from the ability of fresh cranberry juice to acidify the urine, which can be helpful in urinary tract infection. Patients with urinary tract infection are treated with antibiotics, which are far superior to cranberry juice. Most people with kidney disease will get no benefit from cranberry juice, but it sure tastes good.

Because so many people with kidney disease suffer from hypertension, it is important to consider a low-salt diet. A low-fat diet is important in people with an elevated cholesterol or triglyceride level because vascular disease occurs often in people with kidney disease. Patients with diabetes require special diets.

There is a great deal of information available in books, in magazines, and on the Internet about diet. Many supplements are available. It is extremely important that professional advice be obtained before going on any diet. Only a health professional can look at your individual case, review your blood tests and medical history, and determine if a particular diet is right for you. Many people have spent years on restrictive diets only to dis-

Advice that is good in general can be the worst advice for a specific person.

cover that the diet has been of no benefit or, worse, harmful to their medical condition. Advice that is good in general can be the worst advice for a specific person.

9. What medications can prevent my kidneys from getting worse?

The first medications proven to delay the progression of kidney disease are a class of medications called **angiotensin-converting enzyme inhibitors** (**Table 1**). Doctors and other medical professionals call them ACE inhibitors for short. These medications work by blocking an enzyme that activates a protein called **angiotensin**. ACE inhibitors decrease blood flow to the glomeruli. This decrease in blood flow will prevent scarring of the glomerulus and surrounding tissues. ACE inhibitors lower blood pressure. They are most often taken once or twice a day. They help prevent hardening of the arteries, or atherosclerosis. ACE inhibitors are also helpful in preventing heart attacks and in the treatment of congestive heart failure.

Table 1 Common ACE Inhibitors

Brand Name	Generic Name
Aceon	perindopril erbumine
Altace	ramipril
Capoten	captopril
Lotensin	benazepril hydrochloride
Mavik	trandolapril
Prinivil	lisinopril
Univasc	moexipril hydrochloride
Vasotec	enalapril

ACE inhibitors have three major side effects. Cough can occur in 3% to 8% of patients, depending on the study. The cough goes away when the ACE inhibitor is stopped. Skin rash is an uncommon side effect. More severe allergic reactions causing swelling of the face or lips are uncommon. This is called **angioedema** and must be recognized and treated immediately by your doctor. ACE inhibitors can cause an elevation in the potassium level. Potassium is an element in the blood and body. Too high or too low a potassium level can affect the function of the heart. Blood tests will be needed after you start ACE inhibitor medication and afterward on a regular basis to watch your potassium level. If your potassium level is too high, your doctor or healthcare professional may recommend that you decrease your intake of potassium-rich foods. He or she may place you on a potassium-lowering medication called Kayexalate to bind the potassium in your gastrointestinal tract. If your potassium is still too high, you may be told to stop taking your ACE inhibitor. In rare cases, your kidney function may get worse on ACE inhibitors. This is more common in people who have vascular disease or who are dehydrated. Regular blood tests can help your doctor or healthcare professional identify this problem, which will improve after the ACE inhibitor is stopped.

A second and newer class of medications proven to prevent kidney disease from getting worse is **angiotensin receptor blockers**, or **ARBs (Table 2)**. Like ACE inhibitors, these medications are taken orally, lower blood pressure, and help protect the heart. They can raise potassium, cause rashes, and worsen kidney function but they do not cause cough. Because ARBs are newer med-

The Basics

Angioedema

A serious allergic reaction characterized by swelling of a body part, often the face or lips.

Angiotensin receptor blockers (ARBs)

A class of medications that has similar properties to ACE inhibitors. ARBs can treat high blood pressure, stabilize kidney disease, decrease protein in the urine, and treat congestive heart failure.

Table 2   Common Angiotensin Receptor Blockers (ARBs)

Brand Name	Generic Name
Atacand	candesartan cilexetil
Avapro	irbesartan
Benicar	olmesartan medoxomil
Cozaar	losartan potassium
Diovan	valsartan
Micardis	telmisartan
Teveten	eprosartan mesylate

ications, they are more expensive; low-cost generic versions of these drugs are just becoming available.

Many advertisements by drug companies encourage the belief that their ACE inhibitor or ARB is better than all the others. They will list multiple advantages and often feature smiling models posing as patients or doctors testifying to the superiority of their medication and low number of side effects. It is too early to tell if ACE inhibitors or ARBs are better. Medical research may help decide this question. Time will tell. Some kidney doctors (nephrologists) will use ACE inhibitors and ARBs together. If this is done, the patient must come for blood tests and frequent visits to prevent complications.

Other medications may be helpful in stabilizing kidney function. Additional medications to control blood pressure and cholesterol are commonly needed. Patients with diabetes must pay special attention to optimize their medication to control their blood sugar level.

10. What alternative medicine treatments are available for kidney disease?

Alternative medicine treatments are very popular topics in the media and often are the first thought when we are confronted with medical illness. The advantage of alternative therapies is that they are thought to be less toxic than conventional medical treatments. They are often derived from plants, fungi, minerals, or other substances found in nature. In reality, the separation of alternative and traditional medicine is an artificial distinction. The first physicians often grew medical herbs in their gardens. In the modern era, cyclosporine, a product of a fungus, revolutionized kidney transplantation. This is almost never mentioned as an alternative treatment. Physicians interested in kidney diseases have been intrigued with omega-3 fatty acids found in fish oils. They have been used to treat high cholesterol as well as a kidney disease called **IgA nephropathy**. We are all looking for the next new miracle drug. Hopefully, this new treatment will be natural, nontoxic, and will have few side effects. Because of the great interest in alternative medical treatments, the US National Institutes of Health established the National Center for Complementary and Alternative Medicine in 1998. This center will be supervising much-needed scientific research on complementary and alternative medical treatments to see which are effective. For more information, their Web site can be located at *http://nccam.nih.gov.*

I am often brought advertisements for vitamins or dietary supplements by patients who are interested in alternative medical treatments. Some of them contain

The Basics

Alternative medicine

A medical discipline that uses natural products and diet to treat medical illness.

IgA nephropathy

A disease of the kidney that often presents with blood and protein in the urine. The immunoglobulin IgA is seen in the kidney on biopsy.

It is best to get expert medical advice from a medical professional who is experienced in working with kidney and dialysis patients before taking vitamins or alternative treatments.

potassium, magnesium, or other substances that may not be safe for that particular individual. It is best to get expert medical advice from a medical professional who is experienced in working with kidney and dialysis patients before taking vitamins or alternative treatments.

11. How can I stabilize my kidney function and stay off dialysis?

Sonograms

Medical tests in which sound waves are used to obtain pictures of organs in the body. A kidney sonogram requires no injections of substances or exposure to radiation. Also known as an ultrasound.

Immunosuppressive therapy

Immunosuppressive therapy works by suppressing the activity of the cells and antibodies of the immune system. In the treatment of some kidney diseases, immunosuppressive medicines are given intravenously or orally to decrease the immune response. Kidney transplant patients also need immunosuppressive medications to prevent rejection of the transplant.

Many patients feel devastated when diagnosed with a kidney disease. Thinking that the problem is hopeless and that one's life is over is very common. In reality, kidney disease has good treatment options at all stages. Treatment is widely available and is not experimental but proven to be effective. The first step is to look for reversible causes of kidney disease. Medications that cause kidney disease need to be stopped. Tests to look for blockages of the kidney such as **sonograms** need to be considered. The accurate diagnosis of the cause of kidney disease by kidney biopsy can determine if the patient is a candidate for **immunosuppressive therapy** with a variety of medications. Immunosuppressive medications that are available include steroids, cyclosporine, cyclophosphamide, and others. In most kidney diseases, ACE inhibitors and ARBs can delay the deterioration of renal function. Diet and control of blood pressure, blood sugar, and cholesterol are all important. In many cases, kidney disease can be stabilized and patients can be managed without renal replacement therapy.

Erick Lucero writes:

I found out I had kidney disease by going to my regular doctor. He found that I had an elevated creatinine level in my blood and high blood pressure. I was referred to a nephrologist. The nephrologist performed a complete physical exam, sent me for a sonogram of the kidneys, and had me collect my urine for 24 hours. After these tests, I went for a kidney biopsy. The biopsy stung for a few seconds but was not that bad. I was told that both my kidneys were diseased by something called focal segmental glomerular sclerosis. This disease was causing scarring of the kidneys and was causing my high blood pressure. I took blood pressure medication and a medication called cyclosporine to help prevent the scarring of my kidneys. I had a scary feeling about my future. I knew that dialysis would take a lot of time and effort. I didn't want to accept that I had a kidney problem. My medications were very expensive. Once, I didn't take my medications for three weeks because I reached my maximum yearly benefit from my insurance and I couldn't afford them. I had to wait until the end of December when the new year started and my insurance would pay for the medication again. It was hard to keep my diet.

Despite my kidney disease, I worked full time. I was often tired and sad. My girlfriend gave me good support. In March of 2006, we got married. She was never put off by my kidney disease and encouraged me. When I was sad, she was sad. My wife became pregnant, and we have a beautiful little girl. My daughter helped take my mind off my problems.

It was 2 years from the time I learned that I had kidney disease to the time I started dialysis. I stopped drinking alcohol because I figured that if I had one organ damaged, I needed to keep the rest of my body as healthy as possible. To stay off dialysis you have to stay away from salt and potassium and keep your diet. Take your medications. Try and work with your doctor. The better you are at taking your medications and keeping your diet, the longer you will stay off dialysis.

PART TWO

Dialysis

What is dialysis?

Can children be treated with dialysis?

What will happen if I skip a dialysis treatment?

More . . .

12. What is dialysis?

Dialysis is a scientific term for the movement of substances across a membrane by a process called diffusion. If a great deal of a substance is in one place, some of that substance will tend to move out to where the substance is not present. If we gently add a teaspoon of milk to a cup of tea, the milk will diffuse out with time to all areas of the cup. In dialysis, we add a barrier or membrane between two liquids. On one side of the membrane is a liquid with a high concentration of a substance. On the other side of the membrane is a liquid without that substance. If the membrane has small holes or pores, the substance on one side of the membrane will travel or diffuse across the membrane to the other side until the amount on each side is equal. Dialysis membranes are said to be semipermeable. They allow some small substances to pass through while large substances cannot fit through the holes.

In medical dialysis treatments, one liquid is a patient's blood. On the other side of the semipermeable membrane, is another liquid called **dialysate**. Substances in the blood, if they are small enough, will move through the membrane into the dialysate. If the dialysate is then discarded and new dialysate is added, more of the substance can be removed. Removal of substances depends on the size of the substance, the electrical charge of the substance, and also the difference in the amount of the substance on one side of the membrane compared to the other.

If we change the amount of substances in the dialysate, we can remove more or less of a substance. We can even add more of a substance to the dialysate than is in the blood. In this instance, the substance will move

Dialysate

A fluid containing sodium, calcium, bicarbonate, and other substances that is used to remove toxins and poisons during dialysis. Different dialysate solutions are used in hemodialysis and peritoneal dialysis.

from the dialysate into the patient's blood. This can be done with substances that can pass through the semi-permeable membrane. If we put a high concentration of the sugar glucose in the dialysate, it will move or diffuse across the membrane into the blood and raise the level of glucose in the blood.

Dialysis sounds complicated, but it all boils down to the process of diffusion. Large things such as red blood cells, large proteins, and other large substances are trapped on one side of the membrane in the blood. Small things including salts such as sodium and potassium, water, and small proteins can freely move across the membrane from areas where large amounts are present to areas where they are not present.

13. When was dialysis invented?

The first time dialysis is mentioned in scientific literature was by Thomas Graham, a Scottish chemist, who wrote about dialysis in 1854. He used an ox bladder for his membrane. George Haas, working in Germany in the 1920s, was the first person to use dialysis to treat patients. Most kidney doctors consider Dr. Willem J. Kolff to be the father of modern dialysis. Working in the Netherlands during World War II, Dr. Kolff was caring for war casualties who were dying of kidney failure. He decided to design and build an artificial kidney. Because medical supplies were limited, he obtained his membrane for dialysis from a sausage factory. This sausage skin was made of cellulose acetate. He also used an automobile water pump in his machine. Dr. Kolff was able to treat a 68-year-old woman with kidney failure and maintain her on dialysis until her own kidneys recovered. Dr. Kolff's creativity in building his equipment during wartime, his success in the treatment of the first patient, and his work as a teacher make him a legend and an inspiration to generations of kidney doctors.

14. What is hemodialysis?

Hemodialysis is a medical treatment in which dialysis is used to remove poisons and toxins from a patient's blood. Blood is obtained from the patient with needles and plastic tubing. The blood is then pumped past a semipermeable dialysis membrane. Poisons and toxins that are usually removed by the kidneys pass through the membrane by diffusion into a liquid called dialysate. The dialysate is then discarded along with the toxins. The purified blood is then returned to the patient's body.

Because the patient's blood is outside of the body, a modern dialysis machine has a warmer to keep the blood at body temperature. A blood thinner called **heparin** is given to prevent the blood from clotting in the plastic tubing or when in contact with the dialysis membrane. The hemodialysis machine has safety equipment to determine if the hemodialysis is going well (**Figure 3**). These sensors may sound an alarm to help guide the staff. These alarms do not signify danger to the patient. The modern hemodialysis machine has benefitted greatly from the computer age. The electronic chips and integrated circuits in the dialysis machine make dialysis accurate, safe, and reliable. This has improved the quality of care.

Hemodialysis

A medical treatment in which blood is removed from the patient with needles and plastic tubing and pumped past the dialysis membrane. Poisons and toxins cross the dialysis membrane into the dialysate, which is then discarded, and the blood is returned to the patient.

Heparin

An acid that occurs naturally in the liver and lungs that can be purified and used as a medication to prevent blood from clotting. Heparin is used in hemodialysis to prevent blood from clotting in the plastic tubing and when exposed to the dialysis membrane. It can also be injected into the peritoneal dialysis fluid to prevent clots from blocking the peritoneal dialysis catheter.

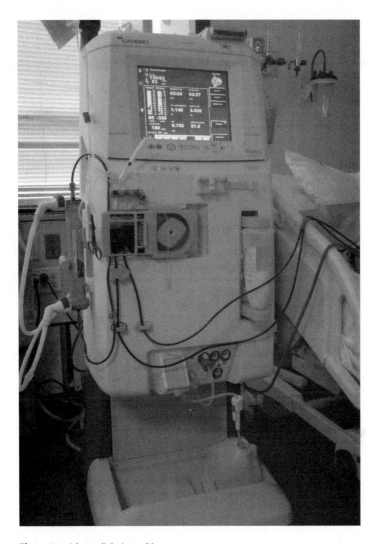

The modern hemodialysis machine has benefitted greatly from the computer age. The electronic chips and integrated circuits in the dialysis machine make dialysis accurate, safe, and reliable.

Dialysis

Figure 3   A hemodialysis machine
Source: K. Neelakantappa, MD

15. What is peritoneal dialysis?

Peritoneal dialysis is a type of dialysis in which a patient's peritoneum is used as the dialysis membrane. The peritoneum is a membrane that covers our intestines inside our abdomen. It is a naturally occurring

Peritoneal dialysis

Dialysis treatments that use the patient's peritoneal membrane in the abdomen as a dialysis membrane to remove toxins and wastes from the body.

membrane. In hemodialysis, an artificial membrane is used. In peritoneal dialysis, we take advantage of the semipermeable qualities of a naturally occurring membrane.

In peritoneal dialysis, a permanent flexible plastic tube is inserted into the abdomen by a physician. This tube is called the peritoneal dialysis catheter. After the tissues around the tube have healed, the tube is used to instill dialysate into the abdomen. The dialysate fluid is allowed to remain in the abdomen for several hours. During this time, poisons and toxins leave the blood vessels of the intestine, pass through the peritoneal membrane, and collect in the dialysate fluid. The dialysate is then drained by gravity through the peritoneal dialysis catheter and collected in a bag. The dialysate fluid containing poisons and toxins can then be discarded into a sink drain or toilet. Another bag of dialysate, usually containing 2 liters of fluid is then infused into the abdomen. Each dialysis drainage and infusion is called an exchange because the fluid is removed and replaced. Patients usually perform four exchanges every day.

The peritoneal dialysis exchanges are initially done by the peritoneal dialysis nurse. The patient on peritoneal dialysis is then trained over a period of weeks to safely perform the dialysis. The exchanges can be done at home, at work, or in any clean, quiet place because no special machine is required. This form of peritoneal dialysis is called **continuous ambulatory peritoneal dialysis**, or **CAPD**. The continuous means that the dialysis will continue throughout the day. Ambulatory refers to the dialysis being done outside of a hospital or medical facility. CAPD is the most popular form of peritoneal dialysis. It is usually done by the person on

Continuous ambulatory peritoneal dialysis (CAPD)

A home dialysis procedure taught to patients who perform their own peritoneal dialysis, CAPD involves the instillation by gravity of dialysate through a catheter into the abdomen. The fluid remains in the abdomen for a time, allowing poisons and toxins to accumulate in the dialysate. The dialysate is then drained and discarded, and fresh dialysate is instilled.

dialysis, but it can also be done by other family members. In the case of children on dialysis, the parents usually perform the dialysis. Elderly patients with many health problems can also have family members perform dialysis. Peritoneal dialysis can also be done at night with the aid of a machine called a **cycler**. This machine is set up before sleep in the patient's bedroom at home. It will then automatically perform the exchanges during the night. This form of peritoneal dialysis is called **continuous cyclical peritoneal dialysis**, or **CCPD**. It allows the patient to be free during the day to work or go to school without performing their exchanges. Family members can also set up the cycler at night without interfering with their daytime activities. Peritoneal dialysis done in a dialysis center is not common but is available in a few dialysis units.

16. Which treatment will be best for me, hemodialysis, peritoneal dialysis, or a kidney transplant?

When faced with kidney disease and the need for renal replacement therapy, most people are overwhelmed. It is difficult to decide which therapy is best. Initially, most patients are treated with hemodialysis at a dialysis center. At the hemodialysis center, the dialysis is performed by the dialysis staff. This allows the patient to get used to the hemodialysis treatment, learn about their diet and medications, and grow stronger. The adjustment to dialysis is both physical and emotional. The dialysis staff will help with this adjustment. Other patients in the dialysis center are able to provide support and advice because they have had to cope with a similar adjustment in the past. Hemodialysis is safe, effective, and well tolerated by most patients. Patients

Cycler

A machine used to automate peritoneal dialysis by performing the exchange of peritoneal dialysis fluid.

Continuous cyclical peritoneal dialysis (CPPD)

A home peritoneal dialysis procedure that uses a cycler to instill and drain fluid into the abdomen. The cycler can perform peritoneal dialysis while the patient is sleeping.

are usually treated three times a week at the same time on Monday, Wednesday, Friday or on Tuesday, Thursday, Saturday. Most dialysis units are closed on Sunday. Treatments are organized in shifts with many patients beginning and ending at about the same time. Patients have 4 days when they do not have hemodialysis treatments. They, however, must keep their diet and take medication 7 days a week.

Patients on peritoneal dialysis start their treatments at a peritoneal dialysis center or unit. The dialysis staff begins the treatment and trains the patients to perform their own dialysis treatment. This training takes several weeks. Most people can learn how to perform the peritoneal dialysis exchanges. Patients usually require 4 exchanges a day, 7 days a week. Because peritoneal dialysis is done 7 days a week, fluid and poisons are removed continuously every day. This continuous treatment allows an increased intake of fluid and a more varied diet. Hemodialysis treatments are typically three times a week. Between hemodialysis treatments, fluid, potassium, salt, and phosphorus intake must be limited. Another advantage of peritoneal dialysis is the ability to vary your dialysis schedule by changing the time or the location of your exchanges. Peritoneal dialysis allows greater flexibility of travel because there is no need to be in a dialysis center or to have a dialysis machine.

Kidney transplantation is a very attractive option for renal replacement therapy because no dialysis is needed. A kidney transplant can come from a family member, a person who is not a blood relative like a spouse or a friend, or from a donor who has died. Most patients need to be treated with some form of dialysis before a kidney transplant can be accomplished. Sometimes a transplant is done before dialysis is needed. Kidney transplant patients must take immunosuppressive medication to prevent rejection of the kidney transplant for as long as the transplant is working.

We are very fortunate to have three good treatments for renal replacement therapy. Many patients start on hemodialysis as an initial therapy. As they become more knowledgeable, they may switch to peritoneal dialysis when they feel capable of performing their own dialysis treatments. Some patients learn to perform home hemodialysis that also requires special training. Many patients on dialysis plan to receive a kidney transplant. Others prefer to remain on dialysis. Transplant recipients facing loss of their transplant from rejection can choose to return to hemodialysis or peritoneal dialysis.

We are very fortunate to have three good treatments for renal replacement therapy.

It is very likely that patients with kidney failure will be treated with more than one kind of treatment modality during their lifetime. The choice of the initial therapy is less important than we tend to think. If we are unhappy with our choice or experience difficulties with one therapy, we can change to another renal replacement therapy.

17. Can children be treated with dialysis?

Children can be treated with hemodialysis or peritoneal dialysis. Between 1995 and 2004, over 7,000 children required renal replacement therapy in the United States. As in adult patients, more children are begun on hemodialysis than on peritoneal dialysis. Kidney transplantation is the preferred treatment in children. This is because children's physical growth is less than normal on dialysis. Three out of four children on dialysis receive a transplant within three years. Transplantation offers the best hope for normal growth and development as well as enabling children to participate in school and athletics. The availability of parents as healthy potential donors makes transplantation a good option. Siblings must be over 18 years of age to donate a kidney.

18. Where will I go for dialysis?

In the early days of dialysis, dialysis units were at major medical centers. As the need for dialysis has grown, many more units have opened. Dialysis has become safer and routine. Instead of being in a hospital, most units are now freestanding. This means they are in the community closer to home. Your dialysis unit may be in a shopping center, may be a separate building, or may be part of an office building. Many of us pass these units every day unaware of their existence. When you walk into a dialysis unit, you will enter a reception area or waiting room. Nearby is the treatment area, which is a large room containing 10 to 20 dialysis stations. Each dialysis station has a dialysis machine, a reclining chair, and usually an individual television set. Many dialysis units have computers for record keeping. The stations are in a line to be easily visible to the dialysis staff. There is a central nursing station with telephones, medications, and other equipment. Close to the treatment area but not visible to patients are rooms to purify water, make dialysate, and service equipment.

More dialysis units have opened in suburban and rural locations. Patients living in a high population area such as a city often have several units close by from which to choose. Units in cities are large, with many able to dialyze 20 or more patients on each dialysis shift. Rural units are smaller and farther apart. When dialysis started, most units were owned by hospitals, single individuals, or not-for-profit organizations. In the 1980s ownership of dialysis units changed. Units owned by hospitals, individuals, and not-for-profit foundations remained about the same. Units run by large chains began to grow. These chains are owned by large public corporations. Some of these corporations also manufacture dialysis machines or equipment. The large size of these chains has enabled them to take advantage of buying larger quantities of supplies and equipment at a lower price, and enabled them to open large numbers of units. The highest concentration of dialysis units is in the eastern half of the country. Areas along the Gulf coast and eastern seaboard have many more units than in the western portion of the United States. How long you need to travel to the dialysis unit will influence your choice of therapy. If it takes you several hours to reach the nearest unit, home dialysis or transplantation would be a definite advantage. Most home dialysis and transplant patients when they are stable visit the dialysis unit or doctor's office once a month for evaluation.

19. Who will perform my dialysis treatments?

With in-center hemodialysis, the dialysis staff will perform your dialysis. The role of the physician is to evaluate the patient, determine the specifics of the dialysis treatment, write dialysis orders, and be available for problems and questions. Other staff include **registered nurses**, **licensed practical nurses**, and

Registered nurse

A healthcare professional who has graduated from a nursing program and passed state qualifying examinations.

Licensed practical nurse

A healthcare professional who has completed a nursing program and passed a licensing exam. An LPN works under the supervision of registered nurses and physicians.

Dialysis technician

A healthcare worker who works in the hemodialysis unit under the supervision of a registered nurse. Dialysis technicians can institute hemodialysis by inserting needles into the access, and can also monitor the dialysis treatment, measure blood pressure, and help educate dialysis patients regarding their treatment, but they are not allowed to administer medication.

Nurse practitioner

A nurse who has received additional training in the diagnosis and treatment of diseases. The nurse practitioner is able to prescribe medication and perform medical procedures.

Physician assistant

A member of the healthcare team who works under the supervision of a physician and diagnoses and manages medical problems.

dialysis technicians. State law determines who can perform which functions in the dialysis unit. In most states, the administration of medications is done by registered nurses. The nurses and technicians connect the patient to the machine and monitor the dialysis treatment. Some units have **nurse practitioners** and **physician assistants** as part of the dialysis staff. **Dietitians** and **social workers** are important members of the dialysis team. Dialysis units have a large support staff. Technicians maintain and service equipment. Housekeeping chores such as taking out the garbage and mopping the floors never end. The clerical staff records treatments, orders supplies, and helps submit insurance claims.

Patients on peritoneal dialysis perform their own dialysis treatments. At first, they will perform their dialysis under the supervision of the dialysis nurse. As the patients become more skilled and comfortable with their dialysis, they will be able to perform it alone without help. This adjustment may take 1 to 2 weeks. They will still need to be carefully followed until they are fully comfortable with the peritoneal dialysis procedure. Patients are also taught to self-administer medications. When the training has been completed, they need to come to the dialysis unit once a month for evaluation by the peritoneal dialysis nurse and physician. The patient is examined by the nurse and physician. Blood tests are obtained every month to monitor the dialysis, and changes in the dialysis prescription may be made. Home hemodialysis patients usually come to the dialysis unit every month. Home visits are useful to help optimize the dialysis treatments.

20. Who will be on dialysis with me at the dialysis center?

Patients on dialysis will reflect the composition of the community in which the unit is located. Most of us do not want to travel to receive health care. We may be willing to travel to see a specialist or to have a complicated procedure or operation. Once we are stable and our lives are back to normal, convenience is much more important. Patients on hemodialysis will come to the dialysis center three times a week. If we are able to go to a center close to our home, we will have more time to spend with family or for recreation, or we will be able to keep working at our job. If a problem arises, it is easier to come in to the dialysis unit to be evaluated by the nursing or medical staff. Rain, snow, storms, tornados, hurricanes are less of a problem if our travel to dialysis is short.

Since 1980, patients aged 45 to 64 years have accounted for about 40% of the patients on dialysis. This statistic is due to the aging of the baby boom generation. The median age of patients on dialysis is 64.8 years. There are few patients younger than 18 and older than 90 years of age. As people live longer and dialysis treatments improve, older patients are now being offered treatment with dialysis. More men are on dialysis than women, with a ratio of 1.2 to 1. More patients live in urban than rural areas. Sixty-six percent of patients are white, 30% are black, 3.5% are Asian, and 1% are Native Americans. Culturally, the number of Hispanic patients is growing, as is the Hispanic population of the United States.

Dietitian

A registered health professional who has special training in nutrition. Dietitians advise patients on which foods to eat and which to avoid based upon their individual needs. They use monthly laboratory tests to monitor the patient's progress.

Social worker

A licensed professional who is part of the multidisciplinary team at the dialysis unit. The social worker assists patients with emotional, financial, and social issues and also provides education and referrals to community resources. A nephrology social worker specializes in services that support patients and families who are adjusting to the major lifestyle changes that are caused by end stage renal disease.

Dialysis

A dialysis unit is a microcosm of society. Patients are from all ethnic groups, occupations, religions, and economic backgrounds.

Patients with diabetes as the primary cause of their renal failure account for about 45% of patients on dialysis. The second largest group of patients has hypertension, but the hypertension may be due to many different causes. Other common causes of renal failure are glomerulonephritis and cystic kidney diseases. A dialysis unit is a microcosm of society. Patients are from all ethnic groups, occupations, religions, and economic backgrounds.

21. Who will pay for my dialysis treatments?

Dialysis treatments are expensive. In-center hemodialysis costs about $40,000 to $50,000 a year. Home hemodialysis or peritoneal dialysis is less costly because the person on dialysis performs the treatment.

In 1972, the United States Congress became concerned that the high cost of dialysis was limiting patients' ability to receive treatment. They amended the Social Security Act, making kidney dialysis patients eligible for **Medicare** regardless of their age. This enabled large numbers of patients to receive dialysis treatments, and led to the rapid growth in the number of dialysis units. Patients can qualify for Medicare by working long enough to be insured under Social Security or under other programs such as the Railroad Retirement Board. You may also receive Medicare if you are the husband, wife, or child (under 18 years of age) of someone who has worked long enough to qualify for Social Security. You may also be eligible for Medicare based upon a disability before you need dialysis treatments.

Medicare will pay for 80% of the cost of dialysis treatment including medications given during the

Medicare

A federally-funded program that provides medical treatments and services to patients over the age of 65 and to patients who are younger than 65 and disabled.

dialysis treatment. It will also pay 80% of the costs of hospitalization, x-rays, and doctor fees. Medicare has two parts, A and B. In order to have part B coverage, a premium must be paid of about $92 a month. More information regarding Medicare can be obtained by calling the Medicare Patient Hotline at 800-442-2620, or by visiting the Medicare Web site at *www.medicare.gov.*

Many private insurances cover some or all of the costs of dialysis treatments. If your insurance covers 80% of the cost, you can be eligible for Medicare to pay the remaining 20%. After 30 months, Medicare will become the primary insurance, paying 80%, and your private insurance will pay the remaining 20%.

Recently, many people have enrolled in health maintenance organizations, or HMOs, to provide for their health insurance. Many HMOs have conditions limiting the dialysis unit in which you can obtain treatment. If this happens, it is important to ask the HMO and your dialysis unit to try to obtain approval for your treatment.

Patients without health insurance may be eligible for the **Medicaid** program. Medicaid is administered by the individual states. Eligibility may be different for patients requiring dialysis treatments than for other patients. Patients who are not United States citizens can also be covered under the Medicaid program.

Medicaid

A federally-funded insurance program that is administered by the states to provide medical services, medications, and transportation to medical treatments for patients who have limited monetary resources.

By now, you are probably totally confused and discouraged by how complicated paying for dialysis treatments seems. You are not alone. Most patients are overwhelmed by the rules and regulations for health insurance. The high cost of dialysis treatments makes

Dialysis

this issue even more anxiety producing. Fortunately, no one is denied dialysis treatments in the United States based on their inability to pay. All dialysis units have dedicated social workers and other staff who are experts in the insurance process and who are available to guide you with these issues.

22. I have heard that dialysis is painful. Is this true?

I often tell people considering dialysis treatments that the worst part of dialysis is thinking about it! Our imaginations are always worse than reality. It is important when considering dialysis treatments to visit a dialysis center, observe treatments, and talk to people actually undergoing treatment.

Access

A device that is inserted or constructed in a patient which connects the patient to the dialysis tubing and allows dialysis to take place. In hemodialysis, an access allows blood to be drawn and can be an arterial-venous (a-v) fistula, a-v graft, or a dialysis catheter. The access for peritoneal dialysis (the peritoneal dialysis catheter) is a plastic tube that allows dialysate to be instilled into the abdomen.

In the pre-dialysis period, an **access** must be created before dialysis can be performed. In hemodialysis, a small tube is constructed in the arm between an artery and a vein. This tube allows needles to be inserted to obtain blood for the dialysis treatment. A plastic tube or catheter may be inserted in the blood vessels in the neck to obtain blood. In peritoneal dialysis, a plastic tube is inserted in the abdomen to instill the dialysis fluid. The creation of these accesses are minor surgical procedures. They are associated with mild to moderate pain that usually is treated with oral pain medications such as Tylenol (acetaminophen), Tylenol with codeine, or similar medications until the pain goes away in a day or two.

The most physically painful part of hemodialysis is the insertion of needles in the access in the arm for obtaining blood for the dialysis treatment. Some patients use an anesthetic spray. Most patients on hemodialysis rapidly get used to having needles inserted. Occasionally, muscle cramps in the arms or legs may occur during treatment when too much fluid is being removed. If you have a cramp, telling the dialysis staff will allow them to stop removing fluid or even to give some fluid back. Massaging the affected muscle can also help. Hemodialysis requires sitting in a reclining chair for about 4 hours of treatment. This can be difficult for some people. If you have arthritis or other chronic painful conditions, it is important to consider taking medication for pain before your treatment. Patients come to dialysis with their favorite travel pillow, blanket, book, iPod, or DVD player to make the treatment more comfortable.

Patients on peritoneal dialysis can have abdominal pain, which is often a sign of infection or peritonitis. It is important that patients recognize this and seek help from their dialysis center for evaluation and treatment.

Beginning dialysis is often psychologically painful. We are concerned about the effect dialysis treatments will have on our lives, loved ones, and our future health. Our sense of "well-being" is shaken. These feelings are often accompanied by depression. All these thoughts and feelings are perfectly normal. It is important to express these thoughts to the dialysis staff as well as your physician. They are specially trained to support people beginning dialysis. Remember, they have seen hundreds of people begin and cope with dialysis. You are beginning dialysis for the first time.

One of my patients, who I will call George, suffers from congenital deafness. Because of high blood pressure and diabetes, he was forced to consider dialysis treatments at age 50. After a great deal of resistance to beginning treatment, he ended up in the hospital and began hemodialysis. After a year, during one of our team meetings, he told me that we should change the name of the dialysis center to the dialysis spa. He said that for him, the idea of dialysis as a medical treatment was too negative and depressing. The idea of a spa treatment, away from the demands and frustrations of everyday life, made dialysis less painful for him. He emphasized that the time on dialysis allowed him to think, rest, and read without interruption.

When you visit a dialysis center before beginning your dialysis treatment, ask patients how they cope with their treatment. Most patients will be glad to talk to you.

Many of my patients cope with dialysis treatments by considering dialysis to be a part-time job. Work for them is a source of pride, something that is difficult but, with effort, can be accomplished. There are as many coping mechanisms as there are patients on dialysis. When you visit a dialysis center before beginning your dialysis treatment, ask patients how they cope with their treatment. Most patients will be glad to talk to you. They will remember beginning dialysis and their own fears and misconceptions. This will help you develop your own strategy that is right for you.

Erick Lucero writes:

When I first started dialysis, I had a catheter inserted by a surgeon. The next procedure I had was an a–v (arterial-venous) fistula in my right arm near my wrist. Dialysis using the catheter was not painful. Instead of using needles, there are small caps on the catheter that are unscrewed, and the catheter is connected to the hemodialysis tubing. When it was time to use my fistula after 3 months, the needles were inserted. This was very painful at first. I got used to the needles with time. They still hurt, but the pain lasts for a very short time.

The other painful parts of dialysis are the cramps I get in my legs when too much fluid is removed. I can take off two and a half liters during my treatment. If I try to take off three liters, I sometimes get severe cramps in my calves. This usually lasts 5 minutes. You have to know your body on dialysis and how much fluid you can take off without having cramps.

23. What will happen if I skip a dialysis treatment?

Most people on dialysis are confronted with obligations and commitments that interfere with dialysis treatments. A child might be sick. A favorite niece may have a wedding on a dialysis day. A bad cold may make us reluctant to leave the house. Things happen at inconvenient times. Bad weather may make travel to the dialysis unit difficult or impossible. Very rarely, power outages or problems with the water supply may make it impossible for a dialysis center to treat patients for a short period of time.

In most instances, missing or postponing a single hemodialysis treatment does not result in a catastrophe. If patients are having effective dialysis treatments, adhering to their diet and fluid restrictions, and taking their medications properly, dialysis can be rescheduled for later the same day or even the next day safely. Patients who are not receiving good dialysis or keeping their diet may develop puffiness around the face, fluid in the legs, and shortness of breath. This is due to fluid overload. Typically, these symptoms occur on Sunday or Monday night because of the longer interval between hemodialysis treatments on those days. Often, patients tend to go off their diets on weekends due to parties or other social occasions.

Dialysis is a renal replacement therapy. Our own kidneys work 24 hours a day, 7 days a week. Dialysis does not replace all of our renal function. Hemodialysis 3 times a week at best replaces 12% to 15% of normal renal function. If we miss one hemodialysis treatment, we miss one-third of our weekly renal replacement therapy. This can result in immediate problems such as too much fluid in our body or a high potassium level in our blood. Weakness, fatigue, and loss of appetite can occur. If dialysis treatments are missed frequently, the toxins and poisons that build up in our blood can damage our **peripheral nervous system**. This is called **uremic neuropathy**. Symptoms include numbness and tingling of the hands and feet, pain, and weakness. The poisons can cause inflammation in the lining of our heart, or pericarditis. Fluid overload from missing many treatments can put a strain on the heart, leading to an enlarged heart that is not able to effectively pump blood. Poisons can affect the lining of our stomach and cause gastritis, which in turn can cause decreased appetite, abdominal pain, nausea, and vomiting. In severe forms, bleeding can occur, which may require admission to a hospital for emergency treatment.

Many patients ask if they can be treated with one or two hemodialysis treatments a week. In the 1980s, physicians tried to decrease the time spent on hemodialysis with treatments called **high-flux dialysis**. These approaches resulted in more complications and a shortened life span in patients on dialysis. Scientific experts now recommend that we increase the amount of dialysis treatment to prevent complications and improve the quality and length of life.

Patients on peritoneal dialysis are fortunate that they can adjust the timing of their treatment. Then can perform their exchanges at times that are convenient because they are not dependent on the dialysis center schedule. The peritoneal dialysis staff can guide you on the proper spacing of exchanges. Peritoneal dialysis patients must be self-motivated. If they fail to perform one of their daily exchanges, no one will remind them. If an in-center hemodialysis patient fails to come for treatment, usually a dialysis staff member will call the person to ask why he or she missed a treatment and try to reschedule the treatment. Patients on home hemodialysis can also vary the time of their treatments to fit their schedule. Home dialysis is often a good choice for people with busy careers who may have to adjust their schedules.

Most long-time survivors on dialysis have certain characteristics. First, they accept the need for their treatments both intellectually and emotionally. They participate in the planning of their treatments and understand the factors that result in a successful treatment. These long-term survivors take the necessary steps to ensure that they receive a better treatment and resist the temptation to cut their treatment. Secondly, these patients engage in a healthy lifestyle. They keep their diet, avoid excess alcohol, abstain from smoking, try to exercise. Thirdly, they are very careful to take their medications correctly. If they have hypertension or diabetes, they control these conditions with diet and medication. By accomplishing these things, they avoid many of the complications for renal failure that interfere with quality of life and longevity. Achieving these goals takes time, and most people are not perfect. By developing good habits when beginning dialysis, a routine can be established that can promote health and effective treatment for renal failure.

24. Now that I am on dialysis, can I eat whatever I want?

Before beginning dialysis, patients are often on very restrictive diets to delay the need for dialysis. As kidney disease progresses, the kidneys have a harder time eliminating fluid, and salts, such as potassium and sodium, from the body. Often, diuretics are prescribed to increase the urine output and the excretion of fluid, sodium, and potassium. Eating less sodium, potassium, phosphorus, and fluid compensates for a decreased ability to get rid of these substances. In the early days in the development of dialysis, a limited number of dialysis facilities resulted in many patients delaying dialysis and becoming increasingly debilitated and malnourished. Patients were often placed on low-protein diets and lost part of their muscle mass. They would begin dialysis in a debilitated state and require months of rehabilitation and nutritional support to get back to a state of good health. Now we know that it is better to begin dialysis before these nutritional changes occur and try to preserve muscle mass and nutritional reserves.

An individual's nutritional needs will vary greatly, and it is very important to get expert advice from a registered dietitian who has experience with dialysis patients. This individual evaluation is much more important for kidney patients than for patients with other medical conditions. Every dialysis center has dietary specialists who can take a dietary history and, in consultation with your doctor, develop a diet that is optimized for you.

What you should eat will depend on many factors. Underlying medical problems such as diabetes, elevated cholesterol, and lactose intolerance are just a few examples of conditions that will affect what you eat. Men and women have different dietary needs. Body size and activity level also determine your nutritional needs. The type of dialysis that you choose will also determine your diet. Some patients continue to make urine and have residual renal function. The kidneys are excreting some salt, fluid, and toxins that allow the patient to ingest an additional amount of fluid equal to this urine output.

Hemodialysis three times a week is the most common dialysis therapy. Because this treatment is intermittent, fluid potassium, sodium, and phosphorus, all increase in the body between dialysis treatments. During a 4-hour treatment, an average of 2 liters of fluid is removed. Fluid will then accumulate in your body until the next treatment. The amount of fluid you can safely consume between treatments will include the fluid you excrete in the urine as well as fluid excreted by the lungs and in stool. The goal is to prevent the need for the removal of large amounts of fluid in a short time. If it is necessary to remove a great deal of fluid, complications during dialysis such as muscle cramps, a fall in blood pressure, and dizziness after treatments can occur. Potassium and salt will also have to be restricted in the diet to prevent them from building up in the body. Protein intake is usually recommended to be 1 to 1.2 grams per kilogram of body weight. Many dietitians have food models to give patients an idea of portion size that is included in their diet. They can also try to incorporate patients' favorite foods into their dietary plan.

In peritoneal dialysis, treatment occurs on a continuous basis every day, enabling the patient to ingest an increased amount of fluid. The treatment can be

An individual's nutritional needs will vary greatly, and it is very important to get expert advice from a registered dietitian who has experience with dialysis patients.

Dialysis

adjusted to remove more or less fluid by varying the dextrose or sugar content of the peritoneal dialysis solutions. If we wish to remove more fluid, a higher dextrose-containing solution will osmotically pull out more fluid from the body. This will enable patients to drink more in the course of the day. Patients may also eat more potassium on peritoneal dialysis. Protein can be excreted in peritoneal dialysis because it can pass through the peritoneal dialysis membrane. It is important to take this into consideration and continue to consume enough protein in your diet.

The role of diet is probably the most underestimated factor affecting the health of patients. The more we learn of the science of nutrition as patients and health-care professionals, the better prepared we will be to achieve good outcomes on dialysis.

25. What medicines are removed by my dialysis treatments?

We think of dialysis as a life-saving procedure that removes dangerous poisons and toxins from our blood and our bodies. Dialysis will also remove substances that are beneficial and healthy for us. Examples of these substances are vitamins and medications. As long as a substance can be dissolved in water (water-soluble), and it is not too large, there is a good chance that it will pass from the blood through the dialysis membrane into the dialysate. Hemodialysis and peritoneal dialysis membranes are different and have different clearances. Insulin, a protein, can easily pass through the peritoneal dialysis membrane but cannot pass through the hemodialysis membrane. Many of the water soluble vitamins such as vitamin C, folate, and the B vitamins are removed during hemodialysis and peritoneal dialysis, which is why many dialysis patients are placed on vitamin supplements. If you eat a healthy, varied diet containing fruits and vegetables, this loss is not significant.

Some antibiotics such as penicillin and ampicillin are removed by dialysis. In general, when taking antibiotics, it is wise to take your dose after your dialysis treatment. This will decrease the amount of medication removed by your treatment. Seizure medicines such as phenytoin are also removed by hemodialysis. It is important for your doctor to check blood levels to guide you on the proper dose of this medicine. Other medications removed by dialysis include aspirin and lithium. In fact, overdoses of some medications are sometimes treated with hemodialysis. Alcohol readily passes through the dialysis membrane.

26. Will I be able to keep my job after beginning dialysis?

Work is an important part of our lives. We often define ourselves by what we do. We are a police officer, farmer, engineer, teacher, secretary, or carpenter. In addition to our salary, we have the benefits of feeling useful to others, camaraderie with fellow workers, and the self-esteem of a job well done. We rely on our jobs for financial security and often for health insurance.

Most people plan to take time off from work when starting dialysis. Beginning dialysis treatments is stressful. You may find that it is difficult to concentrate on work and risk performing poorly. Every occupation is different, some more stressful and demanding than others. How much time you take off from work depends on several factors. Patients who delay beginning dialysis for a long time may feel weak and debilitated. They may eat poorly and lose muscle mass. Their ability to perform tasks at work may decrease. Dialysis patients who also have other medical conditions such as heart problems, recent surgery, and poor nutritional status may need a longer adjustment period. Every job is different. The level of physical activity, amount of time at work, and travel for work all are important considerations.

Most people plan to take time off from work when starting dialysis. Beginning dialysis treatments is stressful.

I tell my patients they should try to take off a minimum of at least 2 weeks while adjusting to dialysis. During the second week, they can review their progress with the dialysis team and begin to plan their return to work. Many patients go back to work part time at first. This allows them to rest more and decreases the stress associated with starting dialysis.

Peritoneal dialysis patients will have to decide on the timing of their peritoneal dialysis exchanges. Most people will perform one exchange at home before going to work, one exchange during their lunch period, one exchange when returning home, and one before bedtime. It is possible to be on peritoneal dialysis at night by using a machine called a cycler. You can set the machine up at home, and it will complete your exchanges automatically while you sleep. In the morning, you can disconnect from the machine and have no dialysis during the day, allowing your full attention to be devoted to work. Peritoneal and home dialysis can help by eliminating your travel time to the dialysis unit. Many patients on hemodialysis can use their time on hemodialysis to be productive. The modern laptop computer can allow highly motivated and accomplished patients to write letters, answer e-mail, and research presentations all while receiving dialysis treatment. Other patients prefer their dialysis treatment time to be work free and would rather watch television, read, or sleep on dialysis. Certainly, you should not depend upon working while receiving dialysis. Episodes of low blood pressure, machine alarms, and the measuring of vital signs including heart rate and blood pressure every 15 to 30 minutes by the dialysis staff may make the idea of working on hemodialysis overly optimistic for many patients.

Some patients beginning dialysis choose to change their careers. They use the first year or two on dialysis to go to school and retrain in a profession that is more compatible with their dialysis lifestyle. Chronic renal failure is sometimes grounds for being placed on disability. Your dialysis team, especially the social worker, will be able to help you determine if you meet the criteria for disability in your state.

Erick Lucero writes:

My doctor and I were working hard to save my kidney function. I was on a medication called cyclosporine that I hoped would stabilize my kidney function and prevent the need for dialysis. Suddenly my blood tests were worse and my potassium was high. I received a call from my doctor on June 1, 2007, that I needed to begin dialysis as soon as possible. For the last 10 years, I have worked in sales, selling electrical components and data processing equipment like fiber-optic cable to contractors. When I learned I was starting dialysis, I met with my two bosses. I had already talked to them about my kidney problems, and they already had an idea that I would need to have dialysis treatments. They explained the benefits that were available and that I was covered for disability for 3 months. On June 5, 2007, I had a dialysis catheter inserted, and I began hemodialysis on June 6, 2007 at a dialysis center. I had another surgery to create an AV fistula in my left arm.

Being out of work was very hard. I felt weak and was depressed that I could not take care of my wife and daughter. Being home made me think too much. My wife was also depressed because she saw me being sad. Luckily, my one-year-old daughter did not understand what was going on. I enjoyed taking her out to the park because it took my mind off my problems.

Little by little, I felt stronger. I never thought I would miss my job, but I did. I was bored being home all day. After 3 months, I returned to work full time. At first, I had some of my accounts assigned to other people, but I soon was back to my old schedule. I tried to do some work while I was on hemodialysis, but the lack of an Internet connection was a problem. Sometimes after dialysis, I work at home until 1:00 a.m. I've had a lot of energy since starting dialysis and enjoy being back at work. I never complain about my job anymore.

27. Am I too old to receive dialysis treatments?

No! You are not too old to consider dialysis treatments at any age. Patients in their late 90s have been treated with dialysis. The most important requirement for patients considering dialysis at any age is a positive mental attitude and the desire to get better.

In the early days of dialysis treatments, the 1970s, older patients were not considered good candidates for dialysis treatments. The hemodialysis machines were primitive compared to today's equipment. Peritoneal dialysis was not readily available for continuous treatments on an outpatient basis. The availability of dialysis was limited to a few centers. Elderly patients were often treated conservatively, and not even offered dialysis as an option.

A great deal has changed. The modern hemodialysis machine allows older and sicker patients to receive treatments. The dialysate used for dialysis in the 1970s contained a substance called acetate. This acetate could pass through the dialysis membrane into the patient's blood. The acetate was then converted to **bicarbonate** to treat the accumulation of acids in the body. In the 1980s, technology changed to allow bicarbonate to be added directly to the dialysate, resulting in gentler and smoother treatments. It reduced the number of times the patient's blood pressure would fall during the treatment. More fluid could be removed safely. Patients with heart conditions could be treated without developing chest pain or other cardiac symptoms. Infirm and weak patients were able to tolerate hemodialysis.

The computer revolution has also improved the modern hemodialysis machine. Microprocessors are part of every machine. These small computers accurately measure how fast and how much fluid is removed. Microprocessors measure the composition and temperature of the dialysate. They detect leaking of blood through the dialysate membrane into the dialysate. Peritoneal dialysis has also benefited by modern technological advances.

The modern hemodialysis machine allows older and sicker patients to receive treatments.

Dialysis

Bicarbonate

A salt of carbonic acid that acts as an important buffer to help keep our blood from becoming too acidic.

Better tubing and connection systems have decreased the rate of infection. Peritoneal dialysis machines or cyclers that automatically perform dialysis benefited from microprocessors. Computers have made dialysis better and safer.

The improvement in medical care has helped older patients receive dialysis treatments. Better cardiac care including coronary artery bypass surgery, coronary angioplasty and stent placement, and implantable defibrillators have improved the life expectancy and quality of elderly patients' lives. Medications have also improved outcomes. The treatment of elevated blood pressure and cholesterol has contributed to people living longer.

In 2003, 26% of new patients beginning dialysis were older than 75 years of age. It is now common for patients over 90 years of age to begin dialysis treatments. Elderly patients are often afraid of dialysis treatments. They feel that treatments may be painful. A common fear is that once you start dialysis you will be trapped on dialysis and will not be able to stop treatment. Both of these fears are best addressed by talking to other elderly patients who are receiving dialysis treatments. Your healthcare professional can arrange for you to tour a dialysis center and to talk to patients while they are actually on dialysis. Most dialysis patients are happy to share their stories and have unique insight into dialysis treatments. They remember vividly what beginning dialysis was like and will honestly answer your questions.

Often the worst part of beginning dialysis is our fear of the unknown. It is impossible to predict who will do well on dialysis and who will not. Many elderly patients surprise themselves and the healthcare team. They expect to survive a few months. After a year or two on dialysis, they have gained strength, are more active, and are glad to have begun dialysis. If you do not know if dialysis is for you, you can give it a try for several months. You can always stop treatment.

28. Can I catch HIV or hepatitis from my dialysis treatment?

There has never been a case of a person contracting HIV (human immunodeficiency virus) from dialysis treatments. HIV can be transmitted by blood transfusions, needle sticks, sexual activity, and by sharing needles while using drugs. It cannot be transmitted by casual contact such as shaking hands, kissing, sitting in the same chair, or using the same toilet as an HIV-infected person. Accurate tests have been developed for HIV allowing the screening of blood donors and making our blood supply safe. It is necessary to get a person's permission to test them for HIV. Some states have laws restricting access to information concerning HIV in the medical record. Orally administered medicines now exist that can greatly reduce the amount of virus in an HIV-infected individual's body. This medical advance has allowed HIV patients to live a more normal life and has greatly improved their longevity.

In hemodialysis, all the tubing that comes into contact with blood is discarded after use. Some centers will reuse the dialysis membrane many times. The membrane is disinfected, carefully tested, and used only on the same person. There is no risk of getting HIV infection or hepatitis from reusing dialysis membranes. Unfortunately, needle sticks can occur in hemodialysis units. They usually involve staff members sticking themselves with a used needle from a patient. This may put the staff member at risk but does not pose a threat to the patient. Some hemodialysis centers allow patients to receive blood transfusions for anemia while they are on hemodialysis. The use of a medication called erythropoietin as well as the use of intravenous iron replacement has decreased the need for transfusions in dialysis patients. Because of the screening of blood donors, the blood supply in the United States and most countries is very safe. The chance of contracting HIV infection or hepatitis from blood transfusion is very small.

In the 1970s there were epidemics of hepatitis B infection in hemodialysis centers. This risk was recognized, and it was decided to treat patients with hepatitis B in special isolation areas within the dialysis unit, dramatically decreasing the transmission of hepatitis B. Today, all dialysis patients and dialysis staff are offered vaccination for hepatitis B. This series of three shots is your best defense against hepatitis B, and I urge you to take the hepatitis B vaccine.

More patients on dialysis have been exposed to hepatitis C infection than to hepatitis B. Hepatitis C is transmitted by blood transfusions, needle sticks, or sharing needles during intravenous drug use. Hepatitis C is not thought to be transmitted by sexual activity. Dialysis is not a risk factor for the transmission of hepatitis C. Most cases are asymptomatic, and people find out that they have been exposed to hepatitis C when blood tests are taken. Most people with hepatitis C recover. A small number of people develop chronic hepatitis, which if left untreated can result in permanent scarring or cirrhosis of the liver. Treatment is available to prevent this scarring, and it is important to have a thorough evaluation if you have chronic hepatitis C to see if you can benefit from treatment. There is no vaccine for hepatitis C. There is a third type of hepatitis called hepatitis A, which can be transmitted by eating contaminated food. People usually recover with no chronic scarring of the liver. A vaccine is available and should be taken when you travel to areas with a high risk of infection, or if you suffer from chronic hepatitis B or C infection to prevent further damage to your liver. Hepatitis A is rare in dialysis patients in the United States.

Home dialysis patients must take special precautions to protect family and household members from exposure to blood, dialysate, and used dialysis needles. These precautions are called **universal precautions** because they are always used all the time with everyone. They involve washing hands before and after contact with a patient. Family members should also wear eye shields, gloves, and protective gowns when close enough to the dialysis procedure to be at risk for blood splashing on them. It does not matter if your family member on dialysis is HIV negative or does not have hepatitis. We still use universal precautions. This is because there are patients who are in what we call the window period of infection, which refers to the early stages of HIV or hepatitis infection. The patient is exposed to the disease, and viruses are reproducing in their body. Their body has not yet made antibodies to the virus. The test for HIV or hepatitis is negative, but the person can still be contagious. The other reason for universal precautions is that some family members may find it difficult to reveal to their loved ones that they have an infection.

Universal precautions

Wearing medical gloves, goggles, and face shields to avoid contact with body fluids such as blood and peritoneal fluid. Universal precautions protect us from the risk of transmission of blood-borne diseases such as hepatitis and HIV-AIDS.

Universal precautions are like looking both ways before crossing the street. If you learn good habits in the beginning, you will be able to avoid an accident for many years to come. If you are splashed with blood from a family member, the first thing to do is wash the blood off. If the splash has gotten into your eye, irrigating the eye with tap water should be done immediately. If you stick yourself with a used needle, again immediately wash the needle stick site with soap and water. Report the needle stick to your doctor or to your family member's doctor. They can counsel you and your family member to determine if special tests for HIV or hepatitis are needed. Most people splashed with blood or dialysate, or who experience a needle stick have nothing serious happen to them.

PART THREE

Preparing to Begin Dialysis

What is a nephrologist?

How does my doctor know I need dialysis?

What is a shunt or access for dialysis?

More . . .

29. What is a nephrologist?

A nephrologist is a medical doctor who has received specialized training in the diagnosis and treatment of kidney diseases. After 4 years of college and 4 years of medical school, an MD or DO (Doctor of Osteopathy) degree is awarded. The nephrologist has also received 3 years of training as a resident in internal medicine where he or she has studied and managed a large number of different medical problems. After completing the residency in internal medicine, the nephrologist will have 2 or more years of fellowship training in nephrology. The fellow will work under the supervision of several experienced nephrologists who are board certified by the American Board of Internal Medicine. These teachers have years of experience in diagnosing and treating patients with kidney disorders. Many of them have conducted research and have written papers on renal disease. Under their guidance, the fellow will learn to diagnose and a large number of kidney diseases.

The training will include working in a hospital and taking care of critically ill patients in the intensive care unit and the emergency department. The fellow will also learn about hemodialysis and peritoneal dialysis, both in the hospital and in the dialysis center. Kidney biopsy and kidney pathology are studied. The fellow will learn about renal transplantation as an option for treating kidney failure. Many fellowship programs require that the fellow be involved in research. The high point of the fellow's training could be presenting his or her research at a national kidney meeting such as the annual meeting of the **American Society of Nephrology**. This national meeting attracts up to 15,000 nephrologists to hear talks and papers pre-

American Society of Nephrology

A national organization of physicians and scientists founded in 1966 to study and treat kidney disease.

sented from the best nephrologists from all over the world. In addition, fellows will attend many conferences at their hospital. Some fellows will take a third year to specialize in transplant medicine, critical care medicine, or other subspecialties of nephrology. They may take an extra year of research. After their fellowship training, fellows can take an examination for board certification by the American Board of Internal Medicine.

The idea of having a floor of the hospital dedicated to the study, teaching, and treatment of kidney disease was first established by Richard Bright (1789–1858) at the Guy's Hospital and Medical School in London, England. His association of the finding of protein in the urine and the diagnosis of kidney disease is still important today. In his honor, the condition of having protein in the urine was called Bright's disease. Many physicians after Dr. Bright were interested in kidney disease, but the modern era of nephrology began in the 1940s. Physicians studying the physiology (or the way the kidney works) began to make great progress. Experimental dialysis treatment was begun in the 1940s and 1950s. In 1954, the first kidney transplant was performed. Physicians developed a method of performing kidney biopsies without surgery by inserting a needle through the skin and obtaining a small piece of tissue to examine under the microscope. In 1960, an association called the International Society of Nephrology held its first meeting in Evian, France. The American Society of Nephrology was founded in 1966. All these advances promoted the establishment of nephrology as an active subspecialty of internal medicine. The development of formal training in nephrology has allowed patients with kidney disease to receive the latest treatment available.

The development of formal training in nephrology has allowed patients with kidney disease to receive the latest treatment available.

If your doctor has diagnosed a kidney problem or if you have a family history of a genetic kidney disease, it is advisable to ask your doctor or healthcare professional for a referral to see a nephrologist. The nephrologist will concentrate on diagnosing the cause of the kidney problem and will attempt to cure or stabilize the problem. The earlier the evaluation, the more likely it will be that the problem can be reversed or stabilized. The hope of early intervention is to prevent or delay the need for kidney dialysis.

30. What is a urologist?

A **urologist** is a medical doctor who specializes in the treatment of diseases of the kidney and urinary tract. Like a nephrologist, the urologist has spent 4 years attending medical school. After graduation, the urologist will spend 1 year training in general surgery followed by 4 or 5 years of residency training in urology. The urologist, as a surgeon, will concentrate on problems such as diseases of the prostate, kidney tumors, kidney stones, and disorders of the bladder. He or she will learn **cystoscopy**, a procedure in which a small fiber-optic tube is inserted in the bladder. Disorders of the bladder and urinary tract can be diagnosed and treated without making a cut or surgical incision. Tubes called **stents** can be inserted during cystoscopy to bypass a blockage caused by a stone or tumor and allow the kidneys to function. A urologist may become skilled in **laparoscopic surgery**, which allows surgery to be done through small incisions in the abdomen, allowing a faster recovery time. After completing the residency training program, urologists can become board certified by the American Board of Urology. They will have to give case presentations of patients they have cared for and pass three examinations to prove competency in urology.

Urologists were important in the development of peritoneal and hemodialysis. A urologist, Dr. J. Hartwell Harrison, was a member of the team that performed the first renal transplant from one identical twin to another at the Peter Bent Brigham Hospital in Boston, Massachusetts, in 1954. As the specialty of nephrology developed, urologists spent less time with dialysis and renal failure and concentrated more on surgical diseases of the kidney. However, nephrologists and urologists have continued to work together on many diseases. Patients suffering from kidney stones will have them removed by urologists. The nephrologist will help treat the patient to prevent more stones from forming. Many times patients are not sure if they should see a urologist or nephrologist as a kidney specialist. You can ask your primary care doctor which is the appropriate kidney doctor for you. Often the urologist will determine that you should see a nephrologist if medical kidney disease is suspected.

31. How does my doctor know I need dialysis?

The evaluation to determine if a person needs dialysis begins with the medical history. Your doctor will ask you questions regarding your health in the past. He or she will ask about symptoms of kidney failure. Early symptoms of kidney failure include a decreased appetite, weight loss, hiccups, nausea or vomiting, and a bitter or metallic taste in your mouth. A general physical examination will be performed. The doctor will measure your blood pressure, examine your heart,

Laparoscopic surgery

Surgery performed under general anesthesia by inserting fiber-optic tubes through several small incisions.

Preparing to Begin Dialysis

Early symptoms of kidney failure include a decreased appetite, weight loss, hiccups, nausea or vomiting, and a bitter or metallic taste in your mouth.

Anemia

A decrease in the number of red blood cells present in the blood, which can be due to blood loss or a decreased production of red blood cells due to iron deficiency, poor nutrition, or disease. Decreased red blood cell survival occurs in kidney disease. Symptoms of anemia include fatigue, weakness, and shortness of breath on exertion.

lungs, and abdomen, and look for evidence of fluid retention in your legs and feet, and around your eyes. Blood and urine tests will be ordered.

One of the most important blood tests is the BUN test, or blood urea nitrogen test. This was the first blood test developed to measure kidney function. As a person's renal function gets worse, the kidney's ability to excrete or remove urea from the blood declines. The urea level in the blood increases. Another important blood test is the creatinine level. Creatinine is a substance produced from our muscles. As the creatinine enters the bloodstream, it is filtered and excreted by the kidneys. As kidney function decreases, the level of creatinine in the blood increases because less creatinine is removed. Another important blood test is for potassium level. If the potassium level is too high, the patient may be at risk for heart problems. A hematocrit and hemoglobin test can determine if you have an **anemia** or low red blood cell count. Anemia is a common finding in kidney failure. A sonogram can be helpful to evaluate the size of the kidneys. Small kidney size can indicate that the kidneys are scarred and are less likely to improve. A 24-hour collection of urine for creatinine clearance can measure the amount of kidney function a person has left and is more accurate than blood tests. This test is done at home and will require you to save all the urine you make during a 24-hour period. If you get up at night to urinate, you must remember to save this urine. After collecting the urine, you will go to the lab or doctor's office to obtain a blood creatinine level to calculate your kidney function.

In some patients, the decision to start dialysis is easy. They look and feel sick. Fluid is building up in their body, and they are short of breath. They have nausea, vomiting, and cannot eat. In these patients, emergency dialysis can be life saving. They often feel much better after one or two dialysis treatments. This makes accepting the need for dialysis treatments much easier. In other patients, these dramatic symptoms are not present. If toxins and poisons from kidney failure build up gradually, the person will adapt and be able to tolerate the kidney failure. This can make the decision to start dialysis more difficult because the person feels well. Despite blood tests showing kidney failure, the symptoms of kidney failure are absent.

In the early days of dialysis, because resources were limited, almost all patients became ill with symptoms. We have learned that it is better not to wait until the last possible moment before starting dialysis. Early intervention helps prevent damage to the heart, nerves, and bones. Doctors often cannot precisely predict when these organs will be damaged. In general, when the creatinine clearance is 18 to 20 mL/minute we begin preparing the patient for dialysis, and we begin dialysis when the creatinine clearance is 12 to 15 mL/minute. This is to keep the patient out of danger. We have learned after years of experience that it is better to start dialysis before a crisis occurs. The first treatment can be scheduled at a specific time, and family members can be available to support the patient psychologically. When starting dialysis is delayed, individuals might have to start dialysis on an emergency basis, requiring them to go to an emergency room during the middle of the night or on a weekend. Their regular doctor might not be available to help treat them.

Because many patients adapt to kidney failure, they often tell me after starting dialysis that they did not realize how bad they actually had felt. Their appetite improves and they regain their taste for their favorite food. They are stronger and can walk faster and longer before getting tired. High blood pressure is often easier to control after starting dialysis because fluid is removed efficiently. Some patients can decrease their blood pressure medications after starting dialysis. Their sense of well-being improves. They no longer have to worry if they will get sick or have an emergency and need to be rushed to the hospital for emergency dialysis.

32. How will my doctor help me prepare for dialysis?

In the most optimal situation, you will meet your doctor before you need to begin dialysis. He or she will discuss dialysis with you and your family and will have reviewed your blood and other tests. The most important thing that your doctor can do at this stage is give you information. The more you understand dialysis, the less frightening it will be. When I began my career in nephrology, we would carefully explain the dialysis procedure to patients and answer their many questions. Now, many doctors will also mention every possible bad outcome even if the chance of that bad outcome is very unlikely. It is important to tell your doctor how much information you feel comfortable receiving. Some patients need to hear about every detail. Others will put themselves in the hands of someone they trust and let them make many of the decisions. Too much information can sometimes be overwhelming. Many patients want a family member or friend to come with them and receive a lot of the information. That person can be your advocate and help you ask questions and make decisions. Some patients learn that they will need dialysis as an emergency and need to begin dialysis right away. Although this news can be very stressful, dialysis is a very safe and effective procedure and the overwhelming majority of patients tolerate their dialysis treatment without difficulty.

Your doctor will discuss the need to create an access for your dialysis treatment. In hemodialysis, the best access is called an a-v fistula (**Figure 4**). This small tube in the arm is created by connecting an artery to a vein during a surgical procedure under local anesthesia. The fistula may take several months to mature due to the thickening of the wall of the vein of the fistula's vein or because of an increased pressure from the arterial blood. When the fistula is mature or ready for use, needles are inserted into the fistula to obtain the blood for the dialysis treatment. The early creation of the a-v fistula can make beginning dialysis easier and safer. A peritoneal dialysis access or catheter takes less time to be ready than an a-v fistula. Most catheters are ready to use in about 2 weeks.

Part of the care you will receive before beginning dialysis is learning the diet you need to follow to keep yourself healthy. In many instances, this diet will include a restriction in the amount of sodium and potassium you will be able to eat. Phosphorus found in meat and dairy products may be restricted. Phosphate binders, medicines that are taken with food, can also decrease the phosphorus that is absorbed by the gastrointestinal tract. Many patients mistakenly believe that drinking extra fluid will be helpful in kidney disease. This is often wrong. Drink if you are thirsty, but avoid drinking extra fluid. The best person to counsel

Figure 4   A-V fistula
Source: K. Neelakantappa, MD

you on your diet is a dietitian who has experience with dialysis patients.

Many patients with kidney failure begin to develop anemia as part of their renal failure because the survival of the red blood cells is decreased. Erythropoietin, a hormone produced by the kidney, is decreased in kidney failure. Erythropoietin is a messenger that tells our bone marrow to increase the production of red blood cells. The erythropoietin and other medications with similar action can be given by subcutaneous injection to increase the production of red blood cells. This injection can be given every week and will decrease the symptoms of anemia that can include weakness, shortness of breath, and pale skin. Many patients also have to take iron supplements with the erythropoietin injection to increase their red blood cell production.

Due to an inability to eliminate or excrete phosphorus from the body, patients with kidney failure often begin to have bone problems before they need dialysis treatments. This increase in phosphorus in the bloodstream causes calcium, the major element in bones, to be deposited back into the bones. This low calcium can stimulate **parathyroid hormone (PTH)** production. Parathyroid hormone is produced by four small glands in the neck that are near the thyroid gland. Overactive parathyroid glands can produce too much parathyroid hormone, which can cause re-absorption of bone and can lead to aches, pains, and in extreme cases bone fractures. Another symptom of too much parathyroid hormone is itching.

Parathyroid hormone (PTH)

A hormone made and released by the chief cells of the four parathyroid glands found in the neck to regulate calcium metabolism.

Your doctor will continue to focus on control of your blood pressure and blood sugar if you are a diabetic. Many patients with kidney failure have an elevated cholesterol level as well as elevated triglycerides. This condition is controlled with diet, exercise, and sometimes medication.

By now, you are thinking that preparing for dialysis is a lot of work and not much fun. Many patients find all these problems overwhelming and depressing. Every situation is different. Many patients have no symptoms of anemia, bone disease and make enough urine to not require a very restrictive diet. These individual differences are why you need to communicate well with your doctor and concentrate on the most important aspects of your care.

Due to an inability to eliminate or excrete phosphorus from the body, patients with kidney failure often begin to have bone problems before they need dialysis treatments.

33. Will I need to be hospitalized to begin my dialysis treatments?

Many patients who have time to prepare for their dialysis treatments will not have to be hospitalized overnight. If your medical condition is stable, and you have a good support system at home, you may begin dialysis as an outpatient. Most of the time, the dialysis access can be created as an outpatient procedure. If your access is in place and ready to use, you can start hemodialysis as an outpatient. Patients beginning peritoneal dialysis will come to the dialysis unit several days a week for training. They may be receiving hemodialysis treatments three times a week during the training until they feel competent in performing their own peritoneal dialysis.

Different dialysis units have different levels of care. Dialysis units in hospitals sometimes have a mixture of inpatients and outpatients. These units have a high nurse to patient ratio. Physicians spend more time in the unit because the patients on dialysis require a higher level of care. The hospital units have beds as well as dialysis chairs because they take care of weaker and more debilitated patients. When patients become stronger and more stable on dialysis, they can be transferred to an outpatient unit that is closer to home. If your medical condition is unstable, or if you have a heart problem, have had recent major surgery, bleeding, or a stroke, you may have to start dialysis as an inpatient. Many patients feel safe and secure in the hospital. As their condition improves, they can continue their treatment as an outpatient.

A great number of patients still meet their nephrologist for the first time when they need urgent or emergency dialysis. This may be because they have not been referred to a nephrologist by their primary care doctor, or they may have been reluctant to see the nephrologist because of fears of starting dialysis. Many people in the United States and other countries do not receive preventative general medical visits. This decreases their chance of receiving treatment that may keep them off dialysis. In general, the sooner you are evaluated the better.

34. I feel that I would rather die than go on dialysis. Is this a common feeling?

Many patients when confronted with beginning dialysis feel that their life is over. I once went to a national conference on dialysis attended by kidney doctors and dialysis nurses where we were asked to choose our own therapy if we were to develop kidney failure. The choices were hemodialysis, peritoneal dialysis, or no dialysis. To my surprise, a significant number of these healthcare workers, about 6%, stated that they would choose not to go on dialysis and to die. These feelings of helplessness have nothing to do with educational level or knowledge about dialysis. Patients with other diseases such as heart disease, diabetes, or cancer have similar feelings. They are a normal part of coping with illness and are part of the recovery process. Having a medical problem changes our idea of who we are. We feel vulnerable, inadequate, and imperfect. These feelings are signs of **depression** that all dialysis patients experience. They decrease with time. Talking about refusing dialysis is often very upsetting to the patient, the patient's family, and sometimes to the medical staff. I find that expressing these emotions rather than suppressing them is important and helpful in the

Depression

A medical term used to describe feelings of intense sadness, loss of interest in activities of daily life, and a decreased appetite and sense of well-being.

healing process. All dialysis patients will have these feelings, some often, others infrequently. The best response is to listen to why the patient feels this way and to avoid stating that these feelings are uncalled for or abnormal. Some patients will voice their concerns to family members but not the dialysis team. At our outpatient dialysis unit, we have a **psychologist** who is available to talk to all patients about this and other issues.

Psychologist

A healthcare professional who works with patients on their mental health problems including depression and anxiety.

The overwhelming number of patients needing dialysis accept treatment, and most do very well. Although the number is very small, some patients choose to not begin dialysis or decide to stop dialysis when their condition deteriorates and their quality of life is very poor. These patients are often elderly and have multiple medical problems. Art Buchwald, the noted columnist and Pulitzer Prize winner, developed acute renal failure in his 80s. He tried dialysis but decided it was not for him and stopped. His kidneys recovered enough for him to survive for a period of time. He wrote a book called *Too Soon to Say Goodbye*, in which he discusses his serious medical problems. He faces medical illness the same way he faced the rest of his life, with humor and good spirits. Most people relate to illness the same way they relate to their life when they are well, even more so. Chronic procrastinators will find a million excuses to delay beginning dialysis until the last minute. Depressed people will become more depressed. People who are decisive and organized in their daily lives will get all the information they can, research which doctor is best for them, and take action to remain healthy.

The over-whelming number of patients needing dialysis accept treatment, and most do very well.

It is important to realize that the decision to start dialysis is not irrevocable. I often tell my patients who are reluctant to begin dialysis to try one dialysis treatment. This makes them understand that they are in control of their treatment. After their first treatment, they realize that dialysis is not that bad and it is something that will help them lead a better and more productive life. Patients may be candidates for a kidney transplant in the future, which will enable them to get off dialysis. Accepting dialysis is 90% of the struggle. The adjustment period to dialysis is about 6 months. At 6 months, if you are still depressed and find dialysis extremely difficult, you may want to see a psychologist or psychiatrist. Medications for depression work well in patients on dialysis and may be helpful to patients who are severely depressed.

Erick Lucero writes:

Before I knew I needed dialysis, I used to take my uncle home from his dialysis treatments. He is older than I am and was often weak after his dialysis treatments. When my nephrologist told me that I would need dialysis, I knew that dialysis would take a lot of time and effort, and would interfere with my life. I had a sad feeling and was scared. Before beginning dialysis, I was very tired. I went to sleep after coming home from work. I started dialysis after my nephrologist found that my blood tests had gotten worse. My wife speaks of that day as "the black day," as if she was in mourning. After beginning dialysis, I began to feel better. I was less tired and had more energy. I spent time with my young daughter who helped take my mind off my problems. After 3 months, I returned to work. I was bored not working and felt better after beginning hemodialysis. Being on dialysis is less stressful than waiting to begin dialysis. When you are on dialysis, you know what to expect. You fall into a routine. When I am on hemodialysis, I am taking care of my health. The rest of the time, I am involved with my family, my friends, and work. Since I feel better on dialysis, I am less sad.

35. What is a shunt or access for dialysis?

Shunt

An old term used to describe an access used to obtain blood for hemodialysis. It initially referred to the Quinton-Scribner shunt first used in the 1960s. Today, the term includes the a-v fistula and a-v graft which "shunt" blood from the artery to the vein, bypassing the small capillaries.

A **shunt** is an old term that has survived from the early days of hemodialysis. It was first used to describe a device invented by Dr. Belding Scribner and Dr. Wayne Quinton to obtain blood for hemodialysis treatments. In the early days of dialysis, a tube or catheter was placed in an artery by a surgical procedure. Blood was removed from the artery and would run through plastic tubing to the hemodialysis machine. Blood would then run back to the patient into another tube that was placed in a vein. Each artery and vein could only be used once. This limited the number of dialysis treatments because patients ran out of usable arteries and veins. Drs. Scribner and Quinton began working on a device that could be used for many dialysis treatments. They inserted Teflon-coated tubing into an artery and a vein in the patient's arms. After dialysis was completed, the two plastic tubes, one in an artery and one in a vein, were connected together. The tubing was outside the skin, and blood flowing through the tubing on a continuous basis prevented clotting. This shunt, which allowed blood to flow from an artery to a vein, bypassing small blood vessels, was first used in 1960. It was later improved by using flexible silicon plastic tubing. This Quinton-Scribner shunt revolutionized hemodialysis and allowed many patients to be treated with hemodialysis for temporary or acute kidney failure. Dr. Scribner's shunt enabled him to treat patients for months and then years. He organized the first dialysis unit for chronic patients who could not recover kidney function at the University of Washington Hospital. In time, even though the Quinton-Scribner shunt is no longer used, the word shunt became used to describe any device that enabled blood to flow from an artery to a vein that is used for hemodialysis. The term dialysis access is a more modern term for shunt. It means a device that allows access to obtain blood from the circulation to perform dialysis.

The best type of access for hemodialysis is an **arterial-venous fistula**, or a-v fistula for short. Instead of using plastic tubing to connect an artery to a vein, the artery is directly connected to the vein by a vascular surgeon. The a-v fistula is usually located in the arm. The operation, done under local anesthesia, causes blood from the artery to go directly into the vein without passing through small blood vessels called capillaries. Blood is "shunted" from an artery to a vein. This arterial blood is under a higher pressure because it is pumped by the heart. This high pressure causes the vein to dilate (become larger). The wall of the vein becomes thicker. After weeks to months, this dilated vein can be used for hemodialysis. This process is called maturation of the fistula. Two needles can be inserted through the skin into the a-v fistula. One needle carries blood out of the fistula to the dialysis machine. After the blood is cleaned of poisons and toxins, it is carried back to the fistula and is returned to the body by the second needle. Blood can be removed and returned continuously during the dialysis treatment. After dialysis is completed, the needles are removed from the fistula. The patient places a sterile gauze over the hole in the fistula until the a small blood clot seals the needle hole. A Band-Aid is then applied over the needle hole. The

Arterial-venous fistula

A tube that connects an artery to a vein and is constructed by a vascular surgeon. When mature, the a-v fistula can have needles inserted into it to carry blood through plastic tubing to and from the hemodialysis machine.

a-v fistula is the best access for dialysis because it is made of natural materials, artery, and vein. The fistula is capable of healing if damaged and is less likely to become infected. It can last a long time. I have many patients whose fistulas are still working after 20 or more years.

Arterial-venous graft

A length of gortex tubing connected between an artery and a vein that is created by a vascular surgeon. The a-v graft is tunneled under the skin to allow needles to be inserted into it to carry blood through plastic tubing to the hemodialysis machine.

An **arterial-venous graft**, or a-v graft, is another type of access or shunt used in hemodialysis. The a-v graft is used in patients who cannot have an a-v fistula because their veins are small. Tubing made of a material called Gortex is connected between an artery and a vein by a vascular surgeon during an operation under local anesthesia. The tubing runs under the skin. Needles are inserted into the plastic tube to obtain blood for hemodialysis. Because the a-v graft is made of plastic, it cannot repair itself if damaged. It is more likely to become infected. If infected, it must be removed by a surgeon. On average, a-v grafts last 9 months to 2 or 3 years. They are not a good choice for patients who plan to spend many years on hemodialysis because they will need to be replaced many times.

Catheter

A plastic tube used for dialysis. Catheters are inserted into blood vessels to obtain blood for hemodialysis treatments. Peritoneal dialysis catheters are inserted in the abdomen, and are used to instill and drain dialysate into and out of the abdomen during peritoneal dialysis treatments.

Patients who do not have a permanent access who need dialysis can use a **catheter**. A catheter is a long plastic tube that is inserted into a vein. Local anesthesia, usually an injection of lidocaine, is used to numb the area. The catheter is sometimes inserted in a vein in the groin called the femoral vein. This procedure is done in the hospital or as an outpatient when dialysis needs to be done on a temporary basis. The catheter can be removed after the dialysis is completed, making it less likely for the catheter to become infected. Catheters can also be inserted in veins in the neck. They can be left in place for a period of time. Longer catheters are placed to come out of the skin in the upper chest. This positioning makes them less visible, as they are under the patient's shirt. Catheters can be used for hemodialysis immediately. There is no need to wait for the a-v fistula to develop or mature, for the surgical incisions to heal, or for swelling after surgery to decrease. The big disadvantage to catheters is a high chance of infection. The catheter comes out of the skin and is covered by a sterile dressing. Bacteria normally found on the skin can enter the opening in the skin and infect the catheter. Patients with catheters cannot take a bath or shower because this will get the catheter wet and increase the chance of infection. If the catheter becomes infected, antibiotics can be given and the catheter will need to be removed.

36. Should I begin dialysis before I really need it?

Most patients will try to delay dialysis as long as possible. This is a natural reaction. If kidney failure develops slowly, patients are able to adapt to the poisons and toxins in their blood. They may eat less protein, have a decreased appetite, and develop itching, hiccups, nausea, and vomiting. All of these symptoms can be tolerated if they are mild. Your remaining kidney function can be measured by a test called a 24-hour urine collection for creatinine clearance. A normal test result is 100 to 125 mL/minute. When the creatinine clearance decreases to 15 to 12 mL/min, it is time to begin dialysis. If you are a diabetic or elderly, you need to start dialysis a little earlier. You will not tolerate high levels of toxins and poisons in your blood as well as other patients. Fluid could also build up in your body and put a strain on your heart. If your appetite is poor, you may lose weight. Especially important is avoiding loss of muscle mass. When we do not eat enough calories, our bodies use fat stores and break down muscle for food. This can result in you being increasingly weak and less able to perform your daily activities. Carrying groceries, getting to work, cleaning your home can all become increasingly difficult if you lose muscle mass and body weight. It is important to look for this loss of weight. Because most patients do not want to begin dialysis, they can easily rationalize that they are fine. They can minimize the symptoms of renal failure, but weight loss is objective evidence that it would be better to begin dialysis.

Neuropathy

Damage to the peripheral nerves of the body. Symptoms include tingling in the hands and feet, weakness, and numbness.

Patients with kidney failure can also develop nerve damage, or **neuropathy**. This begins as numbness in the toes, feet, and hands. This neuropathy is progressive and can lead to weakness of the arms and legs. It can be treated with dialysis. Anemia, or low red blood cell count, is another problem that improves with dialysis. Anemia can cause weakness, fatigue, shortness of breath, and chest pain. An elevated potassium level, swelling in the legs, abdomen, or around the eyes, and an increased amount of acid in the blood are all signs that you need to start dialysis.

In the 1970s when dialysis was not readily available and there was a lack of knowledge about dialysis among patients and doctors, it was common to have patients at death's door before they were started on dialysis. We have learned that doctors are not that skilled in predicting exactly when you must begin dialysis. You may feel fine one day, and be seriously ill the next. It is always better to begin dialysis in a calm and predictable manner. It is terrible to become ill in the middle of the night, be rushed to an emergency room where the doctors and nurses are not familiar with your case, and begin dialysis on an emergency basis. For all these reasons, it is better to begin dialysis before you think you really need it. You may end up on dialysis a few weeks earlier, but you will preserve your strength and sense of well-being. You will decrease the stress and anxiety of your family. Often the worst part of beginning dialysis is thinking about it. Once you commit to starting dialysis, you will have less fear of the future and the unknown. This will make your adjustment to dialysis so much easier and allow you to continue to do the things you want in life.

You may feel fine one day, and be seriously ill the next.

37. Who will help me find out if my insurance covers my dialysis treatments?

Dialysis treatments are expensive, about $30,000 to $50,000 a year. Most medical insurance will cover all or most of the cost of dialysis treatments as a life-saving medical treatment. If you know that you will need dialysis in the future, you should try to meet with a social worker who has experience working with dialysis patients. Every dialysis unit has a social worker who has experience in counseling patients about health insurance. They will be able to help you understand what your insurance does and does not cover. Medicare covers 80% of the costs of dialysis, and patients will need to have a supplementary insurance policy that covers the remaining 20%. Some insurance plans do not cover the cost of medications taken at home. The average dialysis patient takes 8 to 12 medications a day. It is important to try to obtain a prescription plan that will cover the costs of these medications. Medicare has established a plan called part D in 2007, which pays the cost of medications for some patients. Drug companies have programs available for patients who cannot afford their medications and who do not qualify for other programs. The National Kidney Foundation also has grants that can help pay for medications on a one time basis.

Approximately 45 million Americans have no health insurance coverage at all. Uninsured patients who need dialysis are not uncommon. Fortunately, in the United States, no one is denied dialysis treatments because of an inability to pay. The federal government has provided insurance through the Medicaid and Medicare programs. If you have worked and paid taxes, you will be eligible for Medicare coverage 3 months after your first dialysis treatment. Medicaid eligibility will vary from state to state and is income based. It is important to discuss your eligibility with the dialysis or hospital social worker or have your relatives or significant other help you with the application process. Patients who are from other countries legally or illegally are eligible for Medicaid, which pays for emergency dialysis only. Emergency Medicaid for dialysis will not pay for medications, transportation, or doctors visits. The cost of transportation to and from the dialysis center can be significant, especially if the dialysis center is far from home.

Home dialysis patients have their own financial issues. The transportation costs to and from the dialysis center are much less. After their training is complete, they can expect to go to the dialysis center once a month if their condition is stable. Home hemodialysis patients have several additional expenses. The dialysis machine, dialyzers, tubing needles, gauze, and many other supplies are paid for by the insurance. The plumbing for the water for dialysis needs to be equipped with a backflow preventer. Waste lines to discard used dialysate may also need to be installed. The cost of the initial plumbing work could range from $1,000 to $2,000 and is not covered by insurance. The hemodialysis machine requires a dedicated electrical connection with 20 amperes of current. It will also need a ground fault circuit interrupter (GFCI) to turn off the electricity in the event of a short circuit. Your electricity and water bill will increase if you are on home hemodialysis. The cost of a recliner chair may not be covered by your insurance. The cost of home peritoneal dialysis is much less expensive than home hemodialysis. The main requirement for peritoneal dialysis is storage space for supplies.

Financial matters create a great deal of anxiety for patients and their families beginning dialysis. Many people are not used to discussing financial matters with their doctors. Kidney doctors usually have a great deal of experience dealing with patients with social and financial problems. They may not know the answer to your question, but they will know who on the healthcare team is best equipped to work on your problem with you.

38. Will dialysis heal my damaged kidneys?

Dialysis treatments are a renal replacement therapy. Dialysis replaces some of the functions that your kidneys provide. Dialysis does not heal your kidneys. Additional treatment will be required to heal your kidneys. The type of treatment will depend on the cause of your kidney disease. If you have a blockage to your kidneys, surgery or the insertion of a tube or stent to bypass the blockage may be the treatment needed. If you have an inflammation of the kidneys called **glomerulonephritis**, you may be treated with immunosuppressive medications. Patients who have kidney failure due to medications will sometimes improve with time after the medicine has been stopped. The chance of your kidneys healing and of you getting off of dialysis depends on the amount of scarring of your kidneys that has occurred. Dialysis will keep you in good physical and nutritional shape while your doctors diagnose and treat your underlying kidney problem. Dialysis helps you by removing poisons and toxins, fluid, and electrolytes like potassium. It will remove acids that build up in the body. Dialysis can also remove certain medications and vitamins that are beneficial (see Question 25). Many patients have reported a decrease in the amount of urine they produce after starting dialysis. This is very common and does not mean that dialysis is making your kidneys worse. It is a common misconception that dialysis is responsible for some of the conditions associated with kidney failure such as neuropathy, anemia, or bone disease. It is actually the toxins and poisons that build up in the body that are responsible for these conditions, not the dialysis treatment. The buildup of toxins and poisons in the body is called **uremia**. Because dialysis cannot remove all the toxins and poisons, it is an imperfect treatment. Patients who receive more dialysis treatment time have less complications of kidney failure. The more you learn about dialysis by reading, talking to the dialysis team, and attending educational programs about renal failure, the better equipped you will be to actively participate in your care.

Glomerulonephritis

An inflammation of the filter or glomerulus of the kidney caused by many diseases.

Uremia

Symptoms caused by kidney failure that include loss of appetite, itching, hiccups, nausea, vomiting, seizures, and lethargy.

39. Can Jehovah's Witnesses be treated with dialysis?

Jehovah's Witnesses are members of a church that number one million people in the United States and six million people worldwide. Jehovah's Witnesses have a deeply held religious belief that they should not accept blood transfusions. They will not accept whole blood or parts of blood such as red blood cells, white blood cells, platelets, plasma, or serum albumin infusions. Jehovah's Witnesses are not against receiving medical care. I have taken care of many Jehovah's Witnesses, and all of them have accepted hemodialysis treatments. It is important to help minimize the possibility of blood loss to prevent the need for transfusion. This can be done by starting these patients on a medication called erythropoietin early in the course of their renal failure. Erythropoietin is a naturally occurring substance that is produced by the kidneys. It stimulates the production of red blood cells in the bone marrow. Erythropoietin is now manufactured and can be given by injection. Other brand names for erythropoietin are Epogen and Procrit.

Iron supplements given in pills or by intravenous injection can also be helpful. If the red blood cell level in the body is maintained at a near-normal level, the chance that a blood transfusion will be needed will be greatly reduced. It is also important to avoid blood thinners such as aspirin, Coumadin, Plavix, and other medications that can prevent the blood from clotting. If a surgical procedure is needed, a surgeon who is experienced in low-blood–loss surgery should be consulted. If bleeding occurs, a synthetically made product called recombinant factor VII is accepted by most Jehovah's Witnesses because it is not obtained from a blood donor. Kidney transplantation is not seen as the same as blood transfusions. Jehovah's Witnesses have received kidney, pancreas, liver, and bone marrow transplants. There has been a trend in medicine to use fewer blood transfusions in all patients because of the risks of transfusions. In 2001, the Society for the Advancement of Blood Management was formed by health professionals who are interested in reducing transfusions (*www.sabm.org*). Because of their religious beliefs, Jehovah's Witnesses have stimulated healthcare workers to develop new strategies to reduce bleeding and transfusions. Several blood substitutes are currently being evaluated in scientific clinical trials. These advances have benefited all patients, regardless of their religious beliefs.

40. Why do I need hemodialysis three times a week?

Our kidneys work 24 hours a day, 7 days a week. They work when we are sleeping, going to work, and eating meals, and they remove fluids, salts, toxins, and medications on a continuous basis. Hemodialysis removes these substances on an intermittent basis. Peritoneal dialysis is a chronic therapy and is more similar to our normal kidneys. In the early days of dialysis treatment, it was recognized by physicians that one or two hemodialysis treatments a week were not enough because patients had poor outcomes. Because of these observations, three times a week hemodialysis became the standard therapy. Insurance companies recognized three times a week hemodialysis.

Recently, there has been an interest in daily hemodialysis. This therapy is more similar to our normal kidney function and can be accomplished by being on home dialysis with treatments every day. Some patients choose to have dialysis at night. This is known as **nocturnal hemodialysis**. Patients on daily hemodialysis have lower blood pressures because fluid is removed every day. They are on less medication. Their phosphorus levels are lower and they have more energy. Of course, daily dialysis requires a huge commitment by the patient. Many people prefer to have dialysis three times a week because it allows them four days without dialysis treatments. Many patients ask if they will be better off on daily hemodialysis. I tell them to try it. Most patients on daily hemodialysis do not return to three times a week dialysis because they feel better. They are able to eat more varied foods and to increase their fluid intake.

No one therapy is right for everyone. I have seen patients go from home dialysis to in-center dialysis because of medical problems that required them to be under closer medical and nursing supervision. After their condition improved, they were able to return to home dialysis.

41. When will I meet the dialysis team?

You have already met the most important member of the dialysis team. You are that person. In order to have a successful experience on dialysis, you must be an active participant in your own care. The more responsibility you take, the more information you obtain, and the more positive your attitude, the better will be your outcome on dialysis. The next member of the dialysis

Nocturnal hemodialysis

Hemodialysis treatments done at night six or seven days a week at the patient's home while the patient is asleep. Nocturnal hemodialysis treatments utilize a lower blood pump flow and a longer duration of treatment time to achieve gentle treatments with better clearance of toxins and poisons.

team that you will meet is your nephrologist. You may meet this person in his or her office, in an emergency room, in an intensive care unit, or in the dialysis unit itself. Some patients are able to meet with their doctor when they are healthy in a relaxed atmosphere. You should remember that your nephrologist has helped many patients cope with dialysis and has a great deal of experience.

If possible, it is best to meet other members of the dialysis team by visiting a dialysis unit before you begin dialysis. This will allow you to observe other patients on dialysis and talk to them about their experiences. You will spend some time talking with a senior member of the dialysis nursing team. The dialysis nurse will want to know about your medical condition. He or she will want to evaluate the access that will be used for your first dialysis. The dialysis nurse will ask you questions about your other medical conditions including any allergies, your medicines, your job, your family, and where you live, and will try to understand you as a person.

The next member of the team you will meet is the social worker. Social workers have experience helping patients adjust to dialysis. They have special training in understanding the stresses you are experiencing and can recommend strategies to help you cope with dialysis. They understand insurance companies, how to get you to dialysis and back home with transportation, and how to pay for medication. They can advise you on obtaining dialysis treatments while you are traveling or are on vacation. They pretty much tackle everything else that the other members of the team are unable to cope with. They are often the easiest member of the dialysis team to talk with. If you are having a problem, this is a good team member to approach.

You will also meet the dietitian when you visit the dialysis unit. The more I learn about medical care, the more I understand that diet is very important. Being on the right diet can be the difference between success and failure on dialysis. The dietitian has seen many patients in your situation. He or she can give you helpful hints to select the right foods to stay healthy. Many patients have foods in their culture that require expert knowledge about how much of them they can eat. Chances are your doctor will refer you to the dietitian when you have questions about what to eat.

Being on the right diet can be the difference between success and failure on dialysis.

The dialysis technicians will assist the nursing staff. They will take blood pressures, monitor the dialysis treatment, and perform many other tasks in the unit under the direction of the nurses and doctors. You may spend more time with the dialysis technicians than any other team member because they are always by your side. They tend to be caring and interested in people. They often also have a great sense of humor, which helps a lot in coping with dialysis treatments.

The dialysis unit has a team of technical support staff. These team members make sure that the water supply is safe, that the supplies are available, and are able to repair equipment at a moment's notice.

The dialysis administrator is a person who oversees the entire dialysis unit. Often the administrator will hear from other team members about problems and will be able to solve them. This person recruits staff, makes schedules, leads staff meetings, and performs a host of tasks that are often taken for granted but that are crucial to the successful running of the dialysis unit.

Preparing to Begin Dialysis

42. What will happen on my first day of hemodialysis?

Many people will feel more comfortable bringing a family member or friend with them on the first day of hemodialysis. On arrival at the hemodialysis center, you will be seated in a waiting area. A staff member will greet you and bring you into an office for a brief meeting. There are usually a few administrative tasks to complete such as filling out a data sheet of your address, telephone numbers, and emergency contact information, and you will be asked to sign a consent form giving the staff permission to treat you. A medical history and physical examination are often performed on the first day of hemodialysis. These examinations give the physician and other staff members a baseline record of your medical condition and health history, including operations, allergies, immunizations, and medications. They will also give you a chance to bring specific concerns to your doctor's attention and alert him or her to any new medical problems.

Next you will be brought by a staff member into the treatment area. Your weight will be recorded before each treatment. At your first treatment, your height will be measured. If you are beginning dialysis in a hospital hemodialysis unit, you may be placed in a bed. In most hemodialysis units, whether in or out of hospital, you will be seated in a reclining chair that has large arm rests. This chair allows the staff to change your position from seated to reclining, which is important because patients sometimes feel dizzy due to a drop in blood pressure. You will feel less dizzy when placed in a reclining position. It is also more comfortable to be able to change your position several times during the 3 to 4 hours of your treatment.

After you are seated in your reclining chair, you will notice the dialysis machine to your side. A series of tubes and an electrical wire will be going from the machine to a series of connections in the wall behind the hemodialysis machine. These tubes bring water and dialysate to the dialysis machine. Another tube brings used dialysate from the machine to a drain to be discarded. A television set is often present on the other side of your reclining chair. If you forget to bring a set of headphones, the staff may be able to lend you one.

The hemodialysis procedure begins with the staff measuring your blood pressure, pulse, and temperature. Your access will be examined. If you have a catheter, you and the staff member performing your hemodialysis will wear a mask while you are being connected to the dialysis machine. The masks are to minimize the chances of developing an infection. The staff will also perform catheter care, which involves swabbing the part of the catheter that exits the skin with an antiseptic solution to prevent infection and covering it with a clean dressing. If you have an a-v fistula or an a-v graft, it will be cleaned with an antiseptic solution such as chlorhexidine or alcohol. A staff member will insert two needles in the access and securely tape them to the skin on your arm. You are now ready to begin your first hemodialysis treatment.

The machine will begin pumping blood from one of the needles through the plastic tubing that is filled with a saline solution. This needle is called the arterial needle because blood is coming from the patient to the machine. The tubing connected to the arterial needle is color-coded red. The blood will circulate through the machine pump and into a plastic drip chamber that will allow any air in the circuit to rise to the top. It will then go through the **dialyzer**, which is a plastic cartridge that contains about 13,000 small tubes that are surrounded by dialysate. The blood will then return through the tubing to the patient through the second needle, called the venous needle. The venous needle always carries blood from the machine to the patient. The tubing connected to it is color-coded blue. Since this is your first dialysis, it may be a shorter treatment today, perhaps for 3 hours. From time to time, a blood pressure cuff attached to your arm without the a-v access will tighten as it measures your blood pressure. The alarm on your machine may go off, which means that a beeping noise begins with a flashing light on the machine. This alarm does not indicate danger. It is designed to alert the staff to some parameter that needs checking.

As you look around, you will see other patients coming into the unit to begin their dialysis treatment. Other patients will be chatting with the person next to them or with staff members. Some patients will be sleeping, watching television, or reading a book. Other patients will be finishing their treatment and weighing themselves. After your dialysis treatment is finished, your weight, blood pressure, pulse, and temperature are recorded and are useful pieces of information to be used when you return for your next treatment. Staff members will be checking on you during your treatment. They may ask you for information or try to teach you some of the important points about the dialysis treatment. Do not expect to absorb too much

---

Dialyzer

A medical device that contains the dialysis membrane. It is connected to tubing that allows blood to flow into the dialyzer on one side of the membrane and then back to the patient. Dialysate flows on the other side of the membrane, and poisons and toxins move from the blood across the membrane into the dialysate, which is then discarded.

information on your first treatment. After your pre-scribed dialysis time is completed, an alarm (a beeping noise) will sound. The staff will flush the plastic tubing with saline solution. The lines will then be clamped, and the tubing will be disconnected from the needles. One needle will be removed, and a sterile gauze will be held over the needle hole with firm pressure until the bleeding has stopped. A Band-Aid will then be applied over the needle hole. The second needle will then be removed. It is a good idea to get up slowly after your dialysis treatment. Because fluid has been removed, patients can sometimes feel a bit dizzy. Do not forget to weigh yourself after your treatment. You will return for your next treatment in 2 days. Perhaps for your next treatment you will bring something to read or your iPod to listen to your favorite music to help pass the time.

43. How will I begin my peritoneal dialysis?

Peritoneal dialysis begins with the insertion of the peritoneal dialysis catheter. This access is a flexible plastic tube that is inserted into the abdomen during a minor surgical procedure under local anesthesia with sedation. The procedure is usually done as an outpa-tient. You may not have to stay overnight. A dressing or bandage will cover the incision as well as the catheter. It will take about 2 weeks for your catheter to heal before it can be used. This time will be spent learning how to perform your peritoneal dialysis. Peri-toneal dialysis is a home dialysis procedure, but your training will take place at the peritoneal dialysis unit. The unit may be located in a hemodialysis center or

Peritoneal dialysis is a home dialysis procedure, but your training will take place at the peritoneal dialysis unit.

may be in or close to a hospital or doctor's office. Most units have videos, slide shows, and printed material that will be used in your training. During the healing of your catheter, the peritoneal dialysis nurse or your physician may flush the catheter with a saline solution to keep the catheter from becoming clogged.

When your peritoneal dialysis catheter is ready, you will come to the peritoneal dialysis unit for training. After washing your hands, you will put on a face mask to prevent bacteria from your mouth and nose becoming aerosolized and landing on the catheter while it is being connected to tubing. Your peritoneal dialysis nurse will show you how to connect your catheter to plastic tubing. This task is not very hard, but it will take some time to feel comfortable performing it. The tubing is connected to a plastic bag containing 2 liters of peritoneal dialysis solution. This solution will be placed above your abdomen on a pole similar to those used for intravenous solutions in hospitals (**Figure 5**). A clamp will be opened to allow the peritoneal dialysis fluid to gently run into your abdomen. After the plastic bag is empty, you will disconnect the plastic tubing. The catheter will be secured to your abdomen with a dressing or an elastic belt. You are now free to walk around, eat, read, or perform any of the many activities that you normally would participate in during the day. When it is time to drain the fluid from your abdomen, you will again wash your hands and put on your face mask. After connecting your catheter to the plastic tubing, you will open the clamp and let the solution in your abdomen drain out into an empty plastic bag placed on the floor. The fluid from the abdomen flows out because of gravity. After the abdomen is emptied, the new peritoneal dialysis fluid will be hung on the

Figure 5   A peritoneal dialysis patient

Source: National Institute of Diabetes and Digestive and Kidney Diseases, National Institutes of Health.

pole to allow flow into the abdomen. The used peritoneal dialysis fluid containing poisons and waste
products is then discarded down the drain of a sink.
This process of emptying the abdomen of dialysate
and refilling the abdomen with fresh dialysate is called
an **exchange**. The peritoneal dialysis exchange is not
painful. Most patients perform 4 exchanges a day.

Exchange

A term used in peri-
toneal dialysis that
describes fluid being
drained using plastic
tubing from the
abdomen into a col-
lection bag. New
peritoneal dialysate
is infused by gravity
into the abdomen.

Peritoneal dialysis training usually takes place Monday through Friday. You may also be receiving hemodialysis treatments during your training to remove the toxins and waste products until you can perform the exchanges. As part of your peritoneal dialysis training, you will learn how to inject medications into the peritoneal dialysis bag. You will also learn to recognize the signs and symptoms of infection of the abdomen called peritonitis. Nutritional information will be given to you to help you choose healthy foods. The peritoneal dialysis training takes approximately 2 weeks for most people. Some patients learn faster than others. The most important point is to feel comfortable doing the dialysis. When you are confident with your peritoneal dialysis technique, the nurse will arrange for your supplies to be delivered to your home. After your training is completed, you will visit the peritoneal dialysis unit every month. The peritoneal dialysis nurse will check your catheter and draw monthly blood tests. You will review your progress with your physician at this visit. If problems occur between visits, a nurse is available by telephone 24 hours a day. You can contact the nurse who may direct you to come to the peritoneal dialysis unit or give you advice over the telephone.

PART FOUR

Living Well on Dialysis

Since beginning dialysis, I feel tired all the time. Will this improve with time?

Can dialysis patients be sexually active?

Can I travel as a dialysis patient?

More ...

44. Will my friends and family be able to tell I am on dialysis?

Even though I have special training in nephrology, I often cannot tell that people I meet in social situations are on dialysis. In the early days of dialysis, the dialysis was very inefficient in removing waste products and toxins. Patients were pale and had sickly looking complexions. It was common to smell an odor of urea caused by the very high levels of urea in the blood. Patients had severe deformities of the bones caused by metabolic bone disease. Patients today on dialysis are completely different. Modern hemodialysis and peritoneal dialysis are much more efficient at removing toxins and poisons from the blood. Less of these toxins present means there are less deposited in the skin. Erythropoietin is administered to most patients with anemia to raise their red blood cell count. The pale sickly complexion is not present in most patients. Patients are stronger because of their higher red blood cell count and have a much greater exercise tolerance. Because they look and feel better, they do not act like sick people. Of course, everyone is different. Some patients have severe systemic illnesses like hardening of the arteries, poorly-controlled diabetes, lupus erythematosus, or kidney failure associated with cancer. These individuals will appear ill.

The presence of a hemodialysis access in the arm is a tip off that a person is on hemodialysis. The access does not bother most patients. They leave the arm uncovered or wear long sleeves so the access is less noticeable. Some patients will discuss the placement of the access with their vascular surgeon. An a-v access in the upper arm may be less noticeable and is preferred by some patients.

One of the tricks to help you do well on dialysis is paying a little more attention to your appearance. It is important to comb and style your hair, wear a favorite shirt, or dress up a little. Women receiving dialysis treatments will often put on their makeup and tasteful jewelry before they come to their treatment. If you look good, people are less likely to respond to you as a sick person. You will feel better about yourself, have more self-esteem, and transmit these feelings to others who in turn will relate to you in a more positive way. Try this approach and see if it works for you.

If you look good, people are less likely to respond to you as a sick person.

I encourage people to tell their family, friends, and close colleagues at work that they are receiving dialysis treatments. This will give you additional people to talk with about problems. Many times, these people are sources of support. They may volunteer to drive you to dialysis when your car breaks down, help cover you at work when you have a doctor's appointment, and understand why you are having an occasional rough day. People you are close to may sense that you are sick from your actions. Many times people assume you have a worse condition than you actually have. Most of us know people who are on dialysis and are very accepting of the need for dialysis treatments.

45. Since beginning dialysis, I feel tired all the time. Will this improve with time?

Energy levels vary among individuals both before and after starting dialysis. We all know people who are in constant motion. They work hard, find time for a variety of activities and hobbies, and are always ready to go off on another endeavor at a moment's notice. The rest

Living Well on Dialysis

of us feel tired just thinking about doing these things. It is important to realize that dialysis is physically and psychologically demanding. You should take extra care of yourself during the stage when you are beginning dialysis treatments. You should get a full night's sleep. Make sure you sit down and eat three meals a day and a snack even though you are not hungry. It is also wise to avoid extra stress in your life like changing where you live, taking on a new job, or divorcing your spouse. These experiences can take a lot out of you and add to your fatigue.

The first thing to do if you feel tired is to review your medications with your physician. Many medications for blood pressure and pain, and some ulcer medications called histamine H_2-receptor antagonists, have side effects that will make you tired. Patients on dialysis are more likely to have side effects from medications, possibly because they metabolize medications more slowly than patients with normal renal function. Sleeping pills can build up in your body over time and cause you to be tired. Medications prescribed for anxiety and depression can sometimes decrease your energy level.

Because kidney failure causes our sleep-wake cycle to be reversed, many patients with kidney failure have difficulty sleeping at night. Patients may instead fall asleep during the day. This problem is due to changes in the body's hormonal cycle. Better sleep at night can be achieved by avoiding naps during the day. It is a good idea not to drink caffeinated beverages in the hours preceding sleep.

46. Can dialysis patients be sexually active?

Yes. There is nothing about hemodialysis or peritoneal dialysis treatments that would interfere with sexual activity. An interest in and the ability to engage in sexual activity is a sign of good health in kidney dialysis patients.

Some dialysis patients worry that sexual activity will damage their dialysis access. In hemodialysis, an a-v fistula or graft is usually located in the arm and is not affected by sexual activity. A hemodialysis catheter should be protected with a clean sterile dressing that is securely taped to the patient's chest. The peritoneal dialysis access is a catheter located in the lower abdomen. A clean, securely taped dressing over the catheter is all that is needed to protect it during sexual intercourse.

Recent research has discovered that the inability to participate in sexual intercourse in men with erectile dysfunction predicts their cardiac disease. Patients need to have a good vascular system so that blood can travel to the sexual organs as well as the heart. Smoking, poorly-controlled diabetes, high blood pressure, and an elevated cholesterol level can lead to hardening of the arteries. This process, called atherosclerosis, causes blockages in blood vessels all over the body. As a dialysis patient, you may have one or more of these conditions. It is important to decrease your risk of developing atherosclerosis to preserve your sexual function. The most important measure you can take to remain sexually active as you age is to stop smoking.

An interest in and the ability to engage in sexual activity is a sign of good health in kidney dialysis patients.

Living Well on Dialysis

Another major cause of sexual problems in dialysis patients is neuropathy. Neuropathy is damage to the peripheral nerves that exit the spinal cord and go to our arms, legs, skin, blood vessels, sexual organs, and other parts of our body. Poisons and toxins that build up in our blood in kidney failure can cause this nerve damage. Neuropathy can be prevented by having effective dialysis treatments to remove these substances. It is important that your dialysis treatment remove as much poisons and toxins as possible. This means a longer dialysis treatment. The longer we stay on dialysis, the more toxins and poisons are removed. Other causes of neuropathy in dialysis patients include poorly-controlled diabetes, alcohol abuse, vitamin B_{12} and thiamine deficiency, hypothyroidism, HIV/AIDS infection, vasculitis, and amyloidosis.

Medications can interfere with sexual activity. Many of the first blood pressure medications interfered with sexual activity, especially in men. Most of the new blood pressure medications are free of this unfortunate side effect. Medications for depression, anxiety, and sleeping pills can cause a decrease in interest in sexual activity.

If you have concerns about your sexual function, it is important to discuss this with your doctor in private. As a dialysis patient, many of your interactions with your doctor will be in the dialysis unit where there are other patients and staff members present, which is not the best place to discuss your concerns. Many patients are uncomfortable talking about sexual matters. Many doctors are also somewhat uncomfortable. It is a good idea to ask for a meeting in private and indicate why you wish to meet to allow your doctor to think about your case, review your medications, and develop an approach to working with you on your sexual health. You may or may not want to bring your spouse or sexual partner to the meeting. This is up to you.

The approach to treating kidney patients on dialysis with sexual problems is similar to treating patients who are not on dialysis. The evaluation and therapies are the same. If your dialysis physician is unable to treat your problem, he or she may refer you to a physician with special expertise in this field. Traditionally urologists have developed an interest in treating sexual problems. Gynecologists are often a good resource for women. It is important to find a physician with whom you feel comfortable discussing your sexual health in a nonjudgmental way.

Erick Lucero writes:

I began dialysis suddenly after my blood tests took a turn for the worse. At the time, I was tired and depressed. I didn't have much energy. I had a procedure to insert a catheter into my neck and another operation to put an a–v fistula in my arm. My doctor didn't talk to me about sex. My wife also had questions. At first, I was afraid that sexual activity would make me feel worse. After a month on dialysis, my wife and I decided on our own to have sex.

Since beginning dialysis, I feel better and have a lot more energy. My wife and I have sex more often. We use birth control because we are not ready to have another child. I feel that a discussion about when it is advisable to begin sexual activity should be part of the protocol of every patient's counseling about beginning dialysis. This would be really helpful to patients.

47. Can I have children while I am being treated with dialysis?

Men who have kidney failure can father children. Women have difficulty becoming pregnant. This is because many women with kidney failure stop menstruating. They do not release eggs from their ovaries. If they do have menstrual periods, they often have anovulatory cycles. This means that they do not release an egg cell from their ovaries. When women do have a normal period and become pregnant, the fertilized egg has difficulty developing normally, and there is an increased chance of a spontaneous miscarriage. Despite these limitations, a few women become pregnant on dialysis. As dialysis becomes more efficient and patients have higher blood counts due to erythropoietin, it is possible for more women to become pregnant on dialysis. Very few of these pregnancies are successful. Many of the babies are born too early and are premature.

It is important for women on dialysis to discuss their medical condition with their obstetrician-gynecologist. There may be medical reasons why becoming pregnant might be dangerous to a woman's health. If you think you might be pregnant, it is important to tell your physician. Your physician can review your medications to determine which ones are safe in pregnancy. ACE inhibiters and angiotensin receptor blockers used for treating high blood pressure and heart failure should be stopped if you could be pregnant. These drugs can cause a miscarriage. If you are on these medications, do not panic. Many women on these medications have had successful pregnancies after conceiving. Your doctor can guide you in selecting other medications that are safe for pregnancy. Some birth control methods may be safer than others for women with kidney failure.

Women on birth control pills have a higher chance of stroke and clots that can form in their legs. Birth control methods such as condoms and the diaphragm are well tolerated and safe for dialysis patients. Ask your kidney physician which method is right for you. Women who receive kidney transplants have a very rapid return to fertility and could conceive in the first month after receiving their transplant. Patients are most likely to reject their new kidney during the first 2 years of their transplant. Women need to receive counseling on avoiding becoming pregnant during this important time. After 2 years, if all is going well with the kidney transplant, your transplant physician will advise you that it is safe to become pregnant. Kidney transplantation is the best option for women with kidney failure who want to have a family.

Erick Lucero writes:

I got married before I began hemodialysis treatments. I thought my life was over, and I would be bedridden and sick. My wife was very supportive. She encouraged me to get married despite having renal failure. We planned the pregnancy together. One year before beginning dialysis, we had a beautiful baby girl. My daughter helps me a lot by taking my mind off of dialysis. When I started dialysis, I took time off from work and would take her to the park. She is the best.

Since beginning dialysis, we have thought about having another child, but we are not ready yet. We use birth control and will plan on when to have the next baby. I am worried about the finances of having another child. Also my wife does most of the child care because I am at work or on dialysis. It is easy to take care of one baby, but two with one parent during the day will be harder.

48. How long can I live on dialysis?

This is the most frequent question I am asked by patients who are beginning dialysis. Patients who do not ask this important question must be thinking about it. Doctors developed the ability to treat large numbers of patients with chronic kidney failure in the 1970s. The technology to treat these patients with dialysis was poor. The machines were inaccurate. Doctors could not remove large amounts of poisons and toxins. Medications to treat anemia, hypertension, high cholesterol, diabetes, and heart disease were not as effective as modern medications. Despite these limitations, some patients were able to live for over 30 years after beginning dialysis. Patients beginning dialysis today benefit from better dialysis treatments, better medications, better nursing and medical care, and an expectation by the medical community that they will do well on dialysis. In the 1970s, many physicians felt there was no point in treating patients with dialysis because the prognosis was so poor. This attitude has disappeared as doctors began to see long-term survivors on dialysis. Dialysis will continue to improve due to new discoveries and advances in technology. The major causes of death in the United States and other developed countries are heart disease, stroke, and cancer. The outlook for these diseases is rapidly improving and will continue to improve. Improved treatment of these other diseases will also lead to patients living longer on dialysis.

It is hard to answer patients who want to know how long they will live. Doctors do not know the answer to this crucial question. There is no reason why a highly motivated patient with no other serious medical conditions who began dialysis at 20 years of age could not

Patients beginning dialysis today benefit from better dialysis treatments, better medications, better nursing and medical care, and an expectation by the medical community that they will do well on dialysis.

live for 50 years or more on dialysis. What do I mean by a highly motivated patient? There are four goals that every patient must accomplish to live a long life on dialysis:

1. You must achieve a good dialysis. This does not mean just removing lots of fluid. It means that a large amount of poisons and toxins must be removed. To accomplish this, you must have a good dialysis access. You must have enough time on dialysis. If you are on hemodialysis, this probably means at least 4 hours of hemodialysis 3 times a week. You must not skip any dialysis treatments or fail to perform peritoneal dialysis exchanges. Your healthcare team will be meeting with you and discussing with you the adequacy of your dialysis.

2. You must take special care to keep on your diet and fluid restriction. The more we learn about illness, we realize that what we eat and drink is very important. Patients who continually eat and drink inappropriate foods to excess will decrease their chances of being long-term survivors on dialysis.

3. Make sure you always take your medication. Having a high blood pressure, elevated blood sugar if you are a diabetic, elevated cholesterol, or bone disease will take its toll over the years.

4. Listen to common sense advice concerning your health. This means not smoking, drinking to excess, or using drugs. It means wearing your seatbelt and not driving too fast. If you are a biker or skier, it means wearing a helmet. If you have a gun, keep it locked up and away from children. Do not swim alone. These measures are important for you and your family whether you are treated with dialysis or not.

49. Can I shorten my dialysis treatments?

Patients, doctors, and nurses have always been interested in decreasing the amount of time on dialysis. Patients want to spend as little time on dialysis as possible. It is difficult to sit in one place for 4 hours. The last hour of dialysis is physically and mentally difficult for some patients. A hemodialysis treatment which would last 3 hours or $2\frac{1}{2}$ hours would be much easier than a 4- or 5-hour dialysis treatment.

To accomplish this, high-flux (or high-efficiency) hemodialysis was developed during the 1980s. The blood flow running through the dialysis machine was increased from 300 mL/min to 450 mL/min. Large dialysis membranes with large surface areas were used to allow more blood to be in contact with more dialysate. Dialysis times were decreased to 3, $2\frac{1}{2}$, and sometimes even $2\frac{1}{4}$ hours. The owners of dialysis units were encouraged by high-flux dialysis because less hours for dialysis meant less nursing labor costs. The results of the experiment with high-flux dialysis were a disaster. Patients had more complications. Patients treated with high-flux dialysis did not live as long as patients on regular, longer dialysis. High-flux dialysis was abandoned, and patients went back to longer dialysis treatments.

Several important lessons were learned from this experiment. The importance of increasing blood flow to achieve better removal of poisons and toxins was recognized. The need for better dialyzers with increased clearances and surface areas was appreciated. This finding allowed regular, longer dialysis treatments to remove more poisons and toxins, which made dialysis better by decreasing complications of kidney failure such as neuropathy. In the early days of dialysis, many patients suffered from pericarditis (an inflammation of the lining of the heart). Patients accumulated fluid in the lung called pleural effusion, or in the abdomen called ascites. These complications are much less frequent now that dialysis is more efficient and removes more toxins.

Recently, nocturnal hemodialysis has allowed patients to receive dialysis treatments 6 nights a week while they sleep. This home dialysis treatment involves hemodialysis with a low blood flow rate for 6 to 7 hours, 6 nights a week. Patients have much more toxins and poisons removed with this increased dialysis time and feel better. They are able to eat more varieties of food containing potassium and phosphorus that are restricted in the diet of patients on dialysis three times a week. Fluid restriction is not necessary because of daily fluid removal. Blood pressure is decreased by nocturnal dialysis, and some patients can decrease or stop their blood pressure medications. The present trend is to increase the time on dialysis to improve patient outcomes. The best way to decrease time on dialysis is to consider a kidney transplant. This will allow you to stop dialysis completely.

50. Can I travel as a dialysis patient?

Since the 1970s, patients and doctors on dialysis have been trying to overcome the psychological effects of being connected to the hemodialysis machine. Early on, there were few dialysis centers and travel was limited. Several doctors developed miniature portable hemodialysis machines that were set up by the patient and allowed them to travel. These machines never really caught on, though. One problem is water quality. All modern dialysis centers have an extensive water purification system, which consists of a series of filters to remove particulate matter. After passing through these filters, the water is pumped at high pressure through a reverse osmosis membrane to eliminate elements such as aluminum and copper, producing water that is pure. Reverse osmosis membranes and filters are available for home use, but they significantly increase the size of the dialysis machine. This makes traveling with your dialysis machine difficult. There are dialysis systems that regenerate dialysis and do not require large amounts of pure water. Recently, a new machine called the Nx Stage, which is simpler to set up and use, has become available.

Many hemodialysis units will admit patients that travel who are known as transient patients.

As more hemodialysis centers opened, the need for portable dialysis machines that could be taken with the patient decreased. Many hemodialysis units will admit patients that travel who are known as transient patients. You must plan ahead. Arranging for hemodialysis at another center is best done several months before your trip. Most units will require you to send part of your medical record, which includes a copy of your last physical examination and blood tests. Some centers will want a chest x-ray, **EKG**, and HIV testing before they will accept you. Most centers are happy to have you dialyze with them. They realize that their own patients will travel and know that a warm welcome to transient patients will make their trip successful.

Electrocardiogram (EKG)

A medical test in which electrical impulses generated by the heart are recorded by attaching electrodes to the arms, legs, and chest.

Your health insurance will pay for dialysis treatments within the United States. If you want to travel to another country, you will probably have to pay for the treatments. This can be expensive, up to $600 per treatment at some European dialysis units. Some cruise ship lines have organized cruises for dialysis patients. The ship will have hemodialysis machines as well as doctors and nurses on board to allow you to receive your treatments. They will also arrange to serve meals that are healthy for renal patients. One of the difficulties in traveling is the temptation to go off the renal diet because food that is low in sodium, potassium, and phosphorus is harder to find.

Patients on peritoneal dialysis have an easier time traveling. They can arrange to have supplies shipped to their travel destination and do not have to depend on a dialysis unit because they perform their own treatment. They have more flexibility and can change their itinerary at a moment's notice. This is one of the benefits of peritoneal dialysis treatments.

51. Is home dialysis for me?

Home dialysis has many important advantages to the patient. Because home dialysis patients usually perform their own dialysis treatment, they learn a great deal about how to effectively treat kidney failure. The home dialysis patient is able to schedule his or her treatments around work and family responsibilities and has the flexibility to perform an extra treatment if needed. There is no travel time to the dialysis center, which is especially important for patients who live in rural areas who would have to travel several hours to the nearest dialysis center. In some parts of the world, there are no dialysis units, and home dialysis or kidney transplant are the only option. Some patients must leave their country to obtain dialysis treatments. They cannot go back home because dialysis is not available on many of the Caribbean Islands or in some parts of South America, Africa, and Asia. This is rapidly changing. Many countries are developing dialysis centers to offer modern treatments to their citizens. Home dialysis is cheaper. The cost of the dialysis is the supplies and dialysis machine. There is no cost for the person performing the dialysis, as the patient is doing the work. There is no rent for the dialysis unit, no heating or air conditioning costs, insurance costs, or extra telephone service. Patients on home dialysis do not have to wait their turn to begin their treatment.

The disadvantages of home dialysis are few. Some patients feel more comfortable in the dialysis center because their doctor will see them while they are receiving hemodialysis. Dialysis nurses and technicians will perform your hemodialysis at the dialysis unit. Most patients on home dialysis perform their own dialysis treatment. On home dialysis, you will go to the doctor's office once a month. The dialysis team may make a home visit, but for the most part you will be on dialysis at home with your **dialysis partner**. My colleague and friend Dr. Roxanna Bologa, Director of Peritoneal Dialysis at the Rogosin Institute, tells her patients, "Just because you are on home dialysis does not mean you are alone." Your doctor and nurse are just a phone call away.

Most patients on home hemodialysis have a family member help them with their dialysis. A few home hemodialysis patients have a nurse or dialysis technician perform their dialysis at home. Most insurances will not pay for a dialysis nurse at home. Peritoneal dialysis patients usually perform their own treatment at home. Some elderly patients or children have the dialysis performed by a family member.

Dialysis partner

A person who has received special training in performing hemodialysis or peritoneal dialysis and who assists you in performing dialysis at home.

Many hemodialysis patients begin hemodialysis treatments at the dialysis unit under the care of their doctors and nurses. When they feel comfortable on dialysis, they begin training with a partner and learn to perform their own dialysis. These patients then dialyze at home. If their medical condition changes, they can always go back to the dialysis unit for a period of time when they may need closer observation. The best way to determine if home dialysis is for you is to talk with patients on home dialysis. They can give firsthand information about dialysis at home and share some of their experiences with you.

52. Will dialysis frighten my young children?

Children are very adaptable. They are perceptive and can sense when adults are hiding things from them to "protect them." Children are exposed to many different kinds of illness by the media. Human-interest stories on television and the newspapers have graphic pictures of patients with all sorts of medical conditions, including kidney failure. News reports show dead bodies of people who have died by illness, natural disasters, or wars. I am amazed that it is common to view actual operations on daytime television that can be seen by young children. The best approach with your children is to explain to them that you have a kidney problem and that your dialysis treatments will help you remain healthy. Explain to them when you will be having your dialysis treatments and when you will be away from home. The amount of information you give your child will of course depend on your child's age. Teenagers may better understand the scientific aspects of dialysis.

The best approach with your children is to explain to them that you have a kidney problem and that your dialysis treatments will help you remain healthy.

It is best not to take young children into the dialysis unit. Young children could be potentially distracting to the dialysis caregivers who should focus on giving you the best possible dialysis treatment and not be worried about the effect on your child of seeing a parent on dialysis. Having your child keep you company while you are on home dialysis is fine. It is a good time to talk, watch television together, or perhaps review a homework assignment. It is reasonable to have your child visit you if you are hospitalized. In general, it is better if children avoid going to the intensive care unit. They may be exposed to infectious diseases carried by other patients, and the experience of seeing critically ill patients may be upsetting.

I find that older adult children are much more disturbed by a parent on dialysis than are younger children. They are much more fearful that dialysis will mean they will lose you to illness. A good way to cope with these fears is to assign your children tasks to help you. Have them bring your favorite sweater or book to the hospital. Let them drive you to the dialysis unit or to doctors' visits. This involvement will allow them to adjust to seeing you on dialysis and will make them less fearful. It will give you both time to talk about the impact kidney dialysis is having on your life. It is important not to underestimate the impact of your kidney failure and dialysis treatments on your family. Even though you are doing well and are making progress, this is a major stress for your spouse, children, significant other, and friends. Talk about the impact of your dialysis treatment on your family with your doctor and the dialysis team. Your doctor has seen hundreds of patients and their families cope with kidney dialysis. You have the experience of one person.

53. Can I drive my car to my dialysis treatments?

Many patients drive to their dialysis treatments. You should absolutely not drive your car to your first dialysis treatment. You will be under a great deal of stress, and you will need to have someone else get you to dialysis and get you home. Driving to dialysis is not a problem. Driving home after your treatment is more of a concern. During the hemodialysis treatment, 2 to 3 liters of fluid (a little less than 2 to 3 quarts) are removed from your blood. Sometimes this can cause your blood pressure to decrease, and you might feel a bit weak or dizzy after your dialysis treatment. This effect is especially common during the first few weeks on hemodialysis. I generally counsel patients to arrange for 2 weeks of transportation when beginning hemodialysis. Some insurance plans will pay for transportation to and from the dialysis unit. After this time, you can ask your doctor if he or she feels it is safe for you to drive to your treatments. Having kidney dialysis treatments will make you eligible for a handicapped parking permit. Talk to your dialysis social worker who can help you obtain this useful permit.

Erick Lucero writes:

When I first started dialysis, I didn't want to drive to my treatments. I had a new a–v fistula in my arm, and I felt I needed two strong arms to drive safely. After several weeks, I began to drive to my dialysis treatments. Parking can be a problem near my dialysis unit. I have a metrocard in my pocket for emergencies. If I cannot find a parking spot I park at home and take the bus to the dialysis unit. I'm not far away—about 10 blocks. I can walk to dialysis if I have to. After working all day and being on dialysis for 4 hours, I want to be home as soon as possible.

54. What can I do during my dialysis treatments?

Your hemodialysis treatment will last $3\frac{1}{2}$ to 4 hours. Part of this time will be spent talking to the dialysis staff to tell them how you are feeling, checking your blood pressure and temperature, and having any needed prescriptions refilled by your doctor. You will use your time on dialysis to talk to the dietitian to learn which foods are healthy for you to eat and which foods are best avoided. Your nurse and physician will review your medications and let you know how your dialysis treatments are going. The social worker will visit with you from time to time. Our dialysis unit has a **podiatrist** and a psychologist who will see patients while they are on hemodialysis treatment. This allows them to use their days off hemodialysis for other activities.

Patients look forward to chatting with other patients in the waiting area of the dialysis unit and during hemodialysis treatments. They exchange experiences and support each other during difficult times. Many patients on the same dialysis shift have their treatments at the same time for several years, and there is a social aspect to the dialysis unit that is enjoyable. Some patients, especially patients who work full time, take the opportunity to nap. If you work 40 hours a week and have dialysis 4 hours, 3 times a week, using your time on dialysis to catch up on your rest is a good strategy. The laptop computer has enabled many patients to get their work done while on dialysis. Teachers often spend their time on dialysis grading papers or working on lesson plans. Watching television is always an option. Every dialysis unit has televisions,

Podiatrist

A healthcare professional who is trained in the diagnosis and treatment of disorders of the feet.

usually personal flat screen units that are provided free. Bring your headphones. If you forget them, the unit may be able to lend you a pair. It is common to see patients watching movies on DVD players or laptops. Libraries will lend you DVDs and books on CD or tapes. Did I forget to mention reading books? Some patients will bring their Bible or religious reading material to dialysis. Take your time enjoying the newspaper. Read that catalogue of fishing equipment laying on your desk at home. Consider learning a new language on DVD or tape. College lectures are also available to listen to and watch. Crossword puzzles, word puzzles, and sudoku are very popular. Most dialysis units allow you to talk on your cell phone. Call your nephew to see how he is doing in his first year of college. Catch up with old friends. You may need to increase the minutes on you calling plan when you begin dialysis. Patients use their time on dialysis to work on knitting and crochet. One of my patients on hemodialysis is presently knitting beautiful wool hats.

Patients on peritoneal dialysis spend most of their time performing their exchanges. It takes about 20 minutes to drain the fluid from their abdomen and another 20 minutes to infuse the fresh dialysate. This time can be spent doing other activities.

One approach to hemodialysis treatments is to resent every minute you are forced to spend on dialysis. Another approach is to find activities that are useful and productive, either from a recreational or work point of view (**Figure 6**). Remember, dialysis is the perfect excuse for finding some time for you.

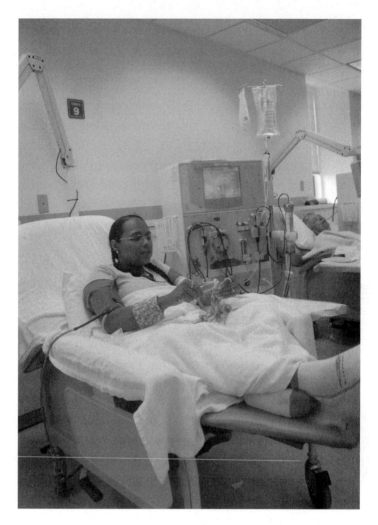

Figure 6   A patient, Yoshi Reynolds, crocheting during her hemodialysis treatment
Source: K. Neelakantappa, MD

55. Will I have the same nurse or technician for every hemodialysis treatment?

Most patients develop close relationships with the members of the dialysis team that take care of them three times a week. It is natural to trust these skilled caregivers and to feel threatened if they are not always available. Team members call in sick, go on vacation, or have responsibilities at home that may make them unavailable for your dialysis treatment. Because no team member can be available all the time, it is common to rotate the dialysis staff within the dialysis unit. This allows a larger number of staff members to be familiar with your treatment. Some patients have difficulty with inserting needles into their dialysis access. There is always one staff member in every unit who is especially skilled at placing dialysis needles. This procedure is called **cannulation** of the access. It is important that staff members in the unit communicate with other staff members about your access. This way, a variety of staff members will be able to place you on dialysis if your regular nurse or technician is not available. Some patients have a fall in blood pressure at the same time during their hemodialysis treatment. Staff members who know this will be able to give you some extra fluid at the right time to prevent you from getting dizzy or sick. As you spend more time on dialysis, you will have less anxiety about new staff members performing your dialysis. Feel free to give them helpful advice about your particular pattern on hemodialysis.

Most patients develop close relationships with the members of the dialysis team that take care of them three times a week.

Cannulation

The insertion of needles into the dialysis access to obtain blood for hemodialysis.

56. Which vaccines should I receive?

When you begin your dialysis treatments, you will be tested for hepatitis B as well as hepatitis C. A series of three immunizations is available to stimulate antibody production by your body against hepatitis B. These antibodies will decrease your chances of developing hepatitis B if you are exposed. Most patients who do not have antibodies decide to receive the hepatitis B vaccine. Vaccination is also available for hepatitis A, but protection only lasts for about 6 months. This vaccine is useful if you will be traveling to areas that have a large number of hepatitis A cases. If you have chronic hepatitis C, you should take the hepatitis B vaccine to prevent further damage to your liver.

Patients on dialysis are offered the pneumococcal vaccine. This can protect you from developing pneumococcal pneumonia. This potentially life-threatening illness can be more serious in dialysis and kidney transplant patients because their immune response to infection is decreased by kidney failure. The anti-rejection medications taken by kidney transplant patients also decrease the body's defense against infection. I always recommend the influenza vaccine to my patients and coworkers at the dialysis unit. Being sick with the flu is no fun. You can transmit influenza virus to members of your family and other people. The risks are small compared to the benefits. Kidney dialysis patients should receive the inactivated influenza vaccine. They should not receive the live attenuated influenza vaccine. Hepatitis B vaccine, pneumococcal vaccine, and the inactivated influenza vaccine are routinely given to patients in the dialysis unit. As part of your dialysis evaluation, you will have a skin test for tuberculosis. In some countries, the **BCG** vaccine is given to patients to prevent tuberculosis. BCG is not recommended for patients in the United States. For more information, the Center for Disease Control and Prevention has prepared Guidelines for Vaccination in Kidney Dialysis Patients and Patients with Chronic Kidney Diseases (*www.cdc.gov*).

BCG

Bacillus Calmette-Guerin is a tuberculosis vaccine given to children in many countries with a high prevalence of tuberculosis. Patients who have received BCG will often have a positive skin test for tuberculosis for the rest of their lives.

PART FIVE

Nutrition on Dialysis

Why do I have to watch what I eat?

What is a renal diet?

Why are potassium and phosphorus so important?

More ...

57. Why do I have to watch what I eat?

As we learn more about the science of medical illness, we realize that diet is very important. As a kidney dialysis patient, you will need expert advice regarding your own individual diet. Many well-meaning people will give you advice, urging you to drink more fluid to flush your kidneys, or to drink cranberry juice. Thank these well wishers for their concern, then discuss your diet with your physician. He or she may not be able to give you all the answers you need, but you will be pointed in the right direction. Your physician can guide you to eat more calories if you need to gain weight or restrict calories to lose weight. He or she will know how much fluid intake is advisable and which foods to avoid if you have high cholesterol, diabetes, heart problems, or other medical conditions. Most physicians have a registered dietitian working with them in the dialysis center who can refine your dietary plan and give you specific information regarding the nutritional content of foods. The dietitian will work with you to help you choose foods that you will like to eat and that are good for you.

If our kidneys are normal, we are able to eat a large variety of foods without a thought. If we eat a large amount of salt, our kidneys will measure the increase and immediately take steps to begin eliminating the salt from our body. If we drink a large amount of fluid, our kidneys will recognize this fluid overload and begin increasing urine formation. If our kidneys become damaged, they lose their ability to respond to variations in diet. Often, diseased kidneys begin retaining salt and fluid when they should be eliminating them. This fluid and salt retention can cause swelling of our legs. The medical term for this is **edema**. As we retain more fluid and salt, some of the

Edema

The medical term for fluid that collects in an area of the body. The most common location for edema is in the legs. The legs appear swollen, especially after walking around. The edema decreases after a night's sleep because it has moved to other areas of the body. Other areas that can collect fluid are the lungs and abdomen.

fluid can back up into our lungs and cause shortness of breath. Fluid retention will also cause our blood pressure to rise and be uncontrolled. This is why kidney patients must measure and restrict the amount of fluid and salt they consume every day.

Once we begin our dialysis treatments, fluid, salt, and other substances are removed during the dialysis treatment. If we are on hemodialysis, about 2 to 3 liters are removed during each treatment. This is about 2.1 to 3.2 quarts of fluid. Removing more fluid on hemodialysis is not that easy or comfortable for the patient. Therefore, it would be advisable to limit fluid intake to the amount we can safely remove. If we are on hemodialysis every other day, this means decreasing our intake to 1 to 1.5 liters a day. Our kidneys no longer can tell that we are gaining fluid. We can tell by weighing ourselves. If we drink 1 liter of fluid, our weight increases by 2.2 pounds. Hemodialysis patients routinely weigh themselves before and after their treatments to see if they have had a successful treatment. Peritoneal dialysis patients weigh themselves every day. Because peritoneal dialysis patients are on dialysis every day, they can often drink more fluid than hemodialysis patients on a daily basis. If they drink too much, and their weight increases, they can increase the amount of fluid removed by changing the dialysate. This ability to remove fluid and salt on a daily basis is one of the advantages of peritoneal dialysis.

While on kidney dialysis, you will be constantly monitoring the levels of potassium, phosphorus, calcium, and cholesterol in your blood. These tests will be measured on a monthly basis, and you will receive a copy of your blood test results and discuss these findings with the dialysis team. If you are a diabetic, you will also monitor your glucose or sugar level on a daily basis. By making small changes in your diet in response to these blood tests, you can improve your results. This seems like a lot of work, but patients will spend a great deal of time learning about diet when they begin dialysis. As time goes on, they will become more accustomed to their diet and will have an easier time making healthy food choices.

58. What is a renal diet?

Renal diet

A diet that avoids foods that contain sodium, potassium, and phosphorus, and limits the amount of fluid intake.

A **renal diet** is a term used to describe the guidelines developed for patients with renal disease. Your dietitian and physician will give you specific recommendations on your own individual renal diet. They will review factors such as your age, weight, blood test results, and your current urine output in preparing your diet.

Most likely, your renal diet will restrict your salt or sodium chloride intake to 2 grams a day. Sometimes food packages list their sodium content per serving in milligrams; 2 grams is equal to 2,000 milligrams. The need to restrict salt is due to salt retention caused by diseased kidneys. We excrete most of our salt in the urine and a small amount in sweat. If a dialysis patient eats too much salt, he or she may have high blood pressure. This can put a strain on the heart or lead to a stroke. If the heart becomes overloaded by too much salt and water, it may fail to pump enough blood, causing shortness of breath as fluid backs up into the lungs. Potassium is another salt that must be restricted to 2 grams, or 2,000 milligrams, a day. Potassium is inside all of the cells that make up our body. If the potassium level in the blood gets too high, it can cause heart problems and muscle weakness. A high potassium level can be diagnosed by a blood test or by an EKG of the heart. Some foods that are high in potassium include oranges, orange juice, cantaloupe, bananas, and tomatoes.

Phosphorus is an important mineral because it is needed to store energy from food for later use. It is also present in our bones. The only way we can excrete phosphorus from our body is through our kidneys. As our kidney function decreases, phosphorus builds up in our bloodstream, causing calcium in our blood to be deposited back into our bones. As the blood-calcium level falls, it stimulates the production of parathyroid hormone, called PTH for short, by the parathyroid gland. Parathyroid hormone will cause more calcium to be absorbed in our small intestine. It will also cause the release of too much calcium from our bones, which can lead to weakening of our bones and even fractures. We must control the phosphorus level in our blood to keep our bones healthy. This is accomplished by taking medications called phosphate binders that bind phosphorus that we eat in our intestine. We also must decrease the amount of phosphorus we eat every day. Phosphorus is contained in meat, dairy products, and beans, such as lentils and kidney beans.

Protein is an important part of the renal diet. You need to eat about 1.2 grams of protein per kilogram of body weight, which is 7 to 8 ounces of meat, chicken, or fish a day. Many people are under the impression that they should not eat protein if they are a kidney dialysis patient. This advice is wrong and could lead to protein malnutrition. Protein is needed to build and repair muscles, make blood cells, fight infection, and perform many other metabolic tasks in our body.

How many calories are needed every day? This depends on our age, how physically active we are, and how much we weigh. About 30 kilocalories per kilogram, or 2,000 to 2,500 calories, will be the ideal daily range for most kidney dialysis patients.

Your own personal diet will also depend on other medical problems. If you have an elevated cholesterol level or diabetes, these conditions will be taken into account when your dietitian and physician formulate your renal diet. Most patients begin to learn about their diet on the first day of dialysis. The dietitian often introduces himself or herself and gives the patient a diet sheet. He or she will remind the patient that alternatives to the diet sheet are possible and will review favorite foods that can fit into the renal diet. The patient then meets the social worker, doctor, and nurses in the dialysis unit. Then they have their first treatment. When patients first look at the diet sheet, they focus on their favorite foods that are prohibited, increasing their feeling of loss. Not only will they be stuck on dialysis, but they will never be able to eat normal foods again. I prefer to think of the renal diet as a voyage. We start in one place and slowly travel to another place. Many patients have some residual renal function when they start dialysis. This means that they are making urine and getting rid of some toxins and poisons, but not enough to stay off dialysis. The renal diet is not as important at the beginning of dialysis as it will be later on when the residual renal function is gone. Most patients have time to adjust to the renal diet. At the beginning of your dialysis treatments, you should concentrate on one or two important points. This may be to decrease your fluid and salt intake. You may be already accustomed to eating a low-salt diet. Ask your doctor and dietitian to tell you the most important part of the renal diet for you. This will prevent you from being overwhelmed and help you concentrate on getting used to your dialysis treatments. Later on, you can learn more when you are feeling better physically and psychologically. Your ability to manage your diet will improve. You will head in the right direction and develop healthier eating habits. Remember that all worthwhile voyages take time.

Erick Lucero writes:

My wife does the cooking in our family. She eats the same food as I do. She doesn't mind the renal diet, and we both try to eat healthy. We have a pamphlet prepared by a nutritionist, which is like a menu. It plans meals on the renal diet for several days. We eat a lot of chicken. I eat a small amount of tomatoes once a week. Instead of oranges, I try to eat lots of raspberries and blueberries. I am a Mexican-American, and a lot of our traditional foods are not on the renal diet. Once in a while, I eat some beans with hot sauce. I watch my lab tests to make sure my potassium and phosphorus levels are not high because of my diet. My father died young at age 51. I want to take good care of myself because I have a young daughter to take care of. I want to live as long a life as I can.

59. Can I eat more foods on peritoneal dialysis?

Yes, one of the joys of peritoneal dialysis is the ability to eat more varieties of food. Patients on hemodialysis must restrict their diet to about 1 to 1½ quarts or liters of fluid a day. Hemodialysis is an intermittent therapy. This means that you are receiving a treatment and then fluid and poisons will build up in your body for 2 days before you will have another treatment. In peritoneal dialysis, you are receiving treatment throughout the day every day. Fluid is removed every day. Potassium is usually a little low or normal, allowing you to eat orange juice, potatoes, tomatoes, and other high-potassium foods. Phosphorus, which is restricted on hemodialysis, is also removed on a daily basis on peritoneal dialysis. Patients on peritoneal dialysis can eat more dairy products such as milk, ice cream, and cheese. Beans and meats also contain phosphorus.

One would think that everyone would want to be on peritoneal dialysis so they could avoid a restrictive renal diet. However, peritoneal dialysis is less efficient than hemodialysis. This means that very large patients are not able to remove enough toxins and poisons to prevent the complications of renal failure. Patients who do well on peritoneal dialysis have some residual renal function. Their kidneys still produce some urine and this helps eliminate more poisons. It is also important to determine if you are willing to be on dialysis every day. As a peritoneal dialysis patient, you will be doing your own dialysis. This allows flexibility but also requires responsibility. If you think peritoneal dialysis may be for you, talk to your dialysis team. They can put you in contact with a peritoneal dialysis nurse. This nurse has a great deal of experience in treating patients on peritoneal dialysis. He or she can give you specific scientific information about peritoneal dialysis and introduce you to patients on peritoneal dialysis. You will be able to hear in these patients' own words the advantages of being on peritoneal dialysis.

As a peritoneal dialysis patient, you will be doing your own dialysis. This allows flexibility but also requires responsibility.

It is important to mention that daily nocturnal home dialysis also allows the patient to eat and drink a larger variety of foods. This is because dialysis is typically done 6 or 7 days a week. Fluid, salt, potassium, phosphorus, toxins, and poisons are all removed on a daily basis. This allows you to eat at your favorite restaurant, then go home and remove all of the substances that can cause problems just like your own kidneys would. Make sure you consider daily nocturnal dialysis if you like to eat.

Patients with renal failure who choose to have a kidney transplant have an increased variety of food choices. Many transplant patients must still restrict the amount of salt they eat because they may still tend to retain salt. They can drink more fluid and eat more potassium and phosphorus than hemodialysis patients. They must still pay attention to their cholesterol intake if they have a high cholesterol level. Diabetic patients will still be diabetic when they are on renal replacement therapy. Many diabetic patients will have a better appetite when they begin dialysis, resulting in an increased intake of calories and an increased blood sugar. It is important to realize that you will need to adjust your diabetes medications after you start renal replacement therapy.

60. How much fluid should I drink every day?

The amount of fluid that you can safely drink on dialysis will depend on the amount of urine you make. If you continue to make a large amount of urine, you are very lucky. This will allow you to drink more. Before you begin dialysis, your doctor will probably order a 24-hour urine collection for creatinine clearance. This important test will determine if you need to start dialysis. It will also give you an idea of how much urine you are producing every day. Most of us have no idea.

We know how many times we urinate but not how much. If you are making a quart of urine a day, you can add that amount to the 1 to 1½ quarts of fluid you should drink each day. If you think in liters and kilograms, that is okay too. Some dialysis units use pounds of weight, but most use kilograms when they weigh you before and after dialysis.

On a daily basis, it is too much work to measure every fluid you drink. You may want to perform this useful exercise once or twice, but life is too short to measure every drop that goes into your body. Fortunately, if you gain 1 kilogram of weight, that corresponds to 1 liter of fluid that you drank. This formula enables us to determine if you are drinking too much. If you drink 1 liter of fluid and urinate 1 liter of fluid, you will lose weight. This seeming imbalance is due to **insensible fluid loss**. Insensible fluid loss is fluid lost in our bowel movements in the form of stool, in sweat, and through water vapor from our lungs. Insensible loss is about one-half to three-quarters of a liter of fluid a day. So, we measure our urine output, add one-half a liter a day of insensible loss of fluid, and another liter a day of fluid that is to be removed on dialysis, and we get a figure that is roughly 1½ to 2 liters of fluid a day. Do not worry if you are confused. Just weigh yourself after dialysis and plan to gain 2 kilograms or 4.4 pounds before your next treatment. Either method will work.

Insensible fluid loss

The fluid that leaves the body in the form of water vapor from the lungs, sweat, and fluid in stool. The amount of insensible fluid loss is about 2 to 3 cups every day.

Many patients on dialysis are very thirsty. The exact reason for this is not known. It may be due to the effect of hormones released by the body, or it may be a signal from the brain that causes patients to seek water to drink. Some medications for blood pressure such as clonidine can make your mouth dry. Many patients resort to eating ice to decrease their thirst.

Unfortunately, melted ice is water, and this is not an ideal solution. It is important to have some sugar-free gum or candy to pop in your mouth when you become thirsty. This will decrease the amount of fluid you consume. It is also important to have a sense of the fluid content of foods. The best example would be watermelon, which contains a large amount of fluid.

61. Can I eat protein on dialysis?

Many people believe that eating protein is harmful to the kidney and may be unhealthy for patients on dialysis. The nutritional content of the food we eat can be divided into protein, carbohydrate, and fat. In the early days of treatment for kidney failure, there was no dialysis. Physicians discovered that reducing the protein intake of patients allowed them to live longer because they produced less poisons and toxins on a low-protein diet. Patients became malnourished but had less symptoms of kidney failure. In the 1980s, a series of experiments with rats showed that rats with kidney failure lived longer on a low-protein rat chow diet than rats with kidney failure on a regular-protein rat chow diet. This research rekindled the interest in low-protein diets in kidney failure. Studies in humans failed to show a clear benefit of low-protein diet in patients with kidney failure. The only role for reducing protein in the diet may be in the pre-dialysis period. Some physicians feel that placing patients on a 30- to 40-gram protein diet may help keep them off dialysis for a time.

The danger of decreasing protein in the diet is the development of protein malnutrition. Protein in the food we eat is broken down into smaller building blocks called **amino acids**. These amino acids are used

Amino acids

Organic acids that are the building blocks of proteins.

Nutrition on Dialysis

to make blood cells, repair injured or damaged organs, make messenger proteins in our blood, and build muscle. If our protein intake and calories are too low, our body begins to use the protein in our own muscle as a fuel source, which leads to **muscle wasting**. This condition can result in weakness, fatigue, anemia, and a decreased ability to repair our body when injured. It can also lead to a decreased ability to fight infection. Anyone considering a low-protein diet for kidney failure should be observed carefully for malnutrition. This is especially important in children, elderly patients, and patients who are losing large amounts of protein in the urine.

Most doctors and nutritionists recommend that patients with kidney failure eat a good amount of **high-biologic-value protein** each day. What is high-biologic-value protein? High-biologic-value protein is protein that contains all of the essential amino acids that we need and that can be easily absorbed by our digestive system. Some amino acids can be built by our body. Essential amino acids cannot be built by the body and must be eaten and absorbed. Many vegetables contain protein, but they do not contain all of the essential amino acids needed for good nutrition. Patients who are vegetarians must take special care to eat a variety of foods that will provide them with all of their protein requirements. This means eating 1.2 grams of protein per kilogram of body weight. This nutritional requirement can be satisfied by eating 4 ounces of meat, poultry, or fish twice a day. Most of us have no idea of the weight in grams or ounces of the food we eat. Your renal dietitian can help you determine the portion size of food that is needed for good nutrition. Food models are available to help you understand portion size.

Muscle wasting

A decrease in the size of the muscles of the body due to poor nutrition or medical illness.

High-biologic-value protein

Proteins found in foods such as eggs, fish, poultry, soy products, and meat. High-biologic-value proteins are easily digestible and are rich in the ten essential amino acids that our body cannot make.

If you are not eating enough protein, you can use protein supplements, which are available in a powder or liquid form. Supplements can be especially helpful if your appetite is poor and if your protein stores have been depleted by illness. Many patients have a poor appetite in the pre-dialysis period because poisons and toxins are building up in their body, and they lose interest in their favorite foods. It is interesting that some patients selectively decrease the amount of protein they eat. These patients may be trying to decrease the amount of poisons and toxins they produce. Patients in the pre-dialysis period often lose weight and some of their protein stores. They may suffer from nausea, vomiting, and hiccups, which interfere with eating. These symptoms usually resolve within several weeks of dialysis treatments. Infections occurring in patients on dialysis can lead to protein malnutrition. Examples of this would be foot infections, access infections, or pneumonia. Attention to adequate nutrition during these episodes of infection can help speed recovery and return you to your normal routine.

62. Can I eat during my dialysis treatments?

If you are a peritoneal dialysis patient, you will be eating during your dialysis treatments. Dialysis is taking place 24 hours a day. The dialysis usually does not interfere with the ability to eat an adequate diet. Peritoneal dialysate contains a sugar called **dextrose** that helps remove fluid from the bloodstream into the peritoneal space so it can be discarded with the dialysate. Some dextrose is absorbed by the body. These extra calories from the dextrose can sometimes act as an appetite suppressor and decrease the patient's desire to

Dextrose

A sugar added to peritoneal dialysis solutions to help remove fluid from the body. It is also added to intravenous fluids to provide calories for nutrition.

eat. Occasionally, patients feel full when their abdomen is full of dialysate. This symptom can be managed by having the patient eat when the abdomen is drained of dialysate.

Hemodialysis centers have different policies regarding patients eating on hemodialysis. You definitely should not eat during hemodialysis in the first few weeks of your treatment. Many patients have episodes of vomiting as the high levels of poisons and toxins are removed during their first hemodialysis treatment. You definitely do not want to have a full stomach. After adjusting to hemodialysis, many patients find that eating a small snack during their treatment is enjoyable. This may be especially important in patients who are diabetic and who are regulating their glucose. It is important to talk to your dialysis nursing staff to find out the eating policy in your hemodialysis unit. Patients on home hemodialysis frequently combine dialysis with their dinner plans. They come home from work, receive their dialysis treatment, and enjoy having dinner with their family while they are receiving their treatment. This can help with a busy schedule and create time for other activities.

After adjusting to hemodialysis, many patients find that eating a small snack during their treatment is enjoyable.

63. Why are potassium and phosphorus so important?

If you spend time in any dialysis unit, you will hear the patients, nurses, dieticians, and doctors talking about these two important elements. Potassium and phosphorus occur inside and outside the cells in our body. They are both needed for healthy living. Potassium and phosphorus levels in our blood reflect the quality of the dialysis treatment and how successful we are in following the renal diet.

Most of the potassium is inside the cells in our body. It also is present in a smaller amount in the liquid part of our blood or serum. Potassium is eaten in our food every day and excreted in our urine, stool, and sweat. In patients with kidney failure, the ability to eliminate potassium in the urine decreases. In order to compensate, we must decrease our intake of potassium in our food and increase our elimination of potassium with the help of the dialysis treatment. We cannot measure the potassium inside the cells of our body. We use the potassium level in our blood to determine if the potassium in our body is at an optimal level. A potassium level that is too high or too low can cause panic in the dialysis unit. This reaction is because very high and very low levels can be associated with heart problems. Irregular or slow heartbeats and cardiac standstill, called cardiac arrest, have been associated with these extreme potassium levels. Muscle weakness and even paralysis are other signs of an abnormally high potassium level. Most patients with these levels do not develop these problems, but it is important to correct a low or high potassium level as soon as possible.

The most common cause of a high potassium level is eating too much potassium in the diet. Orange juice, bananas, cantaloupe, dairy products, tomatoes, salt substitutes, and sports drinks such as Gatorade have too much potassium in them to be safe foods for the hemodialysis patient. The next common cause of a high potassium level is skipping dialysis treatments. An elevated potassium can also be due to a problem with the dialysis treatment. If the access that supplies blood to the hemodialysis machine is not working properly, not enough blood will pass over the dialysis membrane, and a decreased removal of potassium occurs. If there is a blockage in the access, the same blood can go from the patient to the machine over and over again without mixing with the rest of the blood in the body. This is called **recirculation** and is prevented by a frequent evaluation of the a-v access. Patients can also liberate too much potassium from the organs in their body due to disease. This can occur during crush injuries when damaged muscle lets large amounts of potassium that is usually found inside the cells to leak out into the bloodstream. Another cause of a high potassium level is bleeding in the gastrointestinal tract from an ulcer or an inflammation of the lining of the stomach, known as gastritis. Red blood cells contain large amounts of potassium, which can be absorbed from the bowel.

Recirculation

Occurs during hemodialysis treatments when blood that has gone through the dialysis machine does not mix with the patient's blood but returns to the dialysis machine.

The immediate treatment of a high potassium level in a dialysis patient should be to place the patient on dialysis as soon as possible. At the same time, an evaluation should be made of the cause of the high potassium and steps should be taken to decrease the potassium intake in the diet. Low potassium can be the result of vomiting and diarrhea, laxative use, or a decrease in appetite leading to a very low intake of potassium over a long period of time. This problem can often be managed by changing the potassium level in the dialysate and improving the patient's nutritional intake.

Phosphorus, like potassium, is in the food we eat and is eliminated from the body in our urine. As our kidney function decreases, the level of phosphorus in the blood begins to rise. This is managed by decreasing the amount of phosphorus we eat. High phosphorus foods include meat, dairy products, beans, and cola drinks. In addition to eating a reduced phosphorus diet, most dialysis patients will require phosphate binders. These medicines are taken with food and will bind the phosphorus in the gastrointestinal tract and prevent the phosphorus from being absorbed. If the phosphorus level is too high, patients can complain of severe itching. In addition, the high phosphorus will cause the calcium in the blood to be deposited in the bones, causing the calcium level to fall, which will stimulate the production of parathyroid hormone (often referred to as PTH). The parathyroid hormone, if present in high levels, can cause bone disease that can cause pain or even fractures. Although a high phosphorus level is not as dangerous as a high potassium level, longstanding high phosphorus can affect the quality of a patient's life on dialysis and should be avoided. Low phosphorus is uncommon in dialysis patients. If your phosphorus is low, the first thing to do is decrease or stop your phosphorus binders. A small increase in the phosphorus in your diet may also be needed.

64. Can I smoke on dialysis?

A significant number of patients who smoke before they begin dialysis continue to smoke after they begin dialysis. All hemodialysis centers prohibit smoking while on dialysis. Many patients are surprised to learn that smoking cigarettes is an independent risk factor for kidney disease. This risk is because cigarette smoking is one of the causes of hardening of the arteries, or atherosclerosis. Atherosclerosis occurs all over the body. When it occurs in the arteries to the heart, heart disease or a heart attack occurs. Involvement of the

Because kidney patients have a higher chance of having hypertension and high cholesterol, it is especially important that they try to stop smoking.

arteries to the brain can lead to stroke. Atherosclerosis occuring in the arteries to the kidneys, results in a decreased blood supply to the kidney. Atherosclerosis is also caused by hypertension, diabetes, and high cholesterol, and occurs more frequently in patients who have other family members with the disease. Because kidney patients have a higher chance of having hypertension and high cholesterol, it is especially important that they try to stop smoking. Diabetic patients on hemodialysis are especially vulnerable to the effects of cigarette smoking. There is a significant decrease in 5-year survival in hemodialysis patients with diabetes who smoke.

Most smokers want to quit smoking and every year about half of them try to quit. Within 2 days of stopping, the ability to smell and taste food improves. Within 2 to 3 weeks, the chance of a heart attack decreases, and circulation and breathing begin to improve. It is important to obtain help from your doctor or a smoking cessation program. Their help will increase your chance of stopping smoking.

The first step in quitting smoking is to set a quit date in the coming weeks. During this time, you should write down your reasons for quitting smoking. You should also review behaviors that encourage you to smoke, such as drinking alcohol or being around other smokers, and try to avoid them. Contact your doctor about your plan to stop smoking. Ask him or her if nicotine replacement products or other medications might be helpful for you. Nicotine replacement therapy comes in transdermal patches, nicotine gum, lozenges, vapor inhalers, and nasal sprays. Other non-nicotine medications include bupropion, which is also known as Zyban and Wellbutrin. This medicine can be used with nicotine replacement. Varenicline, or Chantix, cannot be used with nicotine replacement therapy and has to be used with great caution in patients with kidney failure at a reduced dose. Get rid of ash trays, cigarettes, and other objects that are associated with smoking. Make your home into a smoke-free zone. If other family members smoke, ask them not to smoke in front of you. Tell your friends and family of your plans to quit, and get their support. Withdrawal from smoking peaks within 1 to 3 weeks after quitting. Be prepared for withdrawal symptoms such as depression, craving for cigarettes, and difficulty concentrating. Beginning dialysis may be the ideal time to consider quitting smoking. You will be getting a great deal of attention from the dialysis team. You will be focused on learning healthy lifestyle choices and may be more motivated than when you get more accustomed to your dialysis treatments.

65. How can I improve my appetite?

Kidney patients on dialysis have many reasons for having a poor appetite. Poisons and toxins that build up in the body of a patient with kidney failure change the way food tastes and smells. It is interesting that smell is such an important sense in good nutrition. If we cannot smell a food or if the smell of a food is not pleasing, we will reject that food. Many patients report a metallic taste in their mouth, which is due to poisons and toxins that are building up in the body. Kidney patients may have a dry mouth, which may cause them to drink large amounts of fluid with no nutritional value, leaving them too full to eat solid foods with more nutrition. Nausea, vomiting, and hiccups are common symptoms of kidney failure in the pre-dialysis period. Patients become afraid that eating will cause them to vomit.

Beginning dialysis will reverse some, but not all of these symptoms. Many patients who delay beginning dialysis will spend several months with poor nutritional intake. As they lose weight, they become physically weaker and less mobile. They suffer from nausea, a decreased appetite, and general malaise. These symptoms decrease their interest in and ability to consume an adequate amount of food. They become accustomed to eating less. When they begin dialysis, they have to get in the habit of eating more again. Patients are often overwhelmed by the renal diet that is presented to them. They may be unsure of what is safe for them to eat. All patients who begin dialysis have an element of depression present. Patients often feel that beginning dialysis is a loss and that life as they knew it is over. This depression is often associated with a decreased appetite.

Improving your appetite and nutrition is fortunately not as hard as it seems. The first thing is to realize that your diet is equally as important as your dialysis treatments and medication in getting well.

Improving your appetite and nutrition is fortunately not as hard as it seems. The first thing is to realize that your diet is equally as important as your dialysis treatments and medication in getting well. Eating is a social experience. We celebrate special occasions like birthdays and holidays with a special meal. You will eat more if you share your meals with family and friends. If you are in the hospital, have a friend or family member visit you at mealtimes. Have them bring a sandwich so they can eat with you. This will help distract you from eating as a task to get through and reconnect you with food as a pleasurable experience. Eat five small meals or snacks a day. Patients who fill up on small amounts of food can let their stomachs empty a bit before they eat again. If you need to consume more calories, do not eat or drink anything with the word diet or low-fat in it. I am always amazed to find patients who are in very poor nutritional health eating a low-fat yogurt or diet soda. What is a good idea for well-nourished individuals may not be the best food for malnourished people. Make sure that everything that goes into you has some caloric value. If you are thirsty, drink a liquid supplement or apple juice, not water. Avoid carbonated beverages. The bubbles can distend your stomach and make you feel full, leaving less room for food. It is important to remember that just about everyone who stops smoking gains a few pounds. If you smoke, this may be the perfect time to quit and gain weight.

Physical activity is one of the best ways to increase your appetite. Active people consume a great deal of calories. They are less likely to suffer from constipation and other bowel complaints. Try to take a short walk several times a day. Find a reason to go out even if you do not have to. Buy a newspaper or pick up a quart of milk or juice. Resist the urge to sit and watch television. Do some work around the house or the garden, even if it is only a small task that can easily be done by someone else. All these activities will increase your appetite.

Medications are sometimes used to increase appetite. Megace is a synthetic derivative of the naturally occurring hormone progesterone. It has been used to treat patients with anorexia and severe malnutrition with wasting, called cachexia. We do not know why Megace works, but it can stimulate appetite and food intake in some patients with kidney failure. It is available as a liquid and must be prescribed by your physician. Another medication that can sometimes be helpful is zinc supplements. Zinc is a metal. Patients with zinc deficiency can lose their taste for foods. Antidepressants can help some depressed patients with kidney failure gain weight. These drugs are called serotonin reuptake inhibitors, or SRIs for short, and must be prescribed by physicians who are expert in their use. Although medications are usually not an easy answer to the problem of poor appetite, they may be useful in selected patients.

66. Who will help me improve my nutrition?

Every dialysis unit has a key person who will be available to help you with your nutrition. This person is the renal dietitian. He or she will have special scientific training to help you understand your nutritional condition, choose healthy nutritious food, and act as your nutritional advocate. It is sad for me to say that I had 1 or 2 days of my medical school curriculum devoted to nutrition. During my training in internal medicine and nephrology, I learned to diagnose nutritional problems but received very little training on the treatment of nutritional disorders. I need to work closely with the dietitian in my dialysis unit, who is a major resource and guide in all matters related to food and nutritional supplements. Dietitians are helpful people. They want to understand where you are coming from. All of us have particular likes and dislikes when it comes to food. The magic of the dietitian is the ability to help you choose food that tastes good and that is good for you. Patients on dialysis come from many different cultures and backgrounds. They are used to eating ethnic foods that may or may not be appropriate for patients with kidney failure. Often the renal dietitian can recommend substitutions in the recipe of your favorite food to make the food more compatible with the renal diet.

The tools that the renal dietitian will use to evaluate your nutritional state are the monthly blood tests that you will be taking and your height and weight. One of the most important values will be the serum **albumin**. This blood test is a reflection of the protein stores in your body. The albumin level can be low for a variety of reasons. You may be malnourished and not eating enough protein. You may be losing albumin in your urine because of your kidney disease. You may be suffering from liver disease and may not be able to build enough albumin protein despite adequate protein intake. The other important lab values include your BUN and creatinine, your phosphorus and calcium levels, and your cholesterol level. If your cholesterol level is too low, it may be a sign that you are not eating enough food. The renal dietitian can use these tests along with your height and weight to give you a nutritional snapshot of where you are now. The more you understand, the better you will be at improving your nutritional condition. Good nutrition will allow you to build muscle and become stronger. It will give you more energy to participate in important events such as family gatherings and will help you return to work if this is your goal.

Most of us are not used to getting advice about our diet. It is important for you to realize that the advice of the renal dietitian is not an attack on your food choices. It is rather an observation on how your food choices will affect your health in the long run. You should always ask your dietitian which dietary recommendation is the most important. This will help you

Albumin

A water-soluble protein found in the blood normally in very minute amounts. Patients with kidney disease often have albumin in their urine because the albumin leaks through the damaged kidneys into the urine.

concentrate on the one change that will help you the most. Remember, the renal diet is a voyage. You are in one place, and you are hoping to arrive at another place, which is healthier. It will take longer than you think to accomplish your goals. Think of the renal dietitian as a fellow traveler. Explain why you feel the way you do about the particular route he or she has suggested. Remember that the renal dietitian has taken this voyage innumerable times following many different paths. With his or her help, try to find the right path for you.

Many other people will be available to help your nutrition, including your physician and nurses in the unit. Some patients with specific medical diseases may have a **gastroenterologist**. Many gastroenterologists have special training in nutrition. The American Association of Kidney Patients, *www.aakp.org*, has a wonderful publication called *Beginnings, Living Well With Kidney Disease*. This publication features many excellent articles concerning nutrition and recipes for great meals, and it is an enjoyable resource for patients on kidney dialysis. Other great recipes can be found at *www.culinary kidneycooks.com* and *www.kidney-cookbook.com*.

Gastroenterologist

A physician who has received training in internal medicine and who has had additional training in the diagnosis and treatment of disorders of the digestive system.

PART SIX

Complications on Dialysis

What should I do if I develop bleeding from my access?

Why does my blood pressure fall too low during my hemodialysis treatment?

Why do I feel weak after my hemodialysis treatments?

More . . .

67. Why is my access so important?

You will be hearing a great deal about access even before you begin your dialysis treatments. The word access includes a variety of devices all used to gain access to the blood circulation. In hemodialysis, the best access is a fistula. The fistula is a tube created by a surgeon in the operating room, by connecting an artery to a vein in the arm (**Figure 7**). Blood from the artery causes the vein in the arm to enlarge and for the wall of the vein to become thicker. The fistula will take 6 weeks to 3 months or more to be ready for use. When it is ready, two needles are inserted into the fistula. One needle will be connected to plastic tubing that will bring blood to the dialysis machine. After the blood has been cleaned of poisons and toxins, the blood will travel through plastic tubing and be returned through a second needle. The fistula is the access of choice for hemodialysis because it will last the longest, be resistant to infection, and be able to repair itself if damaged because it is constructed of living artery and vein.

The fistula is most commonly inserted in the lower arm. It can also be placed in the upper arm and, very rarely, in the patient's upper leg. The fistula takes time to develop or mature. This maturation process can sometimes be facilitated by inserting a small, long balloon in the fistula and inflating the balloon. This process, called **angioplasty**, can increase the size of the vein and enable it to have more blood flowing through the fistula. Angioplasty can help make the fistula ready to use earlier and will make the dialysis more effective because more blood will go through the dialysis machine during a given time.

Angioplasty

A medical procedure in which a balloon catheter is inserted into a blood vessel or dialysis access. When the balloon is inflated, it opens a blockage in the blood vessel to improve blood flow.

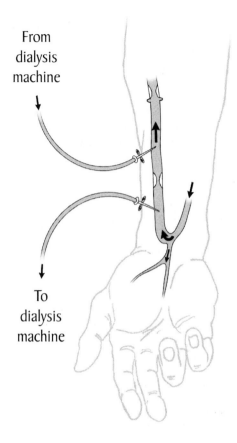

From
dialysis
machine

To
dialysis
machine

Figure 7   An A-V fistula

Source: National Institute of Diabetes and Digestive and Kidney Diseases, National Institutes of Health.

Steal syndrome

A syndrome that
occurs when too
much blood is taken
away from the arm or
hand by an a-v fistula
or a-v graft. The
blood goes from the
artery to the vein,
bypassing the capil-
laries to the hand or
arm, resulting in cool-
ness, pain, and some-
times loss of function
of the hand.

Over time, the fistula can have too much blood flow
and decrease the amount of blood to the hand, making
the hand painful, cold, and pale. This is called a **steal
syndrome** because the fistula steals blood from the
hand. The cold, painful, pale hand is said to be
ischemic. This term describes the lack of blood flow to
the hand. If steal syndrome occurs, surgery may be
required to place a band around the fistula, reducing
blood flow through the fistula so more blood can go to
the hand. If the ischemia is severe, the fistula may need

139

Ischemia

A decrease or lack of blood flow to an organ in the body causing damage or organ dysfunction.

to be closed off to reestablish blood flow to the hand. This is done by having a vascular surgeon place a suture, which is a sterile piece of plastic string, around the fistula and tie a tight knot. The suture causes the blood to stop flowing and the fistula to stop working.

Another complication of fistulas is aneurysm formation. The aneurysm is an outpouching of the vein part of the fistula. This looks like a small balloon and can rupture and cause bleeding if it gets very large. Aneurysms of the fistula must be observed carefully by the vascular surgeon and fixed before they rupture. A fistula can develop a blockage. If this happens, you should immediately contact your doctor to have it fixed as soon as possible. The blockage is sometimes caused by scarring of a portion of the vein and that decreases the blood flow through the fistula and causes the blood to clot. The clot can be removed during a procedure called **thrombectomy**, and a small amount of dye can be injected into the fistula to diagnose the cause of the blockage. If there is a narrowing of the vein, it can be fixed by using a balloon to do an angioplasty to increase the blood flow through the fistula. The fistula should be protected at all times. Blood should not be drawn from the arm with the fistula to prevent damage to the fistula. Tight-fitting jewelry and clothing should never constrict the fistula because this may cause it to clot. Blood pressure should never be taken on the arm with the fistula.

Thrombectomy

A procedure in which a blood clot that is blocking a blood vessel or an a-v access is removed or dissolved with medication. It allows blood to flow through the hemodialysis access so it can be used for hemodialysis.

If the veins in the arms are not very large, an arterial-venous graft, or a-v graft, can be the next best choice for access (**Figure 8**). The graft is constructed by sewing a plastic tube between an artery and a vein. The plastic tube is composed of a material called Gortex. This tube is tunneled under the skin. After about 2 to 3

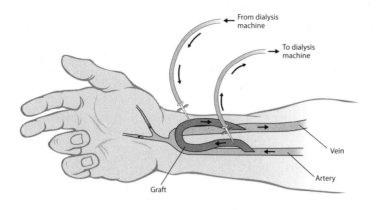

Figure 8 An A-V graft

Source: National Institute of Diabetes and Digestive and Kidney Diseases, National Institutes of Health.

weeks, the swelling after surgery will decrease and the graft will be ready for use. At the beginning of the hemodialysis treatment, two needles are inserted into the plastic tube. Arterial-venous grafts have a high rate of clotting (or thrombosis) and generally last about 9 months to 3 years, making them a poor choice for patients who will need to be treated with hemodialysis for many years. This access will wear out after repeated needle insertions. If the a-v graft gets infected, it will need to be surgically removed because the infection will never really go away. Grafts also can develop blockages and aneurysms, which can be surgically repaired.

The third type of access for hemodialysis is the dialysis catheter (**Figure 9**). The dialysis catheter is a piece of plastic tubing that is inserted in a vein in the neck or leg. A catheter can be temporary, and used for one or two dialysis treatments, or more permanent and used for weeks to months. Catheters can be used right away, as soon as they are inserted. Needles are not necessary so there is no pain associated with using the catheter

141

Figure 9   A hemodialysis catheter

Source: National Institute of Diabetes and Digestive and Kidney Diseases, National Institutes of Health.

for hemodialysis. Catheters are not good accesses for several reasons. The catheter exits the skin and is sutured and taped to the patient's body. This allows bacteria from the skin to enter the bloodstream and cause serious infection. Catheters can also cause scarring of the vein, which can lead to a blockage of the vein and make it impossible to put a fistula in the arm closest to the catheter. Catheters become blocked, kinked, and wear out. You should not get your catheter wet. This means no bathing, showers, or swimming. You must use sponge baths to keep the catheter from becoming infected. I think of a hemodialysis catheter as a temporary access. The next step after getting a catheter for hemodialysis is planning to have an a-v fistula made so the catheter can be removed as soon as possible.

The access in peritoneal dialysis is the peritoneal dialysis catheter. This access is a plastic tube that is inserted into the lower abdomen during a minor surgical procedure. The peritoneal dialysis catheter will take about 2 weeks to heal. This is so tissue can form a seal around the catheter so it does not leak fluid around the catheter. The peritoneal dialysis catheter is used to instill dialysate fluid into the peritoneum where it can draw poisons and toxins into the fluid. The fluid is then drained out by gravity, and fresh dialysate is then infused into the abdomen. Like hemodialysis catheters, peritoneal catheters can be blocked and infected. The catheter can work its way out of the abdomen and could need to be replaced. Your peritoneal dialysis nurse will teach you how to care for your access during your training. Keeping the access clean is called **exit site care** and is done every day. It involves washing the area where the catheter exits the skin in the abdomen with an antiseptic solution, called saline. The exit site is then covered with a sterile dressing. Special care is required not to put too much tension on the catheter and to secure it to the abdomen so it will not move with exercise. Exit site care is done after showering, swimming, or vigorous exercise. This is to decrease the chance of the catheter developing an irritation at the exit site that could lead to an infection.

Exit site care

Exit site care involves swabbing the area where the peritoneal dialysis catheter exits the skin with an antiseptic solution and covering the exit site with a clean sterile dressing.

68. What is an access center?

In the early days of dialysis, the access was inserted by surgeons in the operating room of the hospital. As medical science improved, new techniques were developed. Hemodialysis catheters were invented for temporary use. Fistulas created in the operating room that do not develop properly are enlarged with the use of a procedure called balloon angioplasty (Question 67). Fistulas and grafts that develop clots can have the clots dissolved. Many times the patient would have to wait several days for a simple access procedure because there was no time in the operating room of the hospital. Patients would have their procedure cancelled because of emergencies such as appendicitis or trauma cases. Because of the increasing number of dialysis patients, the **access center** was developed to care for dialysis patients with access-related complications.

Access center

A medical facility that specializes in the creation and care of access for dialysis patients. The access physician uses radiology and ultrasound equipment to evaluate and improve the blood flow in a-v fistulas, a-v grafts, and catheters for hemodialysis.

The access center is often not a part of the hospital. The access center has a physician with special training in dialysis access. The physician could be a surgeon, nephrologist, or radiologist. This physician only works on dialysis access, enabling him or her to develop advanced skills and techniques through specialization and focusing on one problem. The access physician understands the importance of fixing the access as soon as possible. The access physician will have nurses and technicians with special training in access procedures as assistants. Access centers are set up to provide superior care as rapidly as possible. Access centers often allow patients to have their access fixed and to return to the hemodialysis unit the same day for their treatment. They can prevent the need for admission to the hospital and often avoid extra procedures such as the insertion of temporary dialysis catheters. If a dialysis catheter is needed, the access center can insert it. If it is time to remove your catheter because your a-v fistula is working well and your catheter is no longer needed, they can remove it. The access center is often a more pleasant environment than the hospital operating room. Patients in the access center are all on dialysis and are not as sick as patients in holding areas of the operating room of a hospital. The staff is trained about the special needs of dialysis patients and will get to know you and your nephrologist. This will help you get the access care you need with minimal complications and disruption of your dialysis schedule.

Access centers are set up to provide superior care as rapidly as possible.

69. What should I do if I develop bleeding from my access?

Bleeding from the a-v fistula or a-v graft is one of the most common complications of hemodialysis. Bleeding is very upsetting to the patient and dialysis staff, but most of the time it is not life threatening. The first thing to do if you develop bleeding is to apply direct pressure to the part of the access that is bleeding. This can be done with sterile gauze. If you are not in the dialysis unit and do not have a sterile gauze, a clean handkerchief, paper towel, or any clean cloth can be used. If there is a great deal of blood loss, the best thing to do is call 911 and have the emergency medical technician come to your home. This person will take your blood pressure and pulse, put a clean pressure dressing on the access, and transport you to the emergency room for evaluation. If the bleeding is a small amount and stops with pressure, you may want to call or come to the dialysis unit if it is open for evaluation. Most of the time, bleeding occurs after your needles for hemodialysis are removed. This is because you have

Complications on Dialysis

been given a blood thinner called heparin for your dialysis treatment. In this case, the bleeding can be stopped by applying direct pressure to the access. The heparin will be metabolized by your body and the bleeding will stop.

Bleeding from your access on a day you are not on dialysis is a sure sign that something is wrong with the access.

Bleeding from your access on a day you are not on dialysis is a sure sign that something is wrong with the access. It may indicate that the access has an infection. In this case, the bleeding may be accompanied by redness and warmth of the access. Fever may also be present. Infection can be confirmed by obtaining blood cultures to find the bacteria in the blood. A surgeon may have to perform a small incision in the skin to evaluate the problem. During the procedure, if the surgeon sees pus, which is caused by white blood cells attacking the bacteria, he or she may take cultures and have to remove the access if it is an a-v graft. The surgeon may try to remove the infected part of the graft, but this can often fail to control the infection. It is important that medical evaluation is not delayed. A small amount of bleeding can be followed by rupture of the infected access and massive bleeding.

Another cause of access bleeding can be a blockage (or stenosis) at the outflow (or venous side) of the access. This can cause high pressure in the access, making it more likely that bleeding will occur at the needle puncture sites. This problem is best treated by inserting a small balloon across the area with the blockage, inflating the balloon, and opening up the blockage. This procedure is called angioplasty. A surgeon can also fix the stenosis by making a small incision in the access and repairing it in the operating room. Bleeding can also occur from aneurysms of the a-v access. These weaknesses in the wall of the access can enlarge over time and be unsightly. When aneurysms bleed, this is a danger sign, and they should be evaluated by a vascular surgeon and repaired as soon as possible. As noted previously, many patients are on blood thinners that can promote bleeding from the access. Heparin is the most common medication given to prevent clotting while on hemodialysis. If you have frequent bleeding after your needles are removed, ask your nurse and doctor to consider decreasing your dose of heparin. Aspirin, Plavix, Persantine, and Coumadin are other medications that can contribute to bleeding from your access. If you have several episodes of bleeding from your access, your doctor may consider stopping these medications.

70. Why do I have anemia?

Anemia (low blood count) is a common complication of kidney failure. Symptoms of anemia include weakness, fatigue, and shortness of breath while exercising. You may feel your heart racing or beating fast with exertion. Your skin, nails, and lips may appear pale. One of the main reasons is that **red blood cells** have a shortened life span in kidney failure. Our red blood cells are made in our bone marrow from cells called stem cells. The cells are released into our circulation. In normal people, red blood cells last for 90 days in our circulation. Because kidney failure patients have poisons and toxins that remain in the blood despite dialysis, the red cells last much less than 90 days.

Our kidneys produce a hormone called erythropoietin. This protein is a messenger that tells the stem cells in the bone marrow to produce more red blood cells. Patients with kidney disease do not produce enough erythropoietin. Fortunately, erythropoietin is available

Red blood cells

Cells made by the bone marrow that contain an oxygen transport protein called hemoglobin, causing blood to appear red. Red blood cells carry oxygen from the lungs to other organs through the circulatory system.

as a medication that can be given by injecting it under the skin or intravenously. The brand names for erythropoietin are Epogen and Procrit. Another medication for anemia is called Aranesp. Many new medications for anemia are being developed.

Dialysis patients have frequent blood tests. They lose a little bit of blood that remains in the dialysis tubing at the end of the dialysis treatment. They may have blood loss because of bleeding in the gastrointestinal tract and have difficulty absorbing iron supplements from the gastrointestinal tract. Patients on dialysis often suffer from iron deficiency. Many dialysis units will replace iron deficiency by giving intravenous iron during the dialysis treatment. Chronic infection is another common cause of anemia. Chronic infection makes it difficult for the body to produce red blood cells even if erythropoietin and iron are given intravenously on hemodialysis. Good nutrition is important in maintaining a good blood cell count because red blood cells consist of hemoglobin, which is a protein that carries oxygen. Hemoglobin is composed of amino acids and iron. To build hemoglobin and red blood cells, a good intake of high-biologic-value protein is important.

Fortunately, blood transfusions are rarely required to treat anemia these days. Most hemodialysis patients will have their blood count checked every week. Iron stores are tested every month. Peritoneal dialysis patients have their blood tests every month. The successful treatment of anemia is one of the major goals of the dialysis team. You should discuss your blood count with your doctor and nurse when you review your monthly blood tests.

71. Why does my blood pressure fall too low during my hemodialysis treatment?

Your blood pressure will be measured at the beginning of your hemodialysis treatment and at frequent intervals during your treatment. When we remove fluid during hemodialysis treatments, the fluid removed comes directly from the blood within our circulation. Fluid that is present in cells and in other places will move into the circulation slowly. This lag in fluid entering the circulation can result in too little fluid being present in the arteries and veins of the circulatory system, making the blood pressure fall. Most dialysis patients have a decrease in blood pressure during their hemodialysis treatment because 3 to 4 liters of fluid are removed in a 3- to 4-hour treatment. Patients on peritoneal dialysis have a much slower continuous removal of fluid because they are on dialysis 24 hours a day, 7 days a week. This makes peritoneal dialysis a gentler, gradual dialysis treatment. One of the ways to prevent your blood pressure from falling during your hemodialysis treatment is to not drink an excessive amount of fluid between treatments. The more fluid removed, the more likely your blood pressure is to fall dramatically. Some patients find that taking their blood pressure medications after their dialysis treatment is useful. Ask your doctor if this is a good idea for you.

Low blood pressure is bad if you have symptoms. Symptoms of low blood pressure on hemodialysis include dizziness, palpitations or a racing heart beat, nausea, and vomiting or fainting. Many dialysis patients tolerate low blood pressure without symptoms. Occasionally patients begin their dialysis treatment with low blood pressure and have a slight increase in blood pressure as their treatment progresses. The dialysis team will assess your blood pressure on a frequent basis and make changes in your dialysis treatment and medications to try to avoid low blood pressure.

72. My nurse told me my blood clotted in the hemodialysis machine during my treatment. Are these blood clots dangerous?

Our blood contains clotting factors that cause it to clot or turn from liquid into a solid at the right time. Clotting is beneficial when we injure or cut ourselves because the clot forms a plug to seal a hole in our blood vessels to stop bleeding. When blood comes out of our access, it comes into contact with steel needles, plastic tubing, and the dialysis membrane. All these devices tend to stimulate clot formation. Because of this tendency of blood to clot outside of the circulation, heparin, a blood thinner, is given at the beginning of the hemodialysis treatment. This medicine decreases, but does not eliminate, the chance that your blood will clot in the dialysis machine. If you have prolonged bleeding from your needle puncture sites after dialysis, your heparin dose may need to be decreased. If you have active bleeding in your gastrointestinal tract, your doctor may try to eliminate all heparin from your dialysis treatment. Another common cause of clot formation is low blood flow through the hemodialysis machine, which can occur if your dialysis needles are poorly positioned in your access. If the needle is touching the wall of your fistula or graft, it may be difficult to have a high dialysis blood flow. A blood count that is too high because a patient is receiving too much erythropoietin can also cause blood to clot.

One of the first signs of clot formation is an increase in pressure in the dialysis line. This can cause an alarm to go off and alert the nurse or dialysis technician of a problem. They will evaluate the cause of the increased pressure by flushing the tubing and dialyzer with saline solution, making it much easier to see a clot. If a clot progresses, you will be unable to continue your dialysis. If this happens, do not be alarmed. The clot cannot pass into your circulation and cause a medical problem. The nurse or technician will have to disconnect you from the dialysis machine, flush your needles with saline, and set up your machine with new tubing and a new dialyzer to continue your treatment. This occurrence is very common and will probably happen to you at some time if you are on hemodialysis. The blood lost by the tubing clotting is a small amount and is not dangerous. The worst thing that will happen is that your dialysis will take longer because the time it takes to replace your tubing and dialyzer should not be counted as time on dialysis. When you start dialysis, your dialysis team will start you on a heparin dose. They will increase the dose of heparin if you develop clots during your dialysis treatment, to help prevent you from forming more clots during your treatments.

73. Should I be concerned when the alarms go off on my hemodialysis machine?

The modern hemodialysis machine has many electronic sensors to alert the dialysis staff to a variety of events on dialysis. One alarm will sound when your

Figure 10 Frances Brebnor, RN, resets an alarm on a hemodiaysis machine.
Source: K. Neelakantappa, MD

treatment is finished, sort of like the alarm clock that wakes you from sleep. Other alarms will sound if the temperature of the blood or dialysate is too low or high. There are pressure sensors on the tubing bringing blood to the dialysis machine from your access and another pressure sensor for blood returning from the dialysis machine back to your access. The dialysis nurse can adjust these alarms (**Figure 10**). If blood leaks across the dialyzer into the dialysate, an alarm will sound. The most important sensor in the dialysis machine is the air bubble detector. The air bubble detector will shut down the blood pump and clamp the dialysis tubing to prevent the air from entering your access and traveling into your circulation. An alarm will sound to indicate the problem.

Safety sensors and alarms make dialysis safe. If you moved from the country to a busy city, you would be kept awake by the sounds of traffic, police, fire sirens, and car horns. It will take you some time to adjust to the sounds and lights of the sensors of your dialysis machine. You are not in danger when they sound. Most likely, nothing will immediately happen when they alarm. In several minutes, a dialysis team member will walk over to your hemodialysis machine, push a button or two, and then walk away as if nothing important has happened. Ask the staff member the meaning of the alarm. Many dialysis patients understand their dialysis machines and can figure out the meaning of the alarm on their own. Learning the meaning of hemodialysis machine alarms and what to do about them is a good exercise if you are considering going on home hemodialysis. At home, you and your dialysis partner will learn how to react to the alarms during your hemodialysis training. Patients on nocturnal home hemodialysis are asleep during their hemodialysis treatments. Because the blood flow on nocturnal dialysis is lower, there is less chance of an alarm going off during the hemodialysis treatment. A technician is awake monitoring many patients' machines at a remote location at the dialysis center. Nocturnal hemodialysis patients are monitored using the Internet. When an alarm goes off, the technician will call the patient to make sure he or she has correctly responded to the alarm.

The peritoneal dialysis machine is also known as a cycler. It will instill dialysate into the abdomen, drain the dialysate, and repeat the process. Peritoneal dialysis machines are often used at night while the patient sleeps. The most common cause of an alarm on peritoneal dialysis is bent or kinked tubing preventing dialysate flow. The alarm will alert the patient that a

Safety sensors and alarms make dialysis safe. You are not in danger when they sound.

Complications on Dialysis

problem has occurred but does not indicate a dangerous situation.

74. Why do I feel weak after my hemodialysis treatments?

Feeling weak after hemodialysis treatments is a common experience of some hemodialysis patients. Many patients feel well after their treatments. They finish dialysis and rush off to work, leading a busy life. Other patients find that they must rest or lie down after their treatment but feel much stronger the day following their treatment. When we remove poisons and toxins during hemodialysis, we remove these substances from the blood. These poisons and toxins also are found in our brain. When we rapidly remove toxins from our bloodstream, there is a lag before they are removed from the brain. This lag is because the brain and the central nervous system are isolated from the circulation by a covering called the **meninges**. The meninges decrease the movement of substances in and out of the central nervous system. They form what doctors call the blood-brain barrier. When poisons and toxins are rapidly removed from the circulation during hemodialysis, the brain still contains a high concentration of poisons and toxins. Water will move through the blood-brain barrier faster than the poisons and toxins can move out. This causes swelling of the brain. This brain swelling occurs to a greater or lesser extent in every patient on hemodialysis.

Brain swelling during hemodialysis is known as the **disequilibrium syndrome**. Symptoms of the disequilibrium syndrome include headache, weakness, fatigue, nausea, and vomiting. In its extreme form, the patient can become unresponsive or even have a

Meninges

The three membranes that cover the brain and spinal cord. The meninges form a barrier between the central nervous system and the rest of the body, known as the blood-brain barrier.

Disequilibrium syndrome

A syndrome in which the rapid removal of poisons and toxins during hemodialysis results in less toxins being present in the blood than in the brain. This difference causes water to leave the blood stream and enter the central nervous system, leading to brain swelling. Symptoms include headache, nausea, vomiting, fatigue, and weakness. Most of these symptoms are gone by the next day. A severe disequilibrium syndrome can cause seizures and coma.

seizure. Fortunately, doctors know who is at risk for the disequilibrium syndrome, and the severe manifestations of the syndrome are rare. In its mild form, it can cause patients to feel washed out and weak. The swelling of the brain is usually gone by the next day, which is why patients feel better the day after their hemodialysis treatment. The disequilibrium syndrome does not occur in peritoneal dialysis because peritoneal dialysis is a gentle treatment and removes poisons and toxins more slowly over a longer time. This allows the brain to equilibrate slowly with the rest of the body, preventing brain swelling. Patients on nocturnal hemodialysis also do not suffer from the disequilibrium syndrome.

There are many other reasons why patients feel weak after dialysis. If you drink a large amount of liquid between treatments, the dialysis team may try to remove a large amount of fluid during hemodialysis, putting a tremendous strain on the heart and circulation and leading to low blood pressure or hypotension. This lowering of the blood pressure means there is less blood flowing to the brain, heart, and other vital organs of the body. Especially if you are older, or have heart disease or high blood pressure, this low blood pressure can make you feel weak and more debilitated. Some patients are better off removing less fluid, even if they are left with some swelling of the feet, which is called edema.

When you begin your hemodialysis treatment, your body has not adjusted to dialysis. Over time, most patients feel stronger after their dialysis treatment and adjust very well to hemodialysis. This adjustment period is not easy and can take up to 6 months' time. To feel stronger after your dialysis treatment, it is important to receive a good dialysis, which will keep the level of poisons and toxins lower in your body. When you have been having good hemodialysis treatments, there will be fewer poisons removed on each treatment, and this will decrease the amount of brain swelling that occurs. Achieving this means staying on dialysis longer and having a good access that will allow you to have a high flow of blood to the dialysis machine to remove more poisons and toxins. Feeling stronger on dialysis requires keeping to your renal diet and decreasing the amount of fluid you drink between treatments. This will lessen the chance of you developing a low blood pressure and feeling sick.

An exercise program is crucial to feeling stronger on dialysis.

An exercise program is crucial to feeling stronger on dialysis. Many patients begin an exercise program or physical therapy. They have an increased feeling of well-being, better endurance, and greater muscle strength that allows them to perform many of their most difficult daily tasks more easily. When they stop exercising, many patients feel weaker and more fatigued. An exercise program can make the difference between being an independent patient or one who is reliant on others. The psychological benefits of exercise are well known to athletes and doctors. Exercise stimulates endorphin release in the brain. Endorphins are chemical messengers released during pleasurable activities. In one study, patients who exercised have similar improvements in their depression as patients on antidepressants.

75. What will happen if there is an electrical power failure while I am on dialysis?

Electrical power is essential for hemodialysis treatments. Peritoneal dialysis is driven not by electricity but by gravity, so no electrical power is needed. In an emergency, peritoneal dialysis could be performed using flashlights for illumination without difficulty. Most hospitals have emergency generators because a loss of electrical power is extremely dangerous to patients on life support such as ventilators. Patients undergoing major surgery would also be in danger from power failure. Some hemodialysis units that are located in hospitals may be covered by their hospital emergency generator. Dialysis units in parts of the country that have frequent power outages due to storms and downed power lines may have emergency generators. Emergency generators do not cover most freestanding dialysis units.

All dialysis units have emergency plans to cope with electrical power failures. In the event of an electrical power failure, your dialysis machine would immediately stop and the blood flow out of your access would stop. All dialysis machines have a crank to manually turn the blood pump on the dialysis machine. This crank allows the dialysis staff to hand power the blood pump to return your blood to your body. Healthy patients may be able to help the staff in turning the crank to return their blood. Your dialysis unit will instruct you in the procedures to follow in case of emergency, which include what to do during electrical power failure, fire, and other emergencies.

My dialysis unit in Brooklyn experienced an electrical power failure on August 14, 2003, when the electrical grid powering the city and much of the northeastern United States went down. We had 18 patients on dialysis when the power went off, and all of them had their blood returned to their body using the blood pump crank. If it is not possible to return the blood in time, the

Electrical power failure is an inconvenience, not a true emergency.

blood loss will not be very significant and the chance of harm is low. The main adverse effect of electrical power failure is panic and fear in patients and staff. If you do have an electrical power failure in your unit, remain calm. If you are familiar with the emergency procedures to return your blood and disconnect from the dialysis machine, by all means follow them. If you are not comfortable with the emergency plan, wait patiently for the staff to return your blood and disconnect you from the hemodialysis machine. Electrical power failure is an inconvenience, not a true emergency.

76. Why do peritoneal dialysis patients develop peritonitis?

Peritonitis

An inflammation of the peritoneal membrane, which covers the intestines, caused by infection.

Peritonitis is one of the main complications of peritoneal dialysis. Peritonitis is an inflammation of the lining of the intestines. In most cases, peritonitis is caused by bacteria entering the abdomen through the peritoneal catheter. Some patients develop infections because of poor dialysis technique. Because the peritoneal catheter is tunneled through the skin and exits the abdomen, the most likely source of the bacteria is from the skin. To prevent infection, patients on peritoneal dialysis wear a mask while performing their dialysis. They carefully wash their hands with a bactericidal soap. Purell is a bactericidal solution that can be rubbed on the hands to decrease the chance of infection.

Peritoneal dialysis patients should shower and avoid bathtubs. Patients may swim in the ocean or in a private pool. They should avoid hot tubs, saunas, and jacuzzis because these warm environments promote the growth of bacteria on the skin. Patients perform exit site care every day. This involves swabbing the area where the catheter exits the skin with an antiseptic solution and applying a sterile dressing over the exit site. It is important that the catheter be securely taped to the abdomen to prevent it from twisting and turning with activity.

Symptoms of bacterial peritonitis are abdominal pain, fever, chills, and a cloudy peritoneal dialysate. It is important to recognize these signs of infection and to bring the dialysate to the peritoneal dialysis unit or to the emergency room if the unit is closed. The peritoneal dialysis fluid can be cultured by the laboratory to determine which bacteria are causing the infection. As part of the culture, the microbiology lab will test the bacteria causing the peritonitis to determine which antibiotics to use. A cell count will also be performed to measure the white blood cells in your dialysate. In 90% of peritonitis cases, the bacteria causing peritonitis are staphylococcus or streptococcus. These bacteria are normally present on our skin. The cell count and dialysate culture will guide peritoneal dialysis nurses' and physicians' choice of antibiotic. Most of the time the antibiotics will be given by injecting them into the dialysate, which is infused into the abdomen. The antibiotics will be rapidly delivered to the location where they are needed most. Many patients with bacterial peritonitis can be treated as an outpatient. If the peritonitis is severe, your doctor may want to admit you to the hospital.

Other causes of peritonitis in peritoneal dialysis patients are appendicitis, diverticulitis, and perforation of the bowel. The clue to these conditions is a dialysate culture with gram-negative organisms from the bowel, which are unusual in cases of peritonitis. Other clues are the failure of response to antibiotics. A CT scan of

Complications on Dialysis

the abdomen can sometimes diagnose the problem and guide the treatment. Patients can have peritonitis due to fungi such as *Candida*. These patients have often had multiple courses of antibiotics. The peritoneal dialysis catheter should be removed in cases of fungal peritonitis. Antibiotics for fungal peritonitis can be given by mouth or intravenously.

As peritoneal dialysis has improved over the years, the frequency of peritonitis has decreased dramatically. Peritoneal dialysis programs are constantly working hard to decrease the rate of peritonitis in their patients. It is important to realize that hemodialysis patients can also have infections of their access with bacteria, which may result in their catheter or a-v graft being removed. A rare cause of peritonitis is an allergic reaction to dialysate. These patients have a high percentage of **eosinophils** in their cell count. Eosinophils are white blood cells that are frequently released during allergic reactions. Patients can also develop an infection around their peritoneal dialysis catheter, which is called a tunnel infection. Redness around the catheter exit site and drainage of pus or liquid around the catheter are signs of a tunnel infection. You will learn a great deal about peritonitis and catheter tunnel infections during your peritoneal dialysis training.

Eosinophils

White blood cells produced by bone marrow that are active in inflammation caused by allergic reactions as well as other diseases.

77. Will my chest pain or angina get worse on dialysis?

Patients with heart problems are often concerned about the effect of dialysis on their cardiac condition. Beginning dialysis is stressful. The large majority of patients with heart problems can be safely treated with hemodialysis and peritoneal dialysis. It is important

The large majority of patients with heart problems can be safely treated with hemodialysis and peritoneal dialysis.

for your kidney doctor to be aware of your heart condition before you start dialysis and for you to talk to your cardiologist.

Your medications should be optimized so that you will have less of a chance of developing chest pain on dialysis. Many patients who develop chest pain or angina bring their nitroglycerine tablets with them while they are on hemodialysis. If they begin to experience chest pain, they can inform their nurse and immediately place a nitroglycerine tablet under their tongue. Oxygen is sometimes given to patients with heart problems while they receive their dialysis treatments to help prevent episodes of chest pain. Excessive weight gain and water intake between dialysis treatments are best avoided. Removing a great deal of fluid will put strain on your heart and precipitate an angina attack. It can also cause your heart to develop a rapid heart rate and low blood pressure. Patients with heart disease can develop atrial fibrillation or atrial flutter. These episodes of rapid heart rates often resolve by themselves when dialysis is stopped. Medication may be needed to control the heart rate.

Patients with chest pain, irregular heartbeats, or other cardiac symptoms should be carefully evaluated by a cardiologist or heart specialist. Many tests can be performed to determine if the blood vessels to the heart are blocked. If blockages exist, they can often be treated by inserting a balloon across the blockage and inflating it to open up the blocked artery. A cardiac stent or tube, is usually inserted to open the the blockage. This small tube will help prevent the blockage from returning at the same place. If the blockages are too numerous, heart bypass surgery can be done to improve blood flow to the heart. One of the advantages of heart surgery over cardiac stents is that the heart surgery patient does not need to take medications to prevent clotting of the stent. If a patient develops bleeding in the gastrointestinal tract or has had bleeding in the brain, it could be important to stop medications such as aspirin and Plavix, which interfere with platelet function.

Fortunately, medical science has made great strides in developing effective treatments for heart disease. These include medications that lower cholesterol, lower high blood pressure, improve heart failure, and treat angina. Medical devices such as pacemakers and implantable defibrillators can be used in dialysis patients to make sure the heart is beating properly. Revascularization procedures such as cardiac stents and bypass surgery can improve blood supply to the heart. Damaged heart valves can be repaired or replaced. All of these treatments can be successfully used in patients on dialysis. Treatments for heart disease are rapidly becoming more effective and safer, which will help dialysis patients live longer and have a better quality of life.

PART SEVEN

Dialysis: A Healthy Lifestyle

How can I lose weight as a dialysis patient?

Can dialysis patients participate in sports?

How will being a kidney dialysis patient affect my teeth?

More . . .

78. Why do some patients do better on dialysis?

This question of why there is variability in patient outcomes has intrigued doctors. When two patients who are the same age and have the same diagnosis, blood pressure, cholesterol level, financial resources, and support at home begin dialysis, why does one patient have a better outcome? Why do some patients survive longer on dialysis? This phenomenon has also been noticed in cancer patients, patients with infections such as pneumonia, and in patients with many chronic illnesses. The effect of the psyche or the mind on physical illness should never be underestimated. Patients with a positive attitude do better.

The effect of the psyche or the mind on physical illness should never be underestimated. Patients with a positive attitude do better.

When it comes to dialysis, successful patients are those who are able to commit to the dialysis lifestyle. This is hard to do. Many patients with kidney failure have neglected their medical care in the past, leading to kidney damage. Patients may have not taken their medication regularly, kept their doctors' appointments, or stayed on their diet. Beginning dialysis treatments is a wake-up call for many patients. The message is, my health and life are important and I need to do a better job taking care of myself.

In some ways, committing to the dialysis lifestyle is like being a competitive athlete. There is a great deal of loss in beginning dialysis. Your time is not your own. You must show up for your treatments at the hemodialysis center or be on a schedule for your peritoneal dialysis exchanges. An athlete may not want to go to the pool for 2 hours of swimming laps followed by weight training, but he or she does it in pursuit of a goal. You cannot eat what you want as a dialysis patient. Athletes look at that big piece of chocolate cake for dessert and pass it by. They know if they gain weight they will run, bike, or swim slower. They are able to give up their immediate gratification for their long-term goals. They are committed to being the best they can be. Life on dialysis is full of choices. You can go to your treatment, or skip treatment or decrease your treatment time. You can stay on your diet, or eat what you want. You can remember to take your medication, or leave it in the pill container. Successful patients make their treatments time after time. They are not looking for ways to cut corners; they want to be the best they can be. This commitment is not easy or fun, but it will pay off in the long run. As a dialysis patient, you must ask yourself, "Will I do the minimum, or will I be the best I can be?"

Patients on hemodialysis will do better if they have a good dialysis access. The most common complication in hemodialysis is access problems. Patients with catheters have a high rate of infection and scarring of the blood vessels. Arterial-venous grafts have a high rate of clotting or thrombosis and also are prone to infection. It is important to have an a-v fistula. This access is constructed of your own artery and vein, making it less likely to develop infection or clotting. The fistula takes a longer time to develop or mature. If you want to do well on hemodialysis, you should work with your vascular surgeon to develop an a-v fistula. A good a-v fistula with a good blood flow will help you clear more toxins and poisons from your bloodstream, and this will decrease the amount of complications you will have over many years. An a-v fistula will minimize interruptions in your dialysis treatments due to access

Successful patients make their treatments time after time. They are not looking for ways to cut corners; they want to be the best they can be.

Dialysis: A Healthy Lifestyle

failure. It will decrease the chance of an infection in your access spreading to other parts of your body. A good a-v fistula could last 20 years or more.

After access problems, the most common complications in dialysis patients relate to their cardiac health. Heart problems are more common in patients with kidney disease. This is because the risk factors for heart disease such as high blood pressure, diabetes, and elevated cholesterol levels are more common in patients with kidney disease. To do well long term on dialysis, you should do what you can to minimize these risks. If you are a smoker, you must try to stop smoking. Elevated blood pressure should be controlled with medication and diet. Diabetes should be treated aggressively. You will need specialized help from an **endocrinologist**. This doctor has special training in the evaluation and treatment of patients with diabetes and can work with your nephrologist to improve your blood sugars. Many new medications have recently become available to help you. The **diabetes nurse educator** is a nurse with special training in diabetes who can also work with you to help control your diabetes. Ask your nephrologist if a referral to these healthcare professionals would be appropriate for you. Medications to control cholesterol work well in dialysis patients. Your cholesterol should be measured at least once a year, and you should lower an elevated cholesterol with diet and medications. Dialysis patients with cardiovascular risk factors should be evaluated by a cardiologist. The cardiologist can help detect cardiac problems at an early stage by using noninvasive testing such as echocardiograms, stress tests, and nuclear scans. This early detection can help prevent cardiac problems before they happen and help keep you well.

Endocrinologist

A physician who has trained in internal medicine and who has received additional training in the treatment of patients with diabetes, thyroid disease, parathyroid disease, and other glandular disorders.

Diabetes nurse educator

A nurse who has obtained special training and certification in the evaluation and education of patients with diabetes.

79. How can I lose weight as a dialysis patient?

When we discuss weight with dialysis patients, there are several types of weight. One is the weight we lose on dialysis. This corresponds to the fluid removal. The other is what we call our **dry weight**. This corresponds to our weight after dialysis when we do not have extra fluid in our body. Dry weight is the target weight we are aiming for where we feel well and have good blood pressure control. The third weight is called **ideal body weight**. This weight is dependent on your age, height, and body build. Ideal body weights are different for men and women. This weight reflects a healthy weight for you. There are tables available for you to look up your ideal body weight. Your dietitian in the dialysis unit can tell you your ideal body weight. The ideal body weight is based on population studies. It can be used as a guide to determine if you are too light or too heavy. Most of us have a weight that we feel is appropriate for us. Our weight is influenced by cultural and familial factors. In some cultures, being heavy is considered a sign of good health and prosperity. A chubby baby with fat cheeks and fat arms and legs is thought to be healthy and doing well. If our parents are heavy, we are more likely to view a heavy body image as desirable or normal.

Being overweight may have several medical consequences, including elevated blood pressure and difficulty controlling diabetes. Being overweight can also put stress on our heart. It can cause our joints to wear out sooner because our knees and hips are carrying excess weight. Some patients who are very heavy may suffer from a syndrome called sleep apnea. These

Dry weight

The body weight of hemodialysis patients at the end of their hemodialysis treatment. The dry weight is determined by removing fluid until the blood pressure begins to fall.

Ideal body weight

Ideal body weight is dependent upon your age, height, body, build, and sex, and is based on the measured average weight of normal individuals. Ideal body weights can be found in published tables, which are available from your kidney dietitian.

patients have difficulty breathing when they fall asleep. The tube that carries air to the lungs (the trachea) can be blocked, causing the patient to wake up many times during the night and preventing restful sleep. For all these reasons, kidney dialysis patients who are overweight are often encouraged by their physicians to lose weight.

Losing weight as a dialysis patient is similar to losing weight in people not on dialysis. It requires commitment. Decreasing the calories you eat every day and increasing your activity level with exercise is the standard approach. The dietitian at the dialysis unit can help you choose foods that have high nutritional value and fewer calories. Many different diets are advertised in the media for losing weight. Many of these diets are very restrictive. People frequently lose a lot of weight in a short time only to gain it back. Diets that aim for a slower loss of weight by changing your eating habits are more likely to be effective long term. It is important to check with your nephrologist and dietitian before starting any diet to see if the diet is safe for kidney dialysis patients. Diet pills are generally not a good idea for dialysis patients, as they can have some serious side effects. In extreme cases of obesity, weight loss surgery called bariatric surgery can be performed to band the stomach, causing a decrease in your ability to eat too much. Intestinal bypass operations may also be used to treat obesity. These procedures are used as a last resort when dieting and medical management has failed.

Most people find it difficult to lose weight alone. Support groups such as Weight Watchers have been successful in helping people lose weight because they have a structure and a great deal of positive support. It is easier to keep your diet when you have friends who are also trying to lose weight. If your spouse, significant other, or other family members are also overweight, consider encouraging them to join you in your weight loss program. This may make it easier to change your eating habits and to limit some of the high-calorie food that comes into your home. If you do buy high-calorie foods as a treat, consider buying a smaller container. Avoid extra large sizes of cookies, chips, candy, and cakes, even if they cost the same as the small package. This way if you go off your diet, you will not eat as much of these foods. Exercising is also easier to do with others. If you have a regular appointment with a friend to walk, jog, bike ride, or go to the gym, you are more likely to exercise. The best results in losing weight are because of changes in a person's lifestyle that result in a gradual loss of weight.

80. Can dialysis patients participate in sports?

Dialysis patients can participate in a wide range of sports and activities. Studies have shown that regular exercise and physical activity increase patients' sense of well-being, decrease fatigue, improve depression, lower blood pressure, and improve blood sugar control in diabetic patients. It is also fun, especially if you exercise with someone else. It is important to discuss your sports plans with your doctor before you start your exercise program.

Hemodialysis patients with catheters cannot get their catheters wet because of the risks of infection. These patients should not participate in swimming and water sports. Hemodialysis patients with fistulas and grafts can swim and get their access wet. Peritoneal dialysis patients can swim in the ocean or a private pool. Public pools may have a higher bacteria count in the water and are not advised. After swimming, patients on peritoneal dialysis should perform their exit site care. The peritoneal dialysis catheter should be securely taped to the abdomen during swimming or exercise to prevent irritation of the access site.

Patients on peritoneal dialysis should exercise with their abdomen drained of peritoneal dialysis fluid. They should not perform abdominal exercises such as crunches, sit-ups, or leg lifts. They should perform exit site care after their workout because sweat will help bacteria grow on the skin.

Exercises that increase cardiac function such as walking, biking, tennis, and jogging are preferred to exercises that require lifting weights.

Hemodialysis patients with fistulas and grafts are discouraged from lifting weights greater than 20 pounds with their access arm. Lifting heavy weights in general is not the best exercise for dialysis patients because lifting has been associated with increasing blood pressure during the lift. Exercises that increase cardiac function such as walking, biking, tennis, and jogging are preferred to exercises that require lifting weights. Calisthenics are good exercises for dialysis patients. After beginning dialysis, many patients feel fatigued and weak. You should decrease the intensity and level of your activity. If you are used to walking a mile a day, you may want to walk for a quarter of a mile for one week and see how you feel. If you feel capable of more activity, double the distance every week. If you are used to playing tennis for an hour, try 10 or 20 minutes at first. Increase your activity level as long as you are feeling well. It is not important how much exercise you can do, the important point is to start. As we get older, we become more sedentary. We lose the simple joy of shooting a basketball, catching a fly ball, or ice-skating. We all have a thousand reasons to avoid being active. Inertia is the most powerful force in the universe.

It takes effort to overcome the negative feelings of "I cannot do this anymore," "I'm too old," "People will laugh at me," and so forth. Try to overcome these negative feelings. Be prepared for failure. If you become dizzy or feel faint, stop, lie down, and rest. Regroup. Ask your doctor about your symptoms. He or she may recommend changes in your exercise regimen that will help you be active without these symptoms. Avoid exercising in very high temperatures that can lead to dehydration and heat stroke. Use common sense in your exercise. If you bike, rollerblade, or ski, wear a helmet. This is good advice for everyone, on dialysis or not. Do not swim alone. Use the buddy system. Try a new sport. Use beginning dialysis as an excuse to treat yourself to something you always wanted to try but never had the time to try. You need to be active to do well on dialysis. Take lessons to make sure you are using your sports equipment safely and are getting the most out of your exercise time. Have fun!

Erick Lucero writes:

I have always been an active person. At age 12, I became interested in calisthenics at school because I wanted to play baseball. I did exercises that got my legs strong because this would improve the power of my hitting and fielding. I played on traveling baseball teams since I was 12. Later on, I played in baseball leagues on weekends. I play second base. On June 4, 2007, I played for my team. On June 6, I started hemodialysis. At first, I was very weak. Little by little, I began throwing the ball around. In October, I was able to play the last two league games of the season. My team needed me, and they gladly welcomed me back.

The best exercise for dialysis patients is walking. You can do this even if you are not feeling your best. Walking in the park is my favorite. Walking strengthens your leg muscles. If your legs are good, everything else will follow. Stretching is very important for hemodialysis patients. On hemodialysis, you are sitting still for 4 hours. Stretching will make your muscles feel better and decrease cramps on dialysis.

81. How can I keep my bones strong?

Keeping your bones strong requires good nutrition and regular exercise. In addition, kidney dialysis patients are especially susceptible to a type of weakening of the bones that is due to kidney disease. This weakening of the bones is known as **metabolic bone disease** or renal osteodystrophy. Bone problems begin early on in kidney failure, before patients begin dialysis treatments. Most of the calcium and phosphorus in our bodies reside in our bones. Our bones are a large reservoir of these important minerals. As kidney function declines, phosphorus levels rise in the blood. The elevated phosphorus combines with the calcium in the blood and pushes the calcium back into the bones. As a result, the level of calcium in the blood decreases.

Another reason for low calcium is decreased vitamin D activity in kidney patients. The kidney is necessary for the production of active vitamin D. Vitamin D helps absorb calcium that is in the food we eat from the gastrointestinal tract. When the calcium level falls, cells in the parathyroid glands, called chief cells, sense the low calcium level in the blood. The parathyroid glands are four small glands that are located on the thyroid gland

Metabolic bone disease

Bone disease in renal patients is caused by reabsorption of bone by cells called osteoclasts whose growth is stimulated by PTH. Patients with bone disease can have bone pain and are more prone to fractures. Also called renal osteodystrophy.

in front of the neck, at the windpipe near the bulge called the Adam's apple. When the calcium level is low, the chief cells signal the parathyroid glands to produce more PTH. PTH travels through the body in the blood, signaling the gastrointestinal tract to absorb more calcium and telling the kidneys to stop eliminating calcium from the body. PTH also tells cells in the bones called osteoclasts to start releasing calcium from the bones. If the calcium remains low for a long time, the parathyroid gland grows larger and produces abnormally high levels of PTH. The high PTH level can cause too much calcium to leave our bones, resulting in bones that have less structural material holding us up. If the bones lose calcium, they are more susceptible to fractures. Patients develop changes of the bones of their fingers and collarbones that can be seen on x-rays. The most important evidence that bone problems are occurring is from blood tests. Calcium and phosphorus levels are measured every month in dialysis patients to evaluate bone health. Another blood test, alkaline phosphatase can be elevated if the bone is being reabsorbed too rapidly. PTH is also measured on a regular basis.

The first step in maintaining good bone health is to keep your phosphorus level low. This can be done by decreasing intake of phosphorus-containing foods like milk products and beans. Your dietitian will be reviewing these foods with you on a regular basis. Medications can also be helpful in decreasing the absorption of phosphorus from the gastrointestinal tract. Phosphate binders such as PhosLo, which contain calcium acetate, and calcium carbonate binders such as Tums contain calcium that binds phosphorus. Renagel contains sevelamer hydrochloride as a binder. Another binder is Fosrenol, which contains lanthanum carbonate. Fosrenol is a chewable tablet. All the phosphorus binders are taken by mouth and trap phosphorus in the gastrointestinal tract. It is important to remember to decrease the phosphorus in the diet. Vitamin D analogs are also frequently used to keep patients' bones strong. They work by increasing the absorption of calcium from the gastrointestinal tract. They also suppress the production and secretion of PTH. Vitamin D is available as capsules taken by mouth and also as an injection that can be given during the hemodialysis treatment. Some Vitamin D analogs are Rocaltrol, Hectorol, Zemplar, and Calcijex.

Sensipar (cinacalcet hydrochloride) is a medication used to treat kidney dialysis patients who are at risk for developing metabolic bone disease. It is different from other medications that treat bone disease because it is the only medication of its kind available. Sensipar decreases PTH as well as calcium and phosphorus. Vitamin D analogs can decrease PTH, but they can also cause a rise in serum calcium. PTH is produced by the parathyroid glands that are located in the neck. Most people have four parathyroid glands that sit on the thyroid gland. The parathyroid glands have chief cells that have calcium-sensing receptors on their surface. Sensipar increases the sensitivity of these receptors to the calcium in the blood. Sensipar causes a decrease in the PTH secretion as well as a decrease in calcium and phosphorus. This is beneficial because decreasing the amount of calcium circulating in the blood can decrease the calcium that ends up being deposited in blood vessels and other organs of the body.

When Sensipar first became available, it was used in the most difficult cases in patients who had very high

PTH levels. Some of these patients were having multiple fractures and were facing surgical removal of the parathyroid glands. This operation is called a parathyroidectomy. Sensipar was effective in reducing the PTH level in many of these patients and some of them were able to avoid parathyroid surgery. As doctors used Sensipar and found that it was well tolerated by most patients, it began to be used in more patients.

The most frequent side effects of Sensipar are an upset stomach, nausea, vomiting, diarrhea, and muscle cramps. Sensipar comes as a tablet and is available in 30-mg, 60-mg, and 90-mg strengths. Most patients start with the 30-mg tablet. Sensipar is absorbed in 2 to 6 hours and should be taken with food. It is important before you begin taking Sensipar to tell your doctor if you have a history of seizures or liver disease, if you are on any psychiatric medications, or if you are pregnant or are planning to become pregnant. Blood tests including calcium, phosphorus, and PTH levels are followed carefully when you take Sensipar to see if your calcium level falls. Sensipar can be safely used with phosphate binders, as well as vitamin D analogs. Most patients on dialysis are on several medications to prevent bone problems.

When I first started my career treating kidney dialysis patients over 25 years ago, bone disease was a major problem for patients. Many patients had multiple fractures, bone pain, and spontaneous rupture of tendons. Surgery to remove the parathyroid glands was the only option to treat their severe bone disease. Fortunately, we have safe and effective medications that have resulted in better and safer treatment for metabolic bone disease and an improved quality of life for our patients on dialysis.

Do not be discouraged if phosphorus and calcium balance is very confusing to you. It is common for nursing and medical students to have difficulty understanding these concepts. The scientific names are also often overwhelming to patients. Try to concentrate on measures that will keep your phosphorus level normal. You will be reviewing this important subject many times in the future with your nurse, doctor, and dietitian.

82. Why is taking care of my eyes important as a dialysis patient?

We often take for granted our most precious sense, our eyesight. Patients on dialysis have an increased risk of vision loss. This is, in part, due to the fact that about 45% of patients on dialysis have diabetes. Diabetes affects the blood vessels in the kidneys and the eyes at the same time. The first sign of diabetes affecting the eyes is the enlargement of the veins at the back of the eye called the retina. These and other changes in the blood vessels can be seen during an examination by an ophthalmologist or an optometrist. These changes are called retinopathy. As the circulation to the back of the eye gets worse, new blood vessels grow in the retina. Blood vessels can bleed into the back of the eye causing an acute loss of vision. Over time, the blood in the back of the eye can cause scarring and further damage to the retina resulting in permanent loss of vision. Fortunately, damage to the eyes from diabetes can be prevented by careful control of the blood sugar. Damage to the retina can be treated by ophthalmologists with laser treatments. Laser treatments involve exposing damaged areas of the retina to laser light that is able to decrease the growth of new blood vessels. Laser treatments are done in the office and do not require the patient to be admitted to the hospital overnight.

Glaucoma is a group of eye diseases affecting the optic nerve, which is a bundle of nerves that enters the back of the eye and carries visual information from the eyes to our brain. Glaucoma is usually associated with an increased pressure in the eye. More than 2 million Americans over the age of 40 have some form of glaucoma. Risk factors for glaucoma include a family history of glaucoma, black or Hispanic ancestry, diabetes, and hypertension. Glaucoma is diagnosed during a visit to your ophthalmologist or optometrist. These eye doctors will measure the pressure in your eye, examine the optic nerve, and may measure the thickness of your cornea, which is the clear front surface of your eyes. Treatment for glaucoma is usually eye drops to decrease the pressure in the eye. Some forms of severe glaucoma are treated with eye surgery.

Age-related macular degeneration is a common cause of visual loss due to damage to the macula, which is the center of the retina. A healthy macula is needed for clear vision for activities such as reading, driving, recognizing faces, and observing fine details of objects. Macular degeneration generally begins after age 50. More than 14% of patients over the age of 70 suffer from some degree of macular degeneration. Other risk factors besides age include smoking, a family history of macular degeneration, and prolonged sun exposure. It is important not to smoke, and to wear hats and sunglasses to decrease sun exposure to your eyes, and to eat foods such as fresh fruits and vegetables rich in carotenoids, lutens, vitamin C, and vitamin E to decrease your chance of developing macular degeneration as you age. Foods rich in omega-3 fatty acids are also thought to decrease macular degeneration. Your renal dietitian can help you select foods that are part of the renal diet and good for your eyesight.

Dialysis patients should have an eye examination at least once a year. Many patients with diabetes, glaucoma, and macular degeneration should be followed more frequently. Another good practice is to wear glasses and sunglasses that have UV light protection to prevent the formation of cataracts. It is important to wear eye protection when working with tools or participating in sports. Eye guards are protective glasses made of a plastic called polycarbonate. Sports which have a high rate of eye injury include basketball, baseball, water sports, and racquet sports such as tennis, racquetball, and squash. Chemical burns of the eyes from household products such as drain and floor cleaners are common accidents and care should be used when handling these products. Protecting your vision as a kidney patient will help you maintain a good quality of life and decrease your dependency on others.

83. Why is it important to take my medications as a dialysis patient?

Many patients who begin dialysis treatments wonder why they still have to take medication. The average dialysis patient takes between 8 and 12 different pills a day. Taking this amount of medication is difficult for many patients. Dialysis is an imperfect treatment. The normal kidney performs hundreds of different tasks every day. These tasks involve cleaning the blood, metabolizing medications, stimulating the bone marrow to produce red blood cells, activating vitamin D, and regulating blood pressure. The hemodialysis machine and peritoneal dialysis only clean the blood. They can remove some medications. Other functions of the kidney are replaced by medications. To regulate your blood pressure, you will need to take blood pressure medications. To lower your phosphorus level, you will need to take phosphate binders. You will receive erythropoietin injections if you have a low blood count as well as injections of vitamin D. If you are a diabetic, you will continue to take your diabetes pills and injections of insulin. Many patients with diabetes need less medication because the kidneys metabolize the insulin your body produces. As your kidneys become diseased, there is more insulin available to decrease your blood sugar level. Some patients with type II diabetes can come off their diabetes medications. Patients may take medication for their heart to prevent heart attacks, such as aspirin, Plavix, beta blockers, ACE inhibitors, and nitrates. An elevated blood cholesterol is associated with kidney failure and needs to be treated with medication when diet alone is not successful. Bowel complaints such as heartburn and constipation are common in kidney patients. It is easy to see how the number of medications adds up quickly.

It is important to take your medications as a kidney dialysis patient because you will decrease the chances of having a complication that will decrease the quality or length of your life. When you are faced with taking an additional medication, it is important that you learn the reason for the medication from your doctor. The more knowledge you have, the better job you will do taking those pills. Dialysis patients often have several doctors and can end up taking two medications for the same problem. Ask your nephrologist if you can take medicines that can be taken once a day rather than two or three times a day. Many medications have a time-release form that allows you to take them once

It is important to take your medications as a kidney dialysis patient because you will decrease the chances of having a complication that will decrease the quality or length of your life.

a day. It may be possible to simplify by taking higher doses of one or two blood pressure medications and eliminating the third antihypertensive. Some medications are available in an adhesive patch that is applied to the skin. An example is the antihypertensive clonidine, which is available in a patch called Catapress TTS. The Catapress TTS patch is applied once a week. If you are taking clonidine twice a day, that is 14 less pills a week to swallow. Patches are especially useful for confused patients who may not remember to take their medication regularly and patients who do not like taking their pills.

If you are very overweight, the best way to reduce your medications is to lose weight. Many medical problems such as diabetes, hypertension, and elevated cholesterol get better with changes in diet. Increasing the time you spend on dialysis may help normalize your blood pressure and phosphorus level. Patients on daily dialysis therapies such as peritoneal dialysis, nocturnal dialysis, and daily home dialysis often are able to stop some of their blood pressure medication and phosphate binders. Perhaps one of these therapies is best for you.

84. My cholesterol is elevated. Is this a concern?

Cholesterol is a hot topic for everyone. An elevated cholesterol level is associated with hardening of the arteries called atherosclerosis. This hardening of the arteries causes blockages in the arteries to major important organs such as the heart, brain, bowels, arms, legs, and kidneys. If you develop a blockage to the heart, which is called angina, you may have chest pain. If the blockage is very severe, it may lead to a heart attack, which causes a portion of the heart muscle to die. This heart muscle injury is not reversible. If the blockage occurs to the brain, a stroke may occur. Blockages to the legs can cause pain in the calves while walking. Physicians have developed ingenious ways of bypassing these blockages with surgery and other techniques. Coronary bypass surgery for blockages of arteries to the heart involves taking veins in the legs and bypassing the blockage by creating a new tube to carry blood to the heart. Other procedures have been developed to improve circulation to the brain, legs, and kidneys. These procedures are truly wonderful and in some cases lifesaving. It would be better to prevent the blockages caused by hardening of the arteries due to atherosclerosis, which is why everyone is so concerned about cholesterol. An elevated cholesterol level is a major risk factor for developing hardening of the arteries that causes blockages. Other risk factors are high blood pressure, smoking, diabetes, and a family history of hardening of the arteries.

Kidney patients are prone to high cholesterol levels due to several causes. The most common cause of kidney failure is diabetes. Diabetic patients are more likely to have high cholesterol, especially if their diabetes is poorly controlled. Many kidney diseases cause high cholesterol. Patients in the pre-dialysis period with a large amount of protein loss in their urine have high cholesterol because the liver is making more cholesterol along with the protein albumin. Every patient with kidney problems should have their cholesterol measured. The total cholesterol level was the first screening test available. It is best to measure your cholesterol before you have eaten. The fasting cholesterol level will be an accurate measure of your cholesterol. Cholesterol levels rise after your eat. If you have risk factors for hardening of the arteries, it is generally recommended that your fasting total cholesterol be less than 200.

When we measure cholesterol, we typically order a panel of tests, often called the **lipid profile**. The lipid profile contains the total cholesterol level and the triglyceride level, which measures another fat in the blood. An important component of the total cholesterol level is the **low-density lipoprotein** level, referred to as **LDL**. The LDL level is associated with the bad blockages that cause so many problems. In patients with hardening of their arteries, it is recommended that your LDL level be below 100. The **high-density lipoprotein** level, **HDL**, is known as the good cholesterol. A low level of HDL is associated with hardening of the arteries and blockages. A high level of HDL protects people from developing hardening of the arteries. Exercise will raise HDL levels. If your total cholesterol level is high because your HDL is also high, you may not need treatment for a high cholesterol level.

Treatment for high cholesterol begins with diet. Meat, especially organ meat like liver, is high in cholesterol. Some fish, like swordfish, have a lot of cholesterol. Milk, ice cream, and cheese have a large amount of cholesterol. Your kidney dietitian will guide you on your low-cholesterol diet. If diet fails, there are medications available to decrease cholesterol. The statins are a class of medication that work by inhibiting HMG-CoA reductase, which helps synthesize cholesterol in the liver. Some statins are Zocor (simvastatin), Lipitor (atorvastatin), Pravacol (pravastatin), Crestor (rosuvastatin), Welchol (colesevelam), and Lescol (fluvastatin). Another medication for high cholesterol is niacin.

Lipid profile

A lipid profile is a series of blood tests that include total cholesterol, HDL cholesterol, LDL cholesterol, and triglycerides. It is used to evaluate patients for their risk of developing atherosclerosis.

Low-density lipoprotein (LDL)

Composed of proteins, triglycerides, and cholesterol bound together in the blood. A high LDL level is associated with atherosclerosis.

High-density lipoprotein (HDL)

The "good cholesterol" in our blood that protects us from heart disease and other vascular problems. A high level of HDL is protective, and it can be increased by exercising, eating foods such as garlic and onions, and by taking certain medications.

Many people are resistant to taking medications for an elevated cholesterol level. They are not convinced that treatment will be beneficial and will decrease the chances of a serious heart problem or stoke. The benefits of treatment for a high cholesterol level have been shown in many studies with different populations of patients in varying countries. Treatment is not without risk. Statins have risks of liver problems as well as muscle cramps and more serious muscle damage called rhabdomyolysis. It is important to have a frank discussion with your doctor to decide the best course of action for you if you have an elevated cholesterol level. Most people tolerate medications for elevated cholesterol without side effects.

85. How can I live longer as a dialysis patient?

The strategy to live longer as a dialysis patient is to modify the risk factors for the most common causes of demise in dialysis patients, which are cardiac disease and stroke. This means maintaining ideal body weight, controlling blood pressure and cholesterol, treating diabetes, not smoking, and having a regular evaluation with your doctor regarding these risk factors. You do not have to be perfect. You should strive to make improvements in these areas. For example, many people feel they are so heavy that it is no use losing weight. The reality is that losing as little as 5 pounds has beneficial effects on lowering blood pressure. It is important to set realistic goals and reward yourself when you achieve them. If your goal is to lose 40 pounds, there is less of a chance to meet this goal than 5 pounds. After you lose the first 5 pounds, try to lose the next 5 pounds.

Exercise is an important habit to develop. I was on a vacation in France several years ago and was waiting outside in my rented car for my wife to come out of a store. I watched an elderly woman come out of a butcher shop with her purchases. She placed her package in the basket of her bicycle and rode away. I immediately understood why life expectancy is longer in some countries. That woman has probably been riding her bicycle for 75 years. In most instances, we can fit exercise into our daily routine. Park your car 5 blocks from your house and try to go for a walk every day. Use the stairs instead of the elevator. Realize that exercise is best approached in small bits. Exercising for five or ten minutes is better than no exercise at all.

Dialysis patients can live longer by paying attention to their access. If they have a good access, such as an a-v fistula, they can receive better dialysis. Good dialysis is associated with living longer and with less complications of renal failure such as neuropathy. An a-v fistula is less likely to become infected than a hemodialysis catheter. If you are on peritoneal dialysis, ask your doctor how you can increase the amount of dialysis you receive. This may involve increasing the amount of dialysate in your peritoneal dialysis exchange. Avoid missing dialysis or not completing a peritoneal dialysis exchange. If you skip one peritioneal dialysis exchange, you are only receiving 75% of your dialysis for the day. If you miss one hemodialysis treatment, you are missing one-third of your dialysis for that week. Ask your doctor if you are getting enough dialysis. Should you increase your time on dialysis or be treated with a hemodialysis dialyzer with a larger clearance? These questions are best discussed in your doctor's office or during your care plan meeting with the dialysis team.

Patients on dialysis need to be flexible to live longer. You may be faced with changes in your medical condition, develop complications, or need emergency procedures to fix your access. The ability to accept these changes and develop a therapeutic alliance with the dialysis team will improve your chance of long-term survival as a dialysis patient. You may arrive at the dialysis unit before a vacation or other important event and be told that your catheter is infected and must be removed. The ability to understand your dialysis treatment and to respond to crisis will decrease your chances of having a complication that could be life threatening. Try to understand what your doctor and the dialysis team are saying about your problems. Evaluate the information, and adjust your behavior to overcome the obstacle in your way. Be flexible. Stay focused on the big picture.

Patients on dialysis need to be flexible to live longer.

86. How can I avoid being depressed as a dialysis patient?

Being depressed is a normal part of starting dialysis. Being dependent on dialysis treatments to live is very scary. Most patients feel their life is over when they begin dialysis. As they adjust to their treatment and feel better physically, they become more hopeful and realize their life is not over but is continuing in a new way. The ability to accept the dialysis lifestyle and go on with your life by making plans for the future is an important milestone in adjusting to dialysis.

Some of the depression dialysis patients face is due to the poisons and toxins present in kidney failure. If we perform an **electroencephalogram (EEG)** on dialysis

Electroencephalogram (EEG)

A medical test in which electrical impulses generated by the brain are recorded by attaching electrodes to the scalp.

185

patients, we find slowing of their electrical impulses. This typical change in the EEG of dialysis patients is due to the poisons and toxins of kidney failure. These changes are reversed by a successful kidney transplant. Several patients who I observed in the pre-dialysis phase of their kidney failure became depressed when they began hemodialysis. When they received a kidney transplant, they reverted to their previous cheerful, positive personality. It is important to realize that the depression is not your fault.

It is important to realize that the depression is not your fault.

The first thing to do if you find yourself depressed as a dialysis patient is to review your medications with your doctor. Many medications such as sleeping pills, pain medications, some antihypertensives, and medications for ulcers or heartburn can affect your mental function. Medications tend to accumulate in dialysis patients because they metabolize and eliminate medications from the body more slowly than patients not on dialysis. We do not think of alcohol as a medication, but it can increase depression. If you are drinking alcohol, discuss this with your doctor to see if it is increasing your depression.

Exercise can help decrease depression in dialysis patients. Athletes talk about the runner's high. This feeling is due to substances called endorphins, which are released by the brain during intense exercise. These substances cause a sense of well-being and encourage continued exercise. Exercise improves self-esteem, gets you out of the house, and gives you something to do if you have taken time off to adjust to dialysis. Never underestimate the benefits of exercise in your life.

If you continue to be depressed for 6 months after beginning dialysis, or if your feelings of depression are very severe, discuss the possible need for medication and psychiatric consultation with your doctor. Many patients on dialysis benefit a great deal from antidepressants. These medications are taken by mouth and work well in patients on dialysis. Most patients on dialysis who are treated with antidepressants are able to stop them after their depression improves. These medications are safe, effective, and can make life more rewarding if your depression is severe.

Patients with a history of depression before they developed kidney failure can be safely and successfully treated with dialysis. It is important to make sure your psychologist or psychiatrist talks to your nephrologist and maintains communication during your adjustment to dialysis. Some medications for depression such as lithium need to be adjusted or stopped when you develop kidney failure.

Discuss your feelings with your family, significant other, and the dialysis team. Many patients with depression improve because they share their feelings with dialysis patients they encounter in the waiting room of the dialysis unit. The knowledge that you are not alone in being depressed as a dialysis patient and that this is a common response to illness and dialysis treatments can be helpful in decreasing feelings of depression.

When you start dialysis, talk to other patients who are on dialysis. They have faced the same problems you face and have a helpful perspective. Often their stories will give you insight into your own adjustment to dialysis. Most patients starting dialysis feel alone. They speak to their nephrologist, nurse, family, but nothing has the same impact as talking to a fellow dialysis patient. They will help you overcome your depression. Make sure to listen to patients around you in the dialysis center waiting room. Their insight, advice, and support is invaluable.

87. What medications should I avoid as a dialysis patient?

Dialysis patients take a great deal of medication to help replace the function of their kidneys. Often busy physicians feel obligated to prescribe another medication for each new complaint. Many complaints may be due to a side effect of a medication that is then treated with another medication. An example of this is giving a patient painkillers such as codeine or oxycodone for the relief of chronic pain such as arthritis, back pain, or headache. These medications, called opiates, frequently cause side effects such as nausea, vomiting, and constipation. The best thing to do if these symptoms occur is to stop the medication. Stool softeners for constipation and Pepcid or Nexium for nausea and vomiting are frequently prescribed, but they do not get to the root of the problem, which is a drug side effect. It is a good practice to limit pain medication containing opiates to the least amount that can control pain. Many medications are metabolized and eliminated from the body more slowly in kidney dialysis patients, resulting in higher levels of medication in the blood of kidney patients than in people who have normal renal function. This high level of medication can make side effects more likely. With constant use, patients develop **tolerance** to the medication. This means that more medication is needed to get the same reduction in pain. Other approaches to chronic pain such as medications

Tolerance

The need for an increasing amount of medication to produce the same effect over time. A common example is the need to use more pain medication to relieve chronic pain.

that are not opiates, physical therapy, heat, and massage can often be just as effective with fewer side effects. Sleeping pills can also accumulate in the blood of dialysis patients. The side effects of sleeping pills include an inability to wake up in times of danger, such as during a fire in your house. Sleeping pills can cause depression, anxiety, difficulty concentrating, and other problems. They are best used for a short time, if at all.

Medications for diabetes have to be carefully monitored in dialysis patients. Some medications such as Glucophage should not be used at all. The kidney metabolizes insulin, and patients with kidney failure often need less insulin when their kidney disease progresses to prevent the blood sugar from falling too low. Medications called sulfonylureas used to treat type II diabetes are removed from the body by the kidneys. These drugs can accumulate in patients with kidney failure and cause low blood sugar for several days until they are eliminated from the body.

Lithium, a drug used to treat manic depression, is excreted by the kidney and should not be used in patients on dialysis. Most other medications for psychiatric conditions can be safely used in dialysis patients.

Get in the habit of asking your doctor the reason for any new medications that are prescribed. Ask your doctor if the medication is important or if you can do without it. Most dialysis patients end up taking 8 to 12 different medications a day. Many patients are overwhelmed by the number of medications and forget or are unable to take all of them on a regular basis. By trying to take medications that are important in maintaining good health and avoiding unnecessary medications, you will decrease the chances of side effects and drug interactions. You will also be more successful in taking your medications at the right time and be less likely to skip a dose.

88. How will being a kidney dialysis patient affect my teeth?

Patients with kidney problems have more dental problems than patients not on dialysis. This may be because of an increase in the urea and phosphate in the secretions of the salivary glands in the mouth. Patients on dialysis have more plaque and **calculus** formation from bacteria on their teeth. Plaque is a layer of saliva, bacteria, protein, and sugar that forms a film that covers the teeth. When calcium is deposited in the center of the plaque, calculus is formed. Calculus is from the Latin word meaning pebble or stone. Calculus is more difficult to remove. Plaque and calculus can cause an inflammation of the gums, which is called gingivitis. If not treated, gingivitis can lead to serious dental infections and tooth loss. Kidney dialysis patients also have decreased salivary gland secretion, which can lead to parotid gland infection. They can have demineralization of the jawbone due to renal bone disease. Bone demineralization can lead to periodontal disease (disease of the gums), which can cause loose teeth. Dialysis patients are more susceptible to infections of the mouth from *Candida*. They also can get ulcers of the mouth.

The most effective way of removing plaque and calculus from the teeth is brushing and flossing your teeth

Calculus

Comes from the Latin word for stone. A kidney stone is sometimes referred to as a calculus. The term is also used by dentists to describe a calcified layer of saliva, bacteria, protein, and sugar covering the teeth.

at least twice a day. However, brushing alone cannot remove all of the plaque formed daily on your teeth. Plaque is also removed when your teeth are cleaned at your regular visit to your dentist. One study by dentists involving kidney dialysis patients showed that one-half of the patients never brushed their teeth or had regular visits to a dentist. When dialysis patients go to the dentist, it is more likely to be for a specific complaint or problem, not for prevention. This may be because dialysis patients are busy with other health concerns. They may not regard good dental care as a priority. While dental care is also expensive, it is much easier and cheaper to prevent dental disease than to treat it. It is important to keep your teeth and mouth as healthy as possible. Ask your dentist or hygienist to demonstrate proper brushing and flossing techniques. Poor dentition and periodontal or gum disease can interfere with your nutrition, require you to have extensive painful dental procedures, or cause infection in your mouth to spread to other areas of your body such as your lungs and heart. Patients who eat large amounts of sweets and carbohydrates are more likely to have tooth decay. When we eat food with high sugar content, bacteria in the mouth ferment the sugar, which produces acid. The acid encourages the formation of dental caries, also known as cavities. Good oral hygiene will help you live a longer and healthier life on dialysis.

Good oral hygiene will help you live a longer and healthier life on dialysis.

Dialysis patients can safely undergo most dental procedures. Make sure your nephrologist knows when you are scheduled for your dental procedure. It is important to tell your dentist if you are taking any blood thinners like Coumadin, aspirin, Plavix, Persantine, or

Aggrenox, which could cause more bleeding. Also, mention allergies or drug reactions to antibiotics or pain medication. Remind your dentist that the best day for dental procedures is the day after your dialysis treatment. Many dialysis patients receive prophylactic antibiotics during their dental work, which may decrease the chance of an infection in the dialysis access or other areas of the body caused by bacteria entering the bloodstream during the procedure. Dialysis patients are at a somewhat higher risk of complications from general anesthesia. If you need general anesthesia for your dental work, you might want to have it as an outpatient in a hospital setting. If you develop a complication, your nephrologist and other doctors may be more available than in the dentist's office.

Erick Lucero writes:

I began going to the dentist before I was on dialysis. My sister-in-law is a dental hygienist, and she got me to go to the dentist. Before I was on dialysis, I was taking a medication called cyclosporine to help prevent my kidneys from getting worse. The cyclosporine made my gums swell. My dentist explained the need for kidney patients to have regular dental checkups. This got me in the routine of going to the dentist every 6 months. I used to brush my teeth once a day. Now I brush my teeth three times a day (after every meal) and floss. I have a toothbrush I keep at work. Many dialysis patients avoid going to the dentist because they are worried about receiving more bad news about their health. Good oral hygiene is a good thing. It helps you feel better about your health.

89. Why do I have problems sleeping at night?

Most dialysis patients have difficulty sleeping at night at one time or another. The sleep-wake cycle, called the circadian rhythm, that regulates our sleep cycle is disturbed in dialysis patients because of the toxins and poisons in their bodies that are not removed by dialysis. Dialysis patients tend to nap and feel tired in the day and are wide awake at night. They have difficulty falling asleep. It is important to avoid napping during the day, which will make the problem worse. Caffeinated drinks such as coffee and soda should be avoided after noon. Alcohol can help a person fall asleep, but when the alcohol is metabolized and wears off, the patient may wake up. Sleeping pills are not a good long-term solution for sleep disturbances. Eating a large meal close to bedtime can increase your chances of developing heartburn or esophageal reflux, which can also lead to sleep difficulties.

Other medical problems can cause difficulty with sleep. Sleep apnea is a condition that causes patients to wake up because they stop breathing at night. This condition is often due to obstruction of the airway or trachea, which brings air to the lungs. The patient may have loud snoring, gasp for air, and toss and turn excessively at night. Often sleep apnea can be seen in patients who are heavier than normal. Seizures, thyroid disorders, restless leg syndrome, depression, anxiety, and many other medical conditions can interfere with sleep. If you have difficulty sleeping that persists, you may want to see a specialist in sleep medicine. This physician has special training in sleep disorders. He or

Dialysis: A Healthy Lifestyle

she may arrange for you to sleep overnight in a sleep lab. You will be connected to special sensors that will measure your heart rate, EEG, breathing, and other parameters. You will also be videotaped to correlate your physiologic parameters with your behavior. Many patients can learn the cause of their inability to sleep by staying overnight in the sleep lab. Once a diagnosis is made, specific therapy can be prescribed to help you sleep better.

PART EIGHT

Getting Off Dialysis

Can I recover my kidney function?

What will happen if I decide to stop my dialysis treatments?

How can I get a kidney transplant?

More ...

90. Can I recover my kidney function?

This is the most frequently asked question by patients on kidney dialysis. All patients hope their kidneys will regain function and that they can stop dialysis. The chance of this happening depends on the reason your kidneys have failed. If your kidneys have failed because of acute renal failure due to a medication, an infection, uncontrolled blood pressure, or other reversible causes, recovery is a possibility. If you have acute renal failure and make a large amount of urine, say 2 quarts, you have a better chance of improving. If you are not making urine, you are less likely to recover.

Most patients with chronic progressive renal failure will not recover their renal function. This is because the process that is damaging the kidneys continues even though you began dialysis. If diabetes has affected your kidney function, the damage will continue. Patients with kidney damage tend to scar their kidneys further due to a process called **hyperfiltration**. Hyperfiltration takes place when part of a kidney is damaged by disease and is no longer able to filter blood. The remaining healthy part of the kidney filters more blood to make up for the non-functioning kidney tissue. The increase in filtration increases the pressure applied to the glomerulus, which is where the filtration takes place. This increased pressure will damage the filter, causing further kidney damage and scarring, and is harmful to the kidney. This makes the chance of renal function improving with moderate to severe kidney damage less likely. A kidney sonogram is a useful test in determining the chance of your kidneys improving. If the kidney size is small on the sonogram, this is evidence that scarring has occurred that is not reversible. Most patients with chronic renal failure will

Hyperfiltration

Occurs when a damaged kidney increases the blood flow and filtration to the remaining healthy portion of the kidney to compensate for the lost kidney function.

progress and require dialysis or a kidney transplant. Occasionally we do see a patient improving and getting off dialysis. This is a cause for celebration.

91. What will happen if I decide to stop my dialysis treatments?

It is possible to stop dialysis treatments even though renal function has not recovered. Patients stop dialysis when their medical condition deteriorates and they are suffering. Patients who stop dialysis are often elderly with many medical problems. The quality of their life has deteriorated so much that dialysis treatments and other medical treatments become intolerable. This decision is an individual one.

I had a good friend who was on hemodialysis due to kidney failure from diabetes. He also had heart problems, circulation problems, and was losing his vision. Because he lived in a rural area, he had to drive an hour to the nearest dialysis unit. This was difficult because he often felt weak after his dialysis treatments. In winter, the roads were very icy and hard to drive on. Because of his blood pressure falling during hemodialysis treatments, he switched to peritoneal dialysis at home. After a period of time, he was faced with having an amputation of his right leg due to gangrene. His vision was failing, making it more difficult to perform his peritoneal dialysis exchanges. He developed peritonitis due to *Candida*. His nephrologist wanted him to have his peritoneal catheter removed and for him to return to hemodialysis. Instead of returning to hemodialysis my friend chose to end dialysis treatments. His wife was very supportive and felt this was a good decision. Life was becoming more painful and less enjoyable. His multiple medical problems were increasing and were incurable. He stopped dialysis at age 71 and passed away peacefully at home after 10 days of stopping dialysis. This decision was a very personal one. Many patients would have continued dialysis treatments under these circumstances, even if it required spending several months in a hospital. In my many conversations with my friend over the time he was on dialysis, he emphasized quality of life as the reason to have dialysis treatments.

Stopping dialysis is usually not a painful process. The poisons and toxins from kidney failure accumulate in the system and make the patient sleepy. Patients may accumulate fluid in their legs and other parts of the body. Many patients who choose to stop their dialysis treatments feel more comfortable in a hospital or a hospice. If they have pain, breathing difficulty, or other problems, the medical staff is available to help. Patients can benefit from pain medication, oxygen, and other conservative medical therapies that will help relieve suffering.

You should discuss the issue of stopping dialysis with your nephrologist and with your family when you are doing well on dialysis. By making your thoughts and wishes known to your nephrologist and family, they will be better equipped to care for you in the future. In time, it is possible that you will become incapacitated and not fully able to make decisions on your own. Having expressed your thoughts and discussed options when you are well will help guide those you have entrusted with your well-being in the future. A **living will** is a good place to express your wishes about stopping dialysis. This legal document will

Living will

A legal document in which an individual states which procedures, treatments, and food he or she is willing to have in the event that he or she becomes critically ill and is unable to participate in the decision making regarding his or her medical care.

guide your family and physicians in making decisions regarding your medical care. You should identify an individual who can make decisions for you in the event that you cannot make decisions for yourself. This person is called your **healthcare proxy**. The healthcare proxy can be a spouse, blood relative, or someone not related to you. If you are unable to make your own decisions, your healthcare proxy is able to make important decisions on your behalf. It is possible that you will regain the capacity to make medical decisions. At that point, the healthcare proxy will step aside, and you will resume making decisions regarding your medical care.

Your nephrologist may decide at some point to delay your dialysis treatment because dialysis is too dangerous. If your blood pressure is too low, or if you are experiencing bleeding, a stroke, or some other emergency condition, it may be advisable to stop dialysis because the risks of dialysis outweigh the benefits. Your nephrologist will discuss this with you, your family, and your healthcare proxy to explain why it is in your best interest to delay or stop dialysis treatments. Dialysis can be reinstituted when your condition has improved.

92. How long can I live without dialysis treatments?

Living without dialysis treatments is dependent on the amount of urine you make and your residual renal function. Many patients begin dialysis when they still have some residual kidney function. They cannot live a healthy life without dialysis but can survive for a period of time. Patients who have no residual kidney function and make no urine generally can survive an average of 7

Healthcare proxy
An individual designated by a patient to make decisions regarding his or her medical care in the event that he or she is too ill to make his or her own medical decisions.

Getting Off Dialysis

to 10 days without dialysis. Every individual is different and some patients will live less time than others.

A wonderful account of stopping dialysis can be found in Art Buchwald's book *Too Soon to Say Goodbye*. Mr. Buchwald developed renal failure at 80 years of age after undergoing an angiogram for a circulation problem in his leg. After 12 hemodialysis treatments, he decided to stop dialysis against the wishes of his family. He gained some renal function and was able to survive several months and wrote a book about his experiences. His lighthearted account of dialysis, hospitals, hospices, and doctors is of value to anyone trying to decide if dialysis treatments are worthwhile. Another famous author, James Mitchner, decided to stop dialysis treatments in his 90s. As more elderly patients are treated with dialysis, the number of patients who choose to stop dialysis will increase.

Dialysis is not a very aggressive treatment. It is much less invasive than being on a ventilator, having surgery, or undergoing cardio-pulmonary resuscitation (CPR). I think of dialysis in the same category as antibiotics, intravenous fluids, blood transfusions, and food. Many family members of patients on dialysis feel they are killing their loved one if they stop dialysis treatments. This is not true. If the patient were doing well, stopping dialysis would not be an issue. The underlying disease process such as cancer, heart disease, or stroke is what is killing the patient.

Stopping dialysis is appropriate when there is no benefit to the patient and when the patient is truly suffering during treatment. Some religions and cultures do not accept the withdrawal of medical treatment. Some physicians fear that stopping dialysis in a patient who has no hope may make them more likely to face legal action. These cultural factors can make stopping dialysis more difficult. The preservation of life without regard to the quality of that life, the dignity of the patient, and the amount of suffering the person must endure is becoming more common in the United States. This problem is best addressed through education of patients and their families by the dialysis team when the patient is doing well on dialysis. A member of the clergy, sometimes called the hospital chaplain, is often available in hospitals and hospices to discuss end-of-life care with patients and their families. These clergy members have special training and can be very helpful.

93. How can I get a kidney transplant?

A successful kidney transplant is the best option for many patients with kidney failure. The transplanted kidney, like your own kidneys, works 7 days a week removing toxins and poisons from your system. It is able to make hormones such as erythropoietin, to metabolize medications, and to perform a whole host of functions we take for granted.

There are two types of kidney transplants. One is a **cadaveric kidney transplant** from a donor who has died. Each cadaveric donor can donate a kidney to two people. The donor often donates other organs such as the heart, liver, and corneas. The other type of transplant is the **living donor transplant**. This is the older type of transplant and was first performed between identical twins at the Peter Bent Brigham Hospital in Boston in 1954. The living donor donates one of his/her two kidneys to a single transplant recipient.

Cadaveric kidney transplant

A kidney transplant in which the transplanted kidney comes from a donor that has died.

Living donor transplant

A transplant in which a living person donates an organ or part of an organ. Living donor kidney transplants, partial liver transplants, and bone marrow transplants are currently being performed.

Both types of transplants are very successful. The waiting list for cadaveric kidney transplants can be several years because the number of patients who want a transplant is increasing and not enough families consider organ donation when a loved one dies.

It is possible to receive a kidney transplant and never be treated with dialysis. This is the exception rather than the rule. Most patients with kidney failure will spend some time on dialysis before their kidney transplant. Arranging for a kidney transplant takes time. If the donor is a living person, they need to have a complete medical evaluation to determine if they are healthy enough to withstand surgery. They must also be free of kidney disease, infection, and cancer. The kidney is often obtained from the donor using laparoscopic surgery. Several small incisions are made in the abdomen of the patient, and the kidney can be removed through one of these small incisions. This surgery minimizes the recuperation time for the donor. The transplant recipient will also undergo an extensive evaluation by the transplant team. The kidney recipient also must be free of infection and cancer because they will receive medications to prevent the new kidney from being rejected by their body.

Rejection is a process where cells in our immune system recognize the transplanted kidney as a foreign organ. These cells will migrate to and attack the kidney. Other cells produce antibodies, which are proteins that can attach themselves to the cells of the transplanted kidney. These antibodies can injure the transplanted kidney and also make it easier for the cells of the immune system to find and destroy the new kidney. **Anti-rejection medication** must be taken by the kidney transplant recipient every day for as long as the

Rejection

An immunologic process in which the kidney transplant recipient's immune system attacks the transplant with antibodies and cells. Kidney transplant rejection impairs the ability of the transplanted kidney to remove poisons and toxins from the blood. Rejection can be diagnosed after a kidney transplant biopsy.

Anti-rejection medication

Medication used to treat acute rejection of a transplanted organ by the transplant recipient's immune system. The most common anti-rejection medications are steroids.

kidney transplant is working. The medication can make the transplant recipient more susceptible to infections such as pneumonia. They can also allow abnormal cells to grow more quickly in our bodies. If a patient has a small cancer that has not been detected, this small cancer can grow more rapidly because the anti-rejection medication inhibits the immune system's defense against these abnormal cancer cells. Anti-rejection medication can make it harder to control your blood pressure.

When you have undergone all of your tests and have satisfied the transplant center that you are healthy enough to receive a kidney transplant, you will be placed on the transplant list. Several tubes of blood will be collected from you every month to be sent to the transplant unit. These samples will enable the transplant unit to test your blood and compare it to the transplant kidney to see if you are a good match for a kidney that becomes available. The kidney must be compatible with your blood type. The transplant unit will also check to see if you are compatible with the new kidney by testing to see how similar you are genetically to the transplant kidney. The transplant unit will obtain blood tests from you and the kidney donor to measure your histocompatability antigens and can predict the chance of you rejecting your new kidney. The closer you match your new kidney at these loci, the less your chances will be of rejecting the kidney transplant.

The kidney transplant list is based on a seniority system. Available kidneys from cadaveric donors are given to the patients who have been on the transplant list the longest. An exception to this is patients who have a very close match with the kidney that is being transplanted. A patient who matches all the histo-compatability antigens of a kidney will jump the line and receive the kidney because a very well-matched kidney will have much less chance of undergoing rejection, increasing the chance that the kidney will work for a long time.

Despite the side effects of medication, the need to have surgery, and the risks of kidney rejection, kidney transplantation has become the treatment of choice in treating end-stage kidney failure. The kidney transplant recipient can live a life free from the need to have dialysis treatments. He or she can have a more varied diet. The transplant recipient is able to travel more easily without having to make special arrangements to have hemodialysis at a dialysis center or have supplies shipped to perform peritoneal dialysis. When I talk to patients who have experienced both dialysis and a kidney transplant, they all prefer the transplant as the best treatment for their kidney failure.

Erick Lucero writes:

I am hoping to get a kidney transplant. I have been on the transplant list for a year. In 2 weeks I will be going to the transplant clinic for my yearly evaluation. I hope my body accepts a new kidney. I want to live long enough to see my daughter grow up. I want to take care of my wife and daughter. My brother volunteered to donate a kidney for me. He was evaluated, but it was discovered that he had high blood sugar. The transplant team was worried that he might develop kidney problems later in life. My sister was also evaluated but was told to lose 20 pounds and come back. Several friends offered to donate a kidney, but I feel funny accepting their kidney. I do not want anyone to be hurt by donating a kidney to me.

My uncle decided that we should advertise for a kidney donor in Mexico and have the transplant there. I am worried about how safe it is to use a donor who is paid for their kidney. I am doing well on dialysis and am waiting my turn on the transplant list. The reason I want a kidney transplant is to be able to travel. I want to take my wife and daughter to Mexico on vacation. It's hard to travel when you are on hemodialysis. You have to make arrangements for your treatments in advance. If you travel outside of the United States, you have to pay for the treatments. Most insurance companies will not cover dialysis in foreign countries. They will pay for dialysis when you travel in the United States.

94. Is a kidney transplant a dangerous procedure?

Your kidney transplant will require a surgical procedure that is done under general anesthesia. This means you will not be awake during the surgery. All surgery has some risk associated with it. Before you undergo your surgery, you will have a cardiac evaluation. The biggest risk of surgery is a heart attack during or just after the surgery. Some patients with heart disease have had to have cardiac bypass surgery or cardiac stents placed to make sure their kidney transplant could be performed safely. One of the risks of transplantation is that hardening of the arteries develops more rapidly. This may be due to the anti-rejection medication that kidney transplant patients take. It is very important for patients who are considering a kidney transplant to decease their risk factors for coronary artery disease. This means stopping smoking and controlling blood pressure, cholesterol, and blood sugar if you are a diabetic. Overweight patients have an increased risk of

The overwhelming majority of patients who receive kidney transplants do well without serious complications.

heart disease. Overweight patients also have a higher risk of blood clots in their legs during and after surgery. Being able to have a kidney transplant is a good motivation for losing weight if you are heavy. Other less common complications of transplant surgery are bleeding and infection. The overwhelming majority of patients who receive kidney transplants do well without serious complications.

95. Is a kidney transplant expensive?

The average cost of a kidney transplant and the first year of medical care after the transplant is about $90,000. After the first year, the average cost of care is approximately $16,000, most of which is spent on anti-rejection medications. The cost of the surgery for the transplant is paid for by the transplant recipient's insurance. If the kidney transplant is coming from a living, related donor, the cost of the surgery for the donor is also paid for by the transplant recipient's insurance. A living-related transplant is less expensive because the kidney is more likely to function immediately after surgery and the recipient is less likely to require further dialysis. The living-related transplant recipient is more likely to have a shorter hospital stay. The cost of dialysis is about $30,000 to $50,000 a year. The break even point for a kidney transplant is 2.7 years. These numbers do not take into account the possibility that the transplant recipient may be able to return to work.

Some patients experience difficulty paying for their anti-rejection medication, which may not be covered by their insurance. Some insurance plans have maximum amounts they will pay for medications each year.

This potential problem should be discussed with the transplant team's social worker to determine if paying for medication will be a problem after the transplant. The pharmaceutical companies that manufacture anti-rejection medications have special programs for patients who are unable to afford their medications.

96. Will I reject my new kidney?

There are several types of rejections that occur after organ transplantation. **Acute rejection** is most likely to occur in the months after a kidney transplant. Rejection can be suspected when the serum creatinine, a blood test, rises. Some patients require a transplant kidney biopsy to diagnose rejection. This can be done as an outpatient procedure in many cases. Most rejection episodes respond to medications called steroids, which can be given intravenously or by mouth.

Acute rejection

Occurs when a transplant recipient's immune system attacks a transplant with antibodies and cells. It can be treated with steroids and other medication.

A more serious type of rejection is **chronic rejection**. This type of rejection occurs slowly over many years. It is also diagnosed by kidney biopsy. Unlike acute rejection, chronic rejection cannot be reversed. The function of the kidney slowly decreases with time. Chronic rejection is the reason that kidney transplants do not last forever. The average kidney transplant lasts 15 to 20 years because of chronic rejection. When kidney transplants fail, patients face a return to dialysis treatments or will consider a second kidney transplant.

Chronic rejection

A slow process mediated by the immune system in which kidney transplants become damaged and lose function over time.

97. Can I donate a kidney to my spouse?

The first kidney transplant was done between identical twins because medications to prevent rejection did not work very well. Early living-related transplants were done between parents and children or between siblings because the donor and recipient were genetically similar, which resulted in better matching and less rejection. In the 1980s, a new medication called cyclosporine was developed. This medication revolutionized the results in kidney transplantation and made liver and heart transplants more successful. At the same time there was a large increase in the number of patients waiting for kidney transplants. As a result, transplant surgeons began performing living, nonrelated kidney transplants between spouses. These transplants were successful. With the continued improvement in anti-rejection medication, more of these transplants are being done. The newspapers have reported teachers giving a kidney to a student and other inspiring examples of nonrelated kidney donations.

Another type of nonrelated transplant involves swapping kidneys between pairs of donors and recipients. Swaps work when a potential kidney donor is not compatible with a kidney recipient. If another incompatible donor and recipient can be found, it is possible for a spouse to give a kidney to a compatible recipient whose kidney donor can then donate a kidney to the incompatible partner. These kidney transplants require a great deal of counseling and psychological evaluation before they occur. They are usually done at the same time to ensure that both donors go through with the donation.

Recently a debate in the medical transplant literature has discussed the ethics of paying donors for kidney donation. In India and China, poor kidney donors regularly receive compensation for donating a kidney to an unknown recipient. Receiving payment for kidney donation beyond payment for medical expenses is considered inappropriate in the United States and most European countries. It is felt that paying for kidney donation is taking advantage of poor individuals. Many of the ethical and moral considerations regarding transplantation are affected by cultural beliefs. Japan considers using organs from deceased patients ethically wrong. Patients in Japan have had to travel to other countries to receive their transplant.

98. Can I receive more than one kidney transplant?

In a recent survey of patients on a transplant list at the University of Pennsylvania in Philadelphia, 14% of patients on the list had had a prior kidney transplant. Many patients who have had a first kidney transplant that failed have gone on to have a successful second kidney transplant. Most patients who experience the advantages of being off dialysis with a kidney transplant want to have a second transplant when they are back on dialysis. Transplant patients just feel better. They are less depressed, are able to eat a variety of foods, and are free from being attached to a machine three or more times a week on dialysis. Some patients have received more than two kidney transplants. The chances of the third and fourth transplant being successful are less than the chances of the first and second transplant being successful.

The chances of the third and fourth transplant being successful are less than the chances of the first and second transplant being successful.

It is interesting to note that some patients have received more than one type of transplant. One-third of all heart transplant patients have developed kidney failure, often due to the immunosuppressive medication they are taking to prevent the rejection of their heart transplant. If you have already received one transplant, you are on anti-rejection medication. This makes the decision to have a second organ transplant easier since you are already exposed to the side effects of the anti-rejection medication. Other common multiple organ transplants include pancreas and kidney transplants for patients with diabetes, liver and kidney transplants, and bone marrow and kidney transplants.

Transplantation is the great hope of all patients and doctors treating kidney failure. Because of the shortage of available organs, the possibility of organ transplants between species has been proposed as the solution to this important problem. Medical science has utilized tissues from other species such as pig heart valves for many years. In the 1980s several monkey-to-human transplants were performed. This was before the modern era of anti-rejection therapy. The most successful transplant functioned for 9 months. The research on cross-species transplant must make breakthroughs before this is a realistic possibility for treating patients.

99. What will I do if my kidney transplant fails?

One of the great advantages that kidney patients have is the three excellent therapies available for the treatment of kidney failure. Patients who have received a heart transplant are in serious trouble when their heart fails from rejection or other problems. They need a second transplant to survive. Liver failure patients also have no safety net. They need a second transplant when their liver transplant fails. Kidney transplant patients have the safety of dialysis. If their kidney transplant fails, they can resume dialysis treatments that are already familiar to them. The possibility of kidney transplant rejection is very frightening, but it is not medically dangerous. Kidney transplant patients are safe because they have hemodialysis and peritoneal dialysis as a backup. They will be able to resume dialysis and live a good life if their kidney transplant fails.

In the early days of kidney transplantation, patients did not have a long life expectancy. They were treated with high doses of prednisone to prevent rejection, which resulted in many complications. Children who received transplants had stunted growth. Patients developed bone problems due to osteoporosis. They developed hardening of the arteries that resulted in heart problems. They gained weight, developed diabetes, and were susceptible to infections. The present transplant patient has many fewer complications because the dose of prednisone used is very small. Some patients are treated without any prednisone being used with their anti-rejection medications, resulting in many fewer complications. Patients with kidney transplants live longer. Unfortunately transplanted kidneys eventually fail due to chronic rejection. The most successful kidney transplants last about 15 to 20 years. This means that a significant number of patients will someday be faced with resuming dialysis treatments or will need to have a second kidney transplant. Adjusting back to dialysis is not difficult for patients. They have a certain amount of depression due to the loss of their kidney. They have to adjust to a more restrictive diet. They are able to gradually stop their anti-rejection medications. Most of them go right back on the transplant list. Many others receive living-related transplants from a family member or a significant other.

The possibility of kidney transplant rejection is very frightening, but it is not medically dangerous. Kidney transplant patients are safe because they have hemodialysis and peritoneal dialysis as a backup.

Getting Off Dialysis

100. What organizations can help me cope with kidney disease?

The National Kidney Foundation (NKF) is a voluntary health organization whose mission is to prevent kidney disease and diseases of the urinary tract. It was founded in 1950 by Mr. and Mrs. Harry DeBold, who were motivated by the kidney disease of their infant son. Over the years, the National Kidney Foundation has become a powerful force that has successfully advocated for the kidney patient. Their goals are to support research, train healthcare professionals, expand patient services and community resources, educate the public, and shape healthcare policy. You probably have seen one of their walks or runs that they have organized for kidney disease at your local park. They have a wonderful Web site with information on all sorts of topics from diet to prevention of kidney failure to healthcare policy (*www.kidney.org*). The National Kidney Foundation has educational information in Spanish. They have done a wonderful job raising money for research and treatment of kidney disorders.

The American Association of Kidney Patients (AAKP) is a patient-run organization of kidney patients and health professionals. AAKP was founded by six dialysis patients after they met at a Brooklyn Hospital in 1969. From this humble start, this organization has grown into a nationwide group of patients, families, and healthcare professionals that provides support to millions of people with kidney disease. AAKP and its many activities are patient run. AAKP publishes a magazine called *Renalife* that advertises itself as "The Voice of All Kidney Patients." *Renalife* contains articles about dialysis, transplant, diet, travel, and political information written by patients and health professionals. AAKP's 35th annual convention was held in Washington, DC in August 2008. AAKP has support groups for patients and their families. The organization gives awards every year to people who have made contributions to kidney patients. AAKP is actively involved in lobbying government officials to improve the lives of patients with kidney disease. It supports research and education with grants to groups who are making advances in the care of kidney patients. AAKP has electronic newsletters as well as Healthline, a conference call designed to provide information for kidney patients. The cost of membership for patients or family members is $25 annually. More information is available from their Web site, *www.aakp.org*.

Getting Off Dialysis

Appendix

American Association of Kidney Patients
3505 E. Frontage Road, Suite 315
Tampa, FL 33607
Phone: 1-800-749-2257
Fax: (813)-636-8122
Email: info@aakp.org
www.aakp.org

Centers for Disease Control
1600 Clifton Road
Atlanta, GA 30333
Phone: 1-800-CDC-INFO
Email: cdcinfo@cdc.gov
www.cdc.gov

Culinary Kidney Cooks
PO Box 468
Huntington Beach, CA 92648
Phone: (714) 842-4684
Fax: (714) 842-4694
Email: Eric.Brooks@CulinaryKidneyCooks.com
www.culinarykidneycooks.com

Medicare
Centers for Medicare & Medicaid Services
7500 Security Boulevard
Baltimore, MD 21244-1850
Phone: 1-800-MEDICARE
www.medicare.gov
www.cms.hhs.gov

National Center for Complementary and Alternative Medicine (NCCAM)
NCCAM
National Institutes of Health
9000 Rockville Pike
Bethesda, MD 20892
Phone: 1-888-644-6226
Fax: 1-866-464-3616
Email: info@nccam.nih.gov
http://nccam.nih.gov

National Kidney Foundation
30 East 33rd Street
New York, NY 10016
Phone: 1-800-622-9010
Fax: (212) 689-9261
www.kidney.org

The Renal Gourmet
www.kidney-cookbook.com

The Rogosin Institute
505 East 70th Street
New York, NY 10021
Phone: (212) 746-1552
Fax: (212) 288-8370
www.rogosin.org

Society for the Advancement of Blood Management
555 East Wells Street, Suite 1100
Milwaukee, WI 53202-3823
Phone: (414) 276-9339
Fax: (414) 276-3349
Email: info@sabm.org
www.sabm.org

Glossary

Access: A device that is inserted or constructed in a patient which connects the patient to the dialysis tubing and allows dialysis to take place. In hemodialysis, an access allows blood to be drawn and can be an arterial-venous (a-v) fistula, a-v graft, or a dialysis catheter. The access for peritoneal dialysis (the peritoneal dialysis catheter) is a plastic tube that allows dialysate to be instilled into the abdomen.

Access center: A medical facility that specializes in the creation and care of access for dialysis patients. The access physician uses radiology and ultrasound equipment to evaluate and improve the blood flow in a-v fistulas, a-v grafts, and catheters for hemodialysis.

Acute rejection: Occurs when a transplant recipient's immune system attacks a transplant with antibodies and cells. It can be treated with steroids and other medication.

Air bubble detector: A part of the hemodialysis machine that senses when air has entered the tubing. When air is detected, the air bubble detector quickly turns off the machine and clamps the tubing to prevent it from going into the patient.

Albumin: A water-soluble protein found in the blood normally in very minute amounts. Patients with kidney disease often have albumin in their urine because the albumin leaks through the damaged kidneys into the urine.

Alternative medicine: A medical discipline that uses natural products and diet to treat medical illness.

American Society of Nephrology (ASN): A national organization of physicians and scientists founded in 1966 to study and treat kidney disease.

Amino acids: Organic acids that are the building blocks of proteins.

Anemia: A decrease in the number of red blood cells present in the blood, which can be due to blood loss or a decreased production of red blood cells due to iron deficiency, poor nutrition, or disease. Decreased red blood cell survival occurs in kidney disease. Symptoms of anemia include fatigue, weakness, and shortness of breath on exertion.

Angina: Chest pain due to lack of blood to the heart that is often described as a squeezing pain or heaviness. Angina can be precipitated by exercise and is relieved by rest and nitroglycerin, a medication that can be taken intravenously or orally.

Angioedema: A serious allergic reaction characterized by swelling of a body part, often the face or lips.

Angioplasty: A medical procedure in which a balloon catheter is inserted into a blood vessel or dialysis access. When the balloon is inflated, it opens a blockage in the blood vessel to improve blood flow.

Angiotensin: A polypeptide produced in the kidney, which causes blood pressure to rise.

Angiotensin-converting enzyme inhibitors (ACE inhibitors): A class of medications that is useful in treating high blood pressure, stabilizing kidney disease, and improving patients with congestive heart failure. ACE inhibitors stabilize kidney disease by decreasing the amount of protein in the urine and decreasing the damage done by elevated blood pressure.

Angiotensin receptor blocker (ARB): A class of medications that has similar properties to ACE inhibitors. ARBs can treat high blood pressure, stabilize

kidney disease, decrease protein in the urine, and treat congestive heart failure.

Anti-rejection medication: Medication used to treat acute rejection of a transplanted organ by the transplant recipient's immune system. The most common anti-rejection medications are steroids.

Arterial-venuous (a-v) fistula: A tube that connects an artery to a vein and is constructed by a vascular surgeon. When mature, the a-v fistula can have needles inserted into it to carry blood through plastic tubing to and from the hemodialysis machine.

Arterial-venuous (a-v) graft: A length of gortex tubing connected between an artery and a vein that is created by a vascular surgeon. The a-v graft is tunneled under the skin to allow needles to be inserted into it to carry blood through plastic tubing to the hemodialysis machine.

Atherosclerosis: A disease process that involves deposition of cholesterol in the walls of arteries, causing narrowing of the arteries. This can cause blood to clot, further reducing blood flow. Atherosclerosis decreases the amount of blood that can flow to the organs of the body and is increased by an elevated blood pressure, uncontrolled diabetes, smoking, and an elevated cholesterol level.

Autosomal dominant polycystic kidney disease (ADPKD): The most common form of inherited kidney disease. Patients inherit the gene from either parent and many cysts form in the kidneys.

Bacillus Calmette-Guerin (BCG): A tuberculosis vaccine given to children in many countries with a high prevalence of tuberculosis. Patients who have received BCG will often have a positive skin test for tuberculosis for the rest of their lives.

Beta blockers: A class of medication named for its ability to block beta receptors in the heart, blood vessels, and other organs. Beta blockers are used to treat chest pain or angina, congestive heart failure, high blood pressure, and migraine headaches.

Bicarbonate: A salt of carbonic acid that acts as an important buffer to help keep our blood from becoming too acidic.

Blood pump: A circular device that is easily visible on the front of every hemodialysis machine. This roller pump compresses plastic tubing that propels blood from the patient to the dialysis machine and back to the patient.

Blood urea nitrogen (BUN): A common blood test used to screen patients for kidney disease. An elevated BUN can indicate decreased kidney function.

Bright's Disease: An old term, named after Dr. Richard Bright (1789-1858) who first described the association of protein in the urine with kidney disease and renal failure. Although this term is no longer used clinically, it reminds us of Dr.

Bright's great contribution to the treatment of kidney disease.

Bruit: A French word meaning "noise" that is used to describe the sound that blood makes when rushing through a blood vessel or dialysis access. A bruit can be heard with a stethoscope or by holding the access against your ear. A bruit heard in an a-v fistula or a-v graft signifies that blood is flowing through the access and that it is working.

Cadaveric kidney transplant: A kidney transplant in which the transplanted kidney comes from a donor that has died.

Calcium: A mineral found in our bones, blood, and cells.

Calculus: Comes from the Latin word for stone. A kidney stone is sometimes referred to as a calculus. The term is also used by dentists to describe a calcified layer of saliva, bacteria, protein, and sugar covering the teeth.

Cannulation: The insertion of needles into the dialysis access to obtain blood for hemodialysis.

Catheter: A plastic tube used for dialysis. Catheters are inserted into blood vessels to obtain blood for hemodialysis treatments. Peritoneal dialysis catheters are inserted in the abdomen, and are used to instill and drain dialysate into and out of the abdomen during peritoneal dialysis treatments.

Cellcept (mycophenolate mofetil): An immunosuppressant medication that inhibits the proliferation of T and

B lymphocytes, which are important cells in the rejection of kidney transplants. Cellcept is used with other medications to prevent rejection in kidney and other organ transplants. It is also used alone in the treatment of kidney disease due to lupus erythematosus. Cellcept can be taken orally or intravenously.

Cholesterol: A substance manufactured in the liver or ingested that is present in the blood, liver, brain, and other organs. When deposited in blood vessels, cholesterol can lead to atherosclerosis.

Chronic rejection: A slow process mediated by the immune system in which kidney transplants become damaged and lose function over time.

Computerized axial tomography (CT) scan: A computer generated three-dimensional x-ray picture of part of the body used for the diagnosis of disease. It is sometimes called a CT scan.

Continuous ambulatory peritoneal dialysis (CAPD): A home dialysis procedure taught to patients who perform their own peritoneal dialysis, CAPD involves the instillation by gravity of dialysate through a catheter into the abdomen. The fluid remains in the abdomen for a time, allowing poisons and toxins to accumulate in the dialysate. The dialysate is then drained and discarded, and fresh dialysate is instilled.

Continuous cyclical peritoneal dialysis (CCPD): A home peritoneal dialysis procedure that uses a cycler to instill and drain fluid into the abdomen. The cycler can perform peritoneal dialysis while the patient is sleeping.

Creatinine: A substance released into the blood from our muscles. Since it is eliminated from the body by the kidneys, a decrease in kidney function results in an elevation of creatinine in the blood. An elevated creatinine blood test is an indication of decreased kidney function.

Cycler: A machine used to automate peritoneal dialysis by performing the exchange of peritoneal dialysis fluid.

Cyclosporine: A medication, originally isolated from fungi, that is used in preventing the rejection of kidney and other organ transplants. Cyclosporine can also be used to treat some kidney diseases.

Cystoscopy: A surgical procedure performed by a urologist in which a small fiber-optic tube called a cystoscope is inserted through the urethra into the bladder. The urologist can diagnose tumors of the bladder and can perform biopsies and other procedures through the cystoscope.

Depression: A medical term used to describe feelings of intense sadness, loss of interest in activities of daily life, and a decreased appetite and sense of well-being.

Dextrose: A sugar added to peritoneal dialysis solutions to help remove fluid from the body. It is also added to intravenous fluids to provide calories for nutrition.

Diabetes: A disease characterized by an elevation of the glucose level in the blood. This can be caused by a decrease in insulin production by the pancreas or a defect in the insulin receptor.

Diabetes nurse educator: A nurse who has obtained special training and certification in the evaluation and education of patients with diabetes.

Dialysate: A fluid containing sodium, calcium, bicarbonate, and other substances that is used to remove toxins and poisons during dialysis. Different dialysate solutions are used in hemodialysis and peritoneal dialysis.

Dialysis: A scientific term for the movement of substances across a membrane by a process called diffusion.

Dialysis partner: A person who has received special training in performing hemodialysis or peritoneal dialysis and who assists you in performing dialysis at home.

Dialysis technician: A healthcare worker who works in the hemodialysis unit under the supervision of a registered nurse. Dialysis technicians can institute hemodialysis by inserting needles into the access, and can also monitor the dialysis treatment, measure blood pressure, and help educate dialysis patients regarding their treatment, but they are not allowed to administer medication.

Dialyzer: A medical device that contains the dialysis membrane. It is connected to tubing that allows blood to flow into the dialyzer on one side of the membrane and then back to the patient. Dialysate flows on the other side of the membrane, and poisons and toxins move from the blood across the membrane into the dialysate, which is then discarded.

Dietitian: A registered health professional who has special training in nutrition. Dietitians advise patients on which foods to eat and which to avoid based upon their individual needs. They use monthly laboratory tests to monitor the patient's progress.

Disequilibrium syndrome: A syndrome in which the rapid removal of poisons and toxins during hemodialysis results in less toxins being present in the blood than in the brain. This difference causes water to leave the blood stream and enter the central nervous system, leading to brain swelling. Symptoms include headache, nausea, vomiting, fatigue, and weakness. Most of these symptoms are gone by the next day. A severe disequilibrium syndrome can cause seizures and coma.

Dry weight: The body weight of hemodialysis patients at the end of their hemodialysis treatment. The dry weight is determined by removing fluid until the blood pressure begins to fall.

Edema: The medical term for fluid that collects in an area of the body. The most common location for edema is in the legs. The legs appear swollen, especially after walking around. The edema decreases after a night's sleep because it has moved to other areas of the body. Other areas that can collect fluid are the lungs and abdomen.

Electrocardiogram (EKG): A medical test in which electrical impulses generated by the heart are recorded by attaching electrodes to the arms, legs, and chest.

Electroencephalogram (EEG): A medical test in which electrical impulses generated by the brain are recorded by attaching electrodes to the scalp.

Endocrinologist: A physician who has trained in internal medicine and who has received additional training in the treatment of patients with diabetes, thyroid disease, parathyroid disease, and other glandular disorders.

Eosinophils: White blood cells produced by the bone marrow that are normally found in the blood. During allergic reactions, the number of eosinophils increases.

Erythropoietin: A hormone produced by the kidneys that signals the bone marrow to produce more red blood cells. In kidney disease, less erythropoietin is produced and anemia can occur. Erythropoietin can be given by injection to treat anemia.

Exchange: A term used in peritoneal dialysis that describes fluid being drained using plastic tubing from the abdomen into a collection bag. New peritoneal dialysate is infused by gravity into the abdomen.

Exit site care: Exit site care involves swabbing the area where the peritoneal dialysis catheter exits the skin with an antiseptic solution and covering the exit site with a clean sterile dressing.

Focal segmental glomerular sclerosis (FSGS): The most common primary kidney disease in black and Hispanic patients in the United States; it is also found in patients from other ethnic backgrounds. FSGS is suspected when protein is found in the urine and is diagnosed after performing a kidney biopsy.

Gastroenterologist: A physician who has received training in internal medicine and who has had additional training in the diagnosis and treatment of disorders of the digestive system.

Glomerulonephritis: An inflammation of the filter or glomerulus of the kidney caused by many diseases.

Glomerulus: The part of the kidney composed of small blood vessels that filters the blood to produce urine.

Glycogen: A polysaccharide composed of glucose, which is the principal storage unit of carbohydrates in the body.

Health maintenance organization (HMO): An organization that manages a patient's health care for a health insurance company. A patient who is a member of an HMO can select a doctor from a panel available. If they go to a doctor outside of the panel, they may have to pay to see that physician and their health insurance may not reimburse them. The HMO may require approval before your doctor can order certain tests or medications and may have agreements with dialysis units, limiting your choice in where you can receive your dialysis treatments or kidney transplant. By managing health care, the HMO can obtain affordable health care for its patients.

Healthcare proxy: An individual designated by a patient to make decisions regarding his or her medical care in the event that he or she is too ill to make his or her own medical decisions.

Hemodialysis: A medical treatment in which blood is removed from the patient with needles and plastic tubing and pumped past the dialysis membrane. Poisons and toxins cross the dialysis membrane into the dialysate, which is then discarded, and the blood is returned to the patient. A typical hemodialysis treatment lasts four hours.

Heparin: An acid that occurs naturally in the liver and lungs that can be purified and used as a medication to prevent blood from clotting. Heparin is used in hemodialysis to prevent blood from clotting in the plastic tubing and when exposed to the dialysis membrane. It can also be injected into the peritoneal dialysis fluid to prevent clots from blocking the peritoneal dialysis catheter.

Hepatitis B vaccine: A vaccine given to patients in a series of three intramuscular injections. The vaccine stimulates the body to produce antibodies against Hepatitis B. It is recommended for children as part of their routine vaccinations. Patients with kidney disease who have not received the Hepatitis B vaccine should be vaccinated.

High-biologic-value protein: Proteins found in foods such as eggs, fish, poultry, soy products, and meat. High-biologic-value proteins are easily digestible and are rich in the ten essential amino acids that our body cannot make.

High-density lipoprotein (HDL): The "good cholesterol" in our blood that protects us from heart disease and other vascular problems. A high level of HDL is protective, and it can be increased by exercising, eating foods such as garlic and onions, and by taking certain medications.

High flux dialysis: A procedure that uses high blood flows and large dialysis membranes to remove poisons and toxins in a shorter dialysis treatment, although short dialysis treatments are no longer recommended. The experience with high flux dialysis helped kidney doctors improve dialysis treatments by removing more toxins during regular hemodialysis treatments.

Home dialysis: Includes hemodialysis treatments performed by the patient with the help of another person in the family, and also peritoneal dialysis. Occasionally, patients have insurance that covers a hemodialysis nurse or technician to perform their hemodialysis at home.

Horseshoe kidney: A medical condition in which the right and left kidneys are fused at the upper or lower pole. Ninety percent of horseshoe kidneys are fused at the lower pole. The horseshoe kidney is capable of normal kidney function and is usually found when a CT scan or ultrasound (sonogram) is performed for abdominal pain or other symptoms. Patients with a horseshoe kidney are not predisposed to kidney disease.

Human immunodeficiency virus (HIV): The etiologic virus in HIV/AIDS infection. HIV can be transmitted through blood transfusion, intravenous drug use, sexual activity, and through a needle stick. HIV cannot be transmitted during dialysis treatments.

Hyperfiltration: Occurs when a damaged kidney increases the blood flow and filtration to the remaining healthy portion of the kidney to compensate for the lost kidney function.

Hyperparathyroidism: A condition in which the four parathyroid glands, located next to the thyroid gland in the neck, increase their production of the parathyroid hormone (PTH). This is due to a low blood calcium level that is caused by elevated phosphorus production and low Vitamin D production. Hyperparathyroidism is treated by lowering phosphorus levels with

dietary modifications and phosphate binders, and by taking medication to suppress the production of parathyroid hormone. Occasionally, patients have three-and-a-half of their parathyroid glands removed by surgery.

Hypertension: A condition in which the blood pressure is elevated on two or more occasions. High blood pressure can be caused by kidney disease and is associated with increased body weight. Treatment of hypertension includes diet and lifestyle modification and medication.

Hypertrophy: An increase in the size of the kidney.

Ideal body weight: Ideal body weight is dependent upon your age, height, body, build, and sex, and is based on the measured average weight of normal individuals. Ideal body weights can be found in published tables, which are available from your kidney dietitian.

IgA nephropathy: A disease of the kidney that often presents with blood and protein in the urine. The immunoglobulin IgA is seen in the kidney on biopsy.

Immunosuppressive therapy: Immunosuppressive therapy works by suppressing the activity of the cells and antibodies of the immune system. In the treatment of some kidney diseases, immunosuppressive medicines are given intravenously or orally to decrease the immune response. Kidney transplant patients also need immunosuppressive medications to prevent rejection of the transplant.

Insensible fluid loss: The fluid that leaves the body in the form of water vapor from the lungs, sweat, and fluid in stool. The amount of insensible fluid loss is about 2 to 3 cups every day.

Internist: A doctor who has had specialized training in internal medicine. The internist is trained in the prevention, diagnosis, and treatment of disease in adults. An internist can determine if you have kidney disease, begin treatment, and refer you to an appropriate kidney doctor.

Ischemia: A decrease or lack of blood flow to an organ in the body causing damage or organ dysfunction.

Kayexalate (sodium polystyrene): A medication that is taken orally and is used to treat an elevated potassium level. Kayexalate comes as a powder which can be mixed in water or juice and is often given with a sugar called sorbitol to cause diarrhea to eliminate the kayexalate that binds potassium in stool.

Kidney biopsy: A test that can diagnose the cause of kidney failure. It is an outpatient procedure performed by an invasive radiologist or nephrologist in which the exact location of one of your kidneys is visualized with a sonogram or CT scan. Local anesthesia is administered with lidocaine and a small needle is inserted into one kidney. A small piece of kidney tissue is then removed and examined under the microscope by a renal pathologist who will report the diagnosis to your nephrologist.

Kidney cyst: A fluid-filled structure commonly discovered by renal ultrasound (sonogram) or CT scan. Renal cysts are common as we age and are usually benign. Patients with polycystic kidney disease have many cysts that will eventually damage the kidneys and lead to kidney failure.

Kidney stone: Seventy five percent of kidney stones are made up of calcium. They form when there is too much calcium in the urine. Other kidney stones are made of uric acid, cystine, or other substances. Kidney stones may be diagnosed after patients experience severe pain and are often found on kidney sonograms or CT scans.

Kidney transplant rejection: Occurs when the transplant recipient's immune system attacks the new kidney with antibodies and cells; it can be reversed with anti-rejection medication. Chronic rejection occurs over time and is difficult to treat. Kidney transplant rejection can be diagnosed after a biopsy of the transplanted kidney.

Kidney tubule: Tubes composed of cells that carry urine filtered by the glomerulus to the collecting system. Renal tubular cells secrete potassium and acids and re-absorb sodium, bicarbonate, and other substances.

Kidneys: Two fist-sized organs located in the posterior upper abdomen that maintain fluid and salt balance and detoxify the blood by eliminating toxins and poisons from the body in the urine.

Laparoscopic surgery: Surgery performed under general anesthesia by inserting fiber-optic tubes through several small incisions.

Licensed practical nurse (LPN): A healthcare professional who has completed a nursing program and passed a licensing exam. An LPN works under the supervision of registered nurses and physicians.

Lipid profile (lipid panel): A lipid profile is a series of blood tests that include total cholesterol, HDL cholesterol, LDL cholesterol, and triglycerides. It is used to evaluate patients for their risk of developing atherosclerosis.

Living donor transplant: A transplant in which a living person donates an organ or part of an organ. Living donor kidney transplants, partial liver transplants, and bone marrow transplants are currently being performed.

Living will: A legal document in which an individual states which procedures, treatments, and food he or she is willing to have in the event that he or she becomes critically ill and is unable to participate in the decision making regarding his or her medical care.

Low-density lipoproteins (LDL): Composed of proteins, triglycerides, and cholesterol bound together in the blood. A high LDL level is associated with atherosclerosis.

Lupus erythematosus: A disease in which the body's immune system attacks its own organs. Also called systemic lupus erythematosus (SLE).

Medicaid: A federally-funded insurance program that is administered by the states to provide medical services, medications, and transportation to medical treatments for patients who have limited monetary resources.

Medicare: A federally-funded program that provides medical treatments and services to patients over the age of 65 and to patients who are younger than 65 and disabled.

Meninges: The three membranes that cover the brain and spinal cord. The meninges form a barrier between the central nervous system and the rest of the body, known as the blood-brain barrier.

Metabolic bone disease: Bone disease in renal patients is caused by reabsorption of bone by cells called osteoclasts whose growth is stimulated by PTH. Patients with bone disease can have bone pain and are more prone to fractures. Also called renal osteodystrophy.

Microalbumin: A test designed to detect very small elevated amounts of the protein albumin in the urine that are not able to be detected by a routine urine analysis.

Muscle wasting: A decrease in the size of the muscles of the body due to poor nutrition or medical illness.

Nephrologist: A physician who has completed four years of medical school, three years of training in internal medicine, and two or more additional years of specialized training in the diagnosis and management of diseases of the kidney.

Nephrology fellow: A doctor who has completed training in internal medicine and is receiving additional training in the evaluation and treatment of kidney diseases, dialysis, and kidney transplantation.

Nephron: The functional unit of the kidney. Our kidneys contain about two million nephrons, which each consist of a glomerulus that filters the blood, kidney tubules that secrete and absorb substances, and a collecting system to transport urine to the renal pelvis.

Neuropathy: Damage to the peripheral nerves of the body. Symptoms include tingling in the hands and feet, weakness, and numbness.

Nocturnal hemodialysis: Hemodialysis treatments done at night six or seven days a week at the patient's home while the patient is asleep. Nocturnal hemodialysis treatments utilize a lower blood pump flow and a longer duration of treatment time to achieve gentle treatments with better clearance of toxins and poisons.

Nurse practitioner: A nurse who has received additional training in the diagnosis and treatment of diseases. The nurse practitioner is able to prescribe medication and perform medical procedures.

Omega 3 fatty acids: A family of unsaturated fatty acids that is thought to decrease the risk of atherosclerosis. They have also been used to treat IgA nephropathy, which can cause kidney failure.

Parathyroid hormone (PTH): A hormone made and released by the chief cells of the four parathyroid glands found in the neck to regulate calcium metabolism.

Peripheral nervous system: Nerves that leave the spinal cord and go to the organs, muscles, and skin. These nerves carry information from the brain to the body, and also bring information back to the brain.

Peritoneal dialysis: Dialysis treatments that use the patient's peritoneal membrane in the abdomen as a dialysis membrane to remove toxins and wastes from the body.

Peritonitis: An inflammation of the peritoneal membrane, which covers the intestines, caused by infection.

Phosphate binder: Medications taken by mouth at mealtimes to decrease the absorption of phosphorus contained in food.

Physician's assistant: A member of the healthcare team who works under the supervision of a physician and diagnoses and manages medical problems.

Podiatrist: A healthcare professional who is trained in the diagnosis and treatment of disorders of the feet.

Psychologist: A healthcare professional who works with patients on their mental health problems including depression and anxiety.

Recirculation: Occurs during hemodialysis treatments when blood that has gone through the dialysis machine does not mix with the patient's blood but returns to the dialysis machine.

Red blood cells: Cells made by the bone marrow that contain an oxygen transport protein called hemoglobin, which causes blood to appear red. Red blood cells carry oxygen from the lungs to other organs through the circulatory system.

Registered nurse (RN): A healthcare professional who has graduated from a nursing program and passed state qualifying examinations.

Rejection: An immunologic process in which the kidney transplant recipient's immune system attacks the transplant with antibodies and cells. Kidney transplant rejection impairs the ability of the transplanted kidney to remove poisons and toxins from the blood. Rejection can be diagnosed after a kidney transplant biopsy.

Renal diet: A diet that avoids foods that contain sodium, potassium, and phosphorus, and limits the amount of fluid intake.

Renal replacement therapy: Renal replacement therapy replaces kidney function by removing toxins, poisons, salts, fluid, and medications from the body. Renal replacement therapies for patients outside of the hospital include hemodialysis, peritoneal dialysis, and kidney transplant. Patients in intensive care units in hospital can also receive continuous renal replacement therapies such as continuous venovenous hemofiltration (CVVH).

Reverse osmosis (RO): A water purification technique in which water is pushed through a membrane at high pressure to remove impurities. Water treated with reverse osmosis is then used to make dialysate for hemodialysis.

Semipermeable membrane: A membrane used for dialysis that allows small substances such as salts, phosphorus, glucose, and water to pass through while blocking larger substances and cells.

Serum albumin: A protein that constitutes more than one half of the protein found in the blood. During kidney disease, albumin can be lost in the urine resulting in a decreased serum albumin level. The serum albumin is also low in liver disease and malnutrition.

Serum creatinine: A blood test used to screen patients for kidney disease. Creatinine is a breakdown product of muscle. When the kidney function is decreased, the kidneys filter less creatinine and the serum creatinine level rises.

Shunt: An old term used to describe an access used to obtain blood for hemodialysis. It initially referred to the Quinton-Scribner shunt first used in the 1960s. Today, the term includes the a-v fistula and a-v graft which "shunt" blood from the artery to the vein, bypassing the small capillaries.

Sickle cell anemia: An inherited anemia that results in red blood cells forming a crescent shape. Sickle cells block small vessels and can result in injury to the bones, heart, lungs, and kidneys.

Social worker: A licensed professional who is part of the multidisciplinary team at the dialysis unit. The social worker assists patients with emotional, financial, and social issues, and also provides education and referrals to community resources. A nephrology social worker specializes in services that support patients and families who are adjusting to the major lifestyle changes that are caused by end stage renal disease.

Sonogram: A medical test in which sound waves are used to obtain pictures of organs in the body. A kidney sonogram requires no injections of substances or exposure to radiation. Also known as an ultrasound.

Steal syndrome: A syndrome that occurs when too much blood is taken away from the arm or hand by an a-v fistula or a-v graft. The blood goes from the artery to the vein, bypassing the capillaries to the hand or arm, resulting in coolness, pain, and sometimes loss of function of the hand.

Stent: A medical device that looks like a hollow tube. Stents are inserted across blocked blood arteries to the heart, kidneys, and other organs to increase the blood flow. Other kinds of stents are also used to treat blockages in the ureters that transport urine from the kidneys to the bladder.

Thrill: A vibration felt over an a-v fistula or a-v graft caused by blood flowing through the a-v access. A thrill is a sign that the access is working.

Thrombectomy: A procedure in which a blood clot that is blocking a blood vessel or an a-v access is removed or dissolved with medication. It allows blood to flow through the hemodialysis access so it can be used for hemodialysis.

Tolerance: The need for an increasing amount of medication to produce the same effect over time. A common example is the need to use more pain medication to relieve chronic pain.

Transplant list: A list of patients who have successfully completed their transplant evaluation and who are waiting for a cadaveric kidney transplant.

Twenty-four hour urine collection: A test used to measure the amount of protein that a patient is losing in the urine and which also measures the renal function of the patient. The patient typically voids, and then collects all of his or her urine from 8 AM to 8 AM the following day.

Ultrasound: An ultrasound, also known as a sonogram, is a diagnostic test that bounces sound waves off internal organs, such as the kidneys, to obtain a picture of them. Ultrasound does not require x-rays, injection, or dye, and is safe for pregnant patients.

Universal precautions: Wearing medical gloves, goggles, and face shields to avoid contact with body fluids such as blood and peritoneal fluid. Universal precautions protect us from the risk of transmission of blood-borne diseases such as hepatitis and HIV-AIDS.

Urea reduction ratio (URR): A mathematical calculation using the BUN done before and after dialysis that is used to measure the amount of hemodialysis a patient is receiving.

Uremia: Symptoms caused by kidney failure that include loss of appetite, itching, hiccups, nausea, vomiting, seizures, and lethargy.

Uremic neuropathy: Damage to nerves that is caused by the toxins and poisons that build up in the blood in kidney failure. Typical symptoms of uremic neuropathy are tingling or numbness in the feet and hands. Uremic neuropathy is treated by increasing the amount of dialysis that the patient is receiving to remove the build-up of toxins and poisons. Medications are sometimes used to treat the symptoms of uremic neuropathy.

Ureter: A tube that caries urine from the kidney to the bladder.

Urethra: A tube that carries urine from the bladder to the outside of the patient.

Urine analysis: A common screening test that looks for the presence of protein, glucose, and cells in the urine. It can help determine if further tests for kidney disease are indicated.

Urologist: A physician who specializes in the diagnosis and treatment of diseases of the kidney and urinary tract. Urologists have training in surgical procedures used in the treatment of prostate problems, tumors of the urinary tract, and the removal of kidney stones.

Index

^{THE}Quotable
INTELLECTUAL

ᴛʜᴇ Quotable
INTELLECTUAL

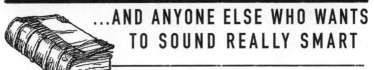

1,417 BON MOTS, RIPOSTES,
AND WITTICISMS
for ASPIRING ACADEMICS, ARMCHAIR PHILOSOPHERS

**...AND ANYONE ELSE WHO WANTS
TO SOUND REALLY SMART**

PETER ARCHER

adamsmedia
Avon, Massachusetts

Published by
Adams Media, a division of F+W Media, Inc.
57 Littlefield Street, Avon, MA 02322. U.S.A.
www.adamsmedia.com

ISBN 10: 1-4405-0589-6
ISBN 13: 978-1-4405-0589-8
eISBN 10: 1-4405-0731-7
eISBN 13: 978-1-4405-0731-1

Printed in the United States of America.

10   9   8   7   6   5   4   3   2   1

Library of Congress Cataloging-in-Publication Data
is available from the publisher.

This publication is designed to provide accurate and authoritative information with regard to the subject matter covered. It is sold with the understanding that the publisher is not engaged in rendering legal, accounting, or other
professional advice. If legal advice or other expert assistance is required, the
services of a competent professional person should be sought.
—From a *Declaration of Principles* jointly adopted by a Committee of the
American Bar Association and a Committee of Publishers and Associations

Many of the designations used by manufacturers and sellers to distinguish
their product are claimed as trademarks. Where those designations appear in
this book and Adams Media was aware of a trademark claim, the designations
have been printed with initial capital letters.

This book is available at quantity discounts for bulk purchases.
For information, please call 1-800-289-0963.

"I might repeat to myself slowly and sooth-
ingly, a list of quotations beautiful from
minds profound—if I can remember any
of the damn things."

—DOROTHY PARKER

"I hate quotations. Tell me what you
know."

—RALPH WALDO EMERSON

"An intellectual is someone who has found
something more interesting than sex."

—EDGAR WALLACE

CONTENTS

Dedication

For Linda and Jocelyn

INTRODUCTION

One afternoon in the 1930s, Dorothy Parker and Claire Booth Luce ran into one another at the front door of the Algonquin Hotel in New York City. Luce stepped back and gestured magnanimously toward the entrance. "Age before beauty," she cracked. "Pearls before swine," replied Mrs. Parker serenely as she glided through the doorway.

It's that sort of comment—witty, barbed, offhand that makes one wish life had a pause and rewind button. How many times have we all encountered a situation in which we could have used the perfect comeback or witticism, if only we'd had time to think about it?

Consider, for instance, another famous encounter, this between the notoriously antagonistic pair Violet Asquith and Winston Churchill, both members of the British Parliament. At a dinner party, as guests looked on in fascination, the two went at it, hammer and tongs, over questions of government policy until Mrs. Asquith's temper gave way.

"Winston," she snapped, "if you were my husband, I'd poison your coffee."

The future prime minister of Great Britain took a long drag on his after-dinner cigar and glowered at her. "Madam," he growled, "if you were my wife, I'd drink it."

How many of us would have thought to say that?

Well, if we can't think of such timely epigrams on our own, the least we can do is borrow from those who can. Hence the purpose of the volume you hold in your hand. Herein are contained quotations from the wildly famous to the justly obscure. Here are thoughts, wisecracks, meditations, japes, wheezes, sneers, eulogies, and observations on a wide variety of subjects. If you find yourself—as you may well—in a conversation in which you wish to give the impression of wit and erudition, drop these sparkling gems into the talk at regular intervals and enjoy the acclaim that will come your way.

There are a few preparations you must undertake for this sort of thing. Memorize quotes appropriate to the occasion—there's nothing more awkward than someone who opens his wallet to pull out a list of epigrams he hoped to employ during the evening.

Also, make sure you get the wording and the attribution right. It's embarrassing to quote, say, Marcus Aurelius on the pleasures of friendship only to have one of your audience point out that actually it was Cicero who said that and he wasn't talking about friendship but about old age.

But apart from these things, you'll find the quotations in this book useful in most social situations—icebreakers at parties, and a way to impress someone you've been wanting to invite out for a quiet drink and possibly a stroll in the summer moonlight after the party is over.

Bonne Chance!

PART I

ART

"There are three forms of visual art: Painting is art to look at, sculpture is art you can walk around, and architecture is art you can walk through."

—DAN RICE

ART

Let's face it: No one really understands why humans create art. Still less do we understand why we create the art we do—is there really an explanation for Abstract Expressionism? Nonetheless, intellectuals have expended a good many words trying to understand the strange, uniquely human propensity to express ourselves in words, in music, in drawing and painting, and in sculpture and architecture.

If you want to impress your friends, the next time conversation at the dinner table lags drop in one of these gems:

"Art is the imposing of a pattern on experience, and our aesthetic enjoyment is recognition of the pattern."

—ALFRED NORTH WHITEHEAD

"Art is the desire of a man to express himself, to record the reactions of his personality to the world he lives in."

—AMY LOWELL (1874–1925)
an American poet from Brookline, Massachusetts, posthumously won the Pulitzer Prize in 1926.

"I believe that if it were left to artists to choose their own labels, most would choose none."

—BEN SHAHN

"Art is a collaboration between God and the artist, and the less the artist does the better."

—ANDRE GIDE

"Let each man exercise the art he knows."

—ARISTOPHANES

"I don't believe in total freedom for the artist. Left on his own, free to do anything he likes, the artist ends up doing nothing at all. If there's one thing that's dangerous for an artist, it's precisely this question of total freedom, waiting for inspiration and all the rest of it."

—FEDERICO FELLINI

"Art, like morality, consists of drawing the line somewhere."

—G. K. Chesterton

(1874–1936)

a prominent Christian author who today is most widely known for the *Father Brown* detective stories.

"What I dream of is an art of balance."

—Henri Matisse

"Every artist dips his brush in his own soul, and paints his own nature into his pictures."

—Henry Ward Beecher

"Through all the world there goes one long cry from the heart of the artist: Give me leave to do my utmost."

—Isak Dineson

"The painting has a life of its own. I try to let it come through."

—Jackson Pollock

"We must never forget that art is not a form of propaganda; it is a form of truth."

—John F. Kennedy

"Creativity is . . . seeing something that doesn't exist already. You need to find out how you can bring it into being and that way be a playmate with God."

—Michele Shea

"I say that good painters imitated nature; but that bad ones vomited it."

—Miguel de Cervantes

(1547–1616)

is among the greatest writers produced by Spain and celebrated for his masterwork, *Don Quixote*.

Is art an expression of the thoughts and urges of its time? Or is it above these things and merely a reflection of the artist's inner drives and psyche? You can join in the conversation with these thoughts.

"I paint my own reality. The only thing I know is that I paint because I need to, and I paint whatever passes through my head without any other consideration."

—FRIDA KAHLO

"Art is on the side of the oppressed. Think before you shudder at the simplistic dictum and its heretical definition of the freedom of art. For if art is freedom of the spirit, how can it exist within the oppressors?"

—EDITH WHARTON

"Works of art, in my opinion, are the only objects in the material universe to possess internal order, and that is why, though I don't believe that only art matters, I do believe in Art for Art's sake."

—E. M. FORSTER (1879–1970) authored such well-known novels as *A Passage to India* and *Howards End.*

Every artist wants to be pure. Every artist wants to change the world through his art. (Every artist also wants to be paid full market value for doing so.) Even if you can't help them in this lofty aim, you can at least quote them.

"Every child is an artist. The problem is how to remain an artist once he grows up."

—PABLO PICASSO

"Art forms of the past were really considered elitist. Bach did not compose for the masses, neither did Beethoven. It was always for patrons, aristocrats, and royalty. Now we have a sort of democratic version of that, which is to say that the audience is so splintered in its interests."

—DAVID CRONENBERG (1943–) a Canadian filmmaker, has made such movies as *The Fly* (1986), *A History of Violence* (2005), and *Eastern Promises* (2007).

"What we play is life."

—LOUIS ARMSTRONG

ARCHITECTURE

Every artist is convinced that his medium of expression is not only the best possible aesthetic but that it is the only one. This accounts for the fact that the average artist has an ego the size of a Texas dust storm— and about as overwhelming. Architects, because they work generally on a large scale, are probably at the top of the ego tree among the creative arts. Thus the best way to approach a gathering of people talking about architecture is to drop a few words from the giants of the profession.

"The mother art is architecture. Without an architecture of our own, we have no soul of our own civilization."

—FRANK LLOYD WRIGHT

"Architecture is the learned game, correct and magnificent, of forms assembled in the light."

—LE CORBUSIER

"Architecture starts when you carefully put two bricks together. There it begins."

—LUDWIG MIES VAN DER ROHE

"Architecture is the reaching out for the truth."

—LOUIS KAHN

"Our architecture reflects truly as a mirror."

—LOUIS SULLIVAN (1856–1924) was one of the foremost American architects of the nineteenth and twentieth centuries.

"A modern, harmonic and lively architecture is the visible sign of an authentic democracy."

—WALTER GROPIUS

"A house is a machine for living."

—R. BUCKMINSTER FULLER

"A great architect is not made by way of a brain nearly so much as he is made by way of a cultivated, enriched heart."

—FRANK LLOYD WRIGHT

Not everyone holds the architectural profession in such reverence. Modern architecture in particular has taken a severe tongue lashing from critics. If you want to deflate an architect's ego—or, at any rate, reduce it to a manageable size—try one of the following:

"Architecture is the art of how to waste space."

—PHILIP JOHNSON

"Architects believe that not only do they sit at the right hand of God, but that if God ever gets up, they take the chair."

—KAREN MOYER

"In my experience, if you have to keep the lavatory door shut by extending your left leg, it's modern architecture."

—NANCY BANKS SMITH

"You have to give this much to the Luftwaffe: when it knocked down our buildings it did not replace them with anything more offensive than rubble. We did that."

—CHARLES, PRINCE OF WALES

"The architecture profession has lost a lot of its integrity, especially in the USA. The general architect here has no scruples, no ambitions."

—HELMUT JAHN

"All architecture is great architecture after sunset."

—G. K. CHESTERTON

"Architect, n. One who drafts a plan of your house, and plans a draft of your money."

—AMBROSE BIERCE
(1842–1914?)
an editor, journalist, and writer, a savage satirist whose writings reflect trends in American literature after the Civil War.

"What has happened to architecture since the Second World War that the only passers-by who can contemplate it without pain are those equipped with a white stick and a dog?"

—BERNARD LEVIN

"A doctor can bury his mistakes, but an architect can only advise his clients to plant vines."

—FRANK LLOYD WRIGHT

"Believe me, that was a happy age, before the days of architects, before the days of builders."

—SENECA

Architects love to be praised, and to hear their profession elevated to the greatest heights. There's no better way to flatter them, and to make yourself appear smart and well-educated, than to toss out something like the following:

"Architecture is music in space, as it were a frozen music."

—FRIEDRICH WILHELM JOSEPH VON SCHELLING

"Architecture is the work of nations."

—JOHN RUSKIN

"Architecture aims at eternity."

—CHRISTOPHER WREN

"Architecture has recorded the great ideas of the human race. Not only every religious symbol, but every human thought has its page in that vast book."

—VICTOR HUGO

"The job of buildings is to improve human relations."

—RALPH ERSKINE

"The principle of Gothic architecture is infinity made imaginable."

—SAMUEL TAYLOR COLERIDGE

"Architecture is inhabited sculpture."

—CONSTANTIN BRANCUSI
(1876–1957)
an internationally known Romanian sculptor, helped usher in the Modernist movement with his works.

"Ah, to build, to build! That is the noblest of all the arts."

—HENRY WADSWORTH LONGFELLOW

"We shape our buildings; thereafter they shape us."

—WINSTON CHURCHILL

ⒹGARRICK THEATRE:CHICAGO

The rules of architecture, are in constant dispute. When listening to arguments about the true art of building and the importance of Vision in Architecture, casually comment along the following lines:

"Architecture begins where engineering ends."

—WALTER GROPIUS

"Architecture is not all about the design of the building and nothing else, it is also about the cultural setting and the ambience, the whole affair."

—MICHAEL GRAVES

"Form ever follows function."

—LOUIS SULLIVAN

"To create architecture is to put in order. Put what in order? Function and objects."

—LE CORBUSIER (1887–1965) was a pioneer of modern architecture, in the movement known as Urbanism.

"Light, God's eldest daughter, is a principal beauty in a building."

—THOMAS FULLER

"I don't think of form as a kind of architecture. The architecture is the result of the forming. It is the kinesthetic and visual sense of position and wholeness that puts the thing into the realm of art."

—ROY LICHTENSTEIN

"The rules of navigation never navigated a ship. The rules of architecture never built a house."

—THOMAS REID

"Even though I build buildings and I pursue my architecture, I pursue it as an artist. I deliberately keep a tiny studio. I don't want to be an architectural firm. I want to remain an artist."

—MAYA LIN

"If a building becomes architecture, then it is art."

—ARNE JACOBSEN

"A structure becomes architectural, and not sculptural, when its elements no longer have their justification in nature."

—GUILLAUME APOLLINAIRE

"I strive for an architecture from which nothing can be taken away."

—HELMUT JAHN

"An architect should live as little in cities as a painter. Send him to our hills, and let him study there what nature understands by a buttress, and what by a dome."

—JOHN RUSKIN

A rchitecture teaches us about the past in a way that no other records can. Perhaps that's one of its real values, you can remind others of this by quoting them something like this:

"If I had to say which was telling the truth about society, a speech by a Minister of Housing or the actual buildings put up in his time, I should believe the buildings."

—KENNETH CLARK (1903–1983) an art historian and author, is best known for his 1968 television series "Civilisation."

"All architects want to live beyond their deaths."

—PHILIP JOHNSON

"Architecture, of all the arts, is the one that acts most slowly but the most surely on the soul."

—ERNEST DIMNET

"Architecture should speak of its time and place, but yearn for timelessness."

—FRANK GEHRY

PAINTING

From the moment Ancient Man, deep in the caves of Lascaux, lifted his brush to paint pictures of bison and deer on the rocky walls, painting has been among the most magical of arts. Not surprisingly, artists have had a good deal to say about it. There are two ways to participate in a conversation about painting. You can draw on your experience of years studying art, walking the galleries of the Louvre or the Prado, examining the paintings of Monet, Velázquez, Goya, and Leonardo . . . . Or you can casually drop into the discussion something like the following:

"Painting is the grandchild of nature. It is related to God."
—REMBRANDT VAN RIJN

"Painting is silent poetry."
—SIMONIDES

"There are painters who transform the sun to a yellow spot, but there are others who with the help of their art and their intelligence transform a yellow spot into the sun."
—PABLO PICASSO

"Art is either plagiarism or revolution."
—PAUL GAUGUIN

"The position of the artist is humble. He is essentially a channel."
—PIET MONDRIAN

"All art is an imitation of nature."

—SENECA

"I don't paint things. I only paint the difference between things."
—HENRI MATISSE

"There is nothing more difficult for a truly creative painter than to paint a rose, because before he can do so he has first to forget all the roses that were ever painted."
—HENRI MATISSE (1869–1954)
widely regarded as one of the most important artists of the twentieth century, noted for his revolutionary use of color.

Painters don't like to talk about money or the fact that they sell their art. Such conversation is considered vulgar, since Art should be above mere Commerce. (Asking a painter how much she or he sold a picture for is a bit like asking your grandmother how much she spent on your Christmas present.) If the subject does comes up, try one of the following quotations to ease the flow:

"I'd asked around ten or fifteen people for suggestions. Finally one lady friend asked the right question. 'Well, what do you love the most?' That's how I started painting money."

—ANDY WARHOL

"An amateur is someone who supports himself with outside jobs which enable him to paint. A professional is someone whose wife works to enable him to paint."

—BEN SHAHN

"Art is making something out of nothing and selling it."

—FRANK ZAPPA

Nothing is more repulsive to the artist than the critic. To endear yourself to an artist, always have a few nasty things to say about critics, reviewers, and criticism in general.

"Painting, n. The art of protecting flat surfaces from the weather and exposing them to the critic."

—AMBROSE BIERCE

"Every time I paint a portrait I lose a friend."

—JOHN SINGER SARGENT

"The artist is not a reporter, but a Great Teacher. It is not his business to depict the world as it is, but as it ought to be."

—H. L. MENCKEN (1880–1956)
an American journalist, editor, and writer, is best known for his book *The American Language.*

"A painting in a museum hears more ridiculous opinions than anything else in the world."

—EDMOND DE GONCOURT

Artists love to be asked why and how they paint. They won't necessarily give you an answer, but they love to be asked. To get the conversation going, try one of the following.

"The world today doesn't make sense, so why should I paint pictures that do?"

—PABLO PICASSO

"Only when he no longer knows what he is doing does the painter do good things."

—EDGAR DEGAS

"A man paints with his brains and not with his hands."

—MICHAELANGELO

"I experience a period of frightening clarity in those moments when nature is so beautiful. I am no longer sure of myself, and the paintings appear as in a dream."

—VINCENT VAN GOGH

"Painting is just another way of keeping a diary."

—PABLO PICASSO (1881–1973)
is sometimes denoted as the greatest
artist of the twentieth century.

"A good painter is to paint two main things, men and the working of man's mind."

—LEONARDO DA VINCI

"Painting is the nail to which I fasten my ideas."

—GEORGES BRAQUE

"Art is the imposing of a pattern on experience, and our aesthetic enjoyment is recognition of the pattern."

—ALFRED NORTH WHITEHEAD

"I've been doing a lot of abstract painting lately, extremely abstract. No brush, no paint, no canvas, I just think about it.

—STEVEN WRIGHT

"Artists who seek perfection in everything are those who cannot attain it in anything."

—EUGENE DELACROIX
(1798–1863)
was a French nineteenth-century painter

"Every good painter paints what he is."

—JACKSON POLLOCK

Then again . . .

"Good painting is the kind that looks like sculpture."

—MICHAELANGELO

"I sometimes wonder if the hand is not more sensitive to the beauties of sculpture than the eye. I should think the wonderful rhythmical flow of lines and curves could be more subtly felt than seen. Be this as it may, I know that I can feel the heartthrobs of the ancient Greeks in their marble gods and goddesses."

—HELEN KELLER

"A sculptor wields the chisel, and the stricken marble grows to beauty."

—WILLIAM CULLEN BRYANT

SCULPTURE

The first thing any self-respecting sculptor will explain to you is that sculpting is much harder and more demanding than painting. The second thing is that he is unappreciated by critics—especially the ones who have trashed his last six shows. The third is that he'd never dream of creating his Art for anything so vulgar as money. Be ready to join in the conversation by quoting something along the following lines.

"Sculpture is more divine, and more like Nature,

That fashions all her works in high relief,

And that is Sculpture.

This vast ball, the Earth,

Was moulded out of clay, and baked in fire;

Men, women, and all animals that breathe

Are statues, and not paintings."
—HENRY WADSWORTH LONGFELLOW

"Sculpture is the art of the intelligence."

—PABLO PICASSO

"I say that the art of sculpture is eight times as great as any other art based on drawing, because a statue has eight views and they must all be equally good."

—BENVENUTO CELLINI

(1500–1571)

the quintessential Renaissance figure: a goldsmith, sculptor, painter, and politician.

"A fellow will hack half a year at a block of marble to make something in stone that hardly resembles a man. The value of statuary is owing to its difficulty. You would not value the finest head cut upon a carrot."

—SAMUEL JOHNSON

"As paradoxical as it may seem a great sculptor is as much a colourist as the best painter, or rather the best engraver. He plays so skillfully with all the resources of relief, he blends so well the boldness of light with the modesty of shadow, that his sculptures please one, as much as the most charming etchings."

—AUGUST RODIN

If a sculptor seems to be getting a bit above him or herself, you can always comment along the following lines. However, if the sculptor picks up a hammer after you've quoted your authority, be ready to duck.

"Sculpture, a very noble art, is one that does not in the execution require the same supreme ingenuity as the art of painting, since in two most important and difficult particulars, in foreshortening and in light and shade . . . the painter has to invent a process, [whereas] sculpture is helped by nature."

—LEONARDO DA VINCI

(1452–1519)

was a poet, painter, sculptor, muralist, musician, scientist, mathematician, and writer.

"I did my sculpture as a painter. I did not work as a sculptor."

—HENRI MATISSE

Once they've convinced you of the superiority of their art over all others, sculptors are eager to explain their philosophy and methods. It turns out that there are exactly as many of these as there are sculptors, whether working in bronze or marble, wood, or wind. If you want to get them going for an entire afternoon, start them off with a quotation such as these.

"A piece of sculpture can have a hole through it and not be weakened if the hole is of a studied size, shape, and direction."

—HENRY MOORE

"There is no substitute for feeling the stone, the metal, the plaster, or the wood in the hand; to feel its weight; to feel its texture; to struggle with it in the world rather than in the mind alone."

—WILLIAM M. DUPREE

"Bronze is the mirror of the form, wine of the mind."

—AESCHYLUS

"Sculpture occupies the same space as your body."

—ANISH KAPOOR

"A hole in the block of a piece of sculpture is in most cases nothing but the expression of impotence and weakness."

—FRITZ WOTRUBA (1907–1975) was a prominent Austrian sculptor who created many works in the form of megalithic abstractions.

"The essence of a sculpture must enter on tip-toe, as light as animal footprints on snow."

—JEAN ARP (1886–1966) was a leading figure in the Dada art movement.

"As picture teaches the colouring, so sculpture the anatomy of form."

—RALPH WALDO EMERSON

"A great sculpture can roll down a hill without breaking."

—MICHAELANGELO

"Sculpture is the art of the hole and the lump."

—AUGUST RODIN

One thing many sculptors do agree on (particularly those who carve in stone) is that the form of the finished sculpture lies hidden in the material. Display your erudition and extensive knowledge of the art (even if you don't have any) by quoting one of the following.

"Within every block of wood and stone, there dwells a spirit, waiting to be released. Direct carving is a way of freeing the spirit—my own and that of the stone or wood."

—HAP HAGOOD

"The stone unhewn and cold

Becomes a living mould,

The more the marble wastes

The more the statue grows."

—MICHAELANGELO

"I saw the angel in the marble and carved until I set him free."

—MICHAELANGELO

T o impress any art-
ist and elevate the
level of your conversa-
tion, quote from one of
the masters of the art.

"There are two devices which
can help the sculptor to judge
his work: one is not to see it for
a while. The other . . . is to look
at his work through spectacles
which will change its color and
magnify or diminish it, so as to
disguise it somehow to his eye,
and make it look as though it were
the work of another."

—GIANLORENZO BERNINI

"Where did I learn

to understand sculp-

ture? In the woods

by looking at the

trees, along roads by

observing the forma-

tion of clouds, in the

studio by studying

the model, every-

where except in the

schools."

—AUGUST RODIN

Cinema

When writing of his experiences as a successful Hollywood screenwriter, William Goldman observed, "Nobody knows anything." Although many others have made similar observations about the essentially anarchic process of movie making, nonetheless, some 400 movies are produced and released every year. This is something of a miracle, considering the vast amounts of ego, money, and influence that are common currency in Hollywood. Tinseltown is first and foremost about appearance—substance is very low down on the list of things that matter there. So toss out something like these sentiments, and you'll be welcomed into the world of America's showfolk.

"Drama is life with the dull bits cut out."

—ALFRED HITCHCOCK

"[M]ovie-making is the process of turning money into light. All they have at the end of the day is images flickering on a wall."

—JOHN BOORMAN

"A film is—or should be—more like music than like fiction. It should be a progression of moods and feelings. The theme, what's behind the emotion, the meaning, all that comes later."

—STANLEY KUBRICK

"Cinema should make you forget you are sitting in a theater."

—ROMAN POLANSKI

"Of all our inventions for mass communication, pictures still speak the most universally understood language."

—WALT DISNEY

"Film is one of the three universal languages; the other two: mathematics and music."

—FRANK CAPRA

"A film is never really good unless the camera is an eye in the head of a poet."

—ORSON WELLES

"A director makes only one movie in his life. Then he breaks it into pieces and makes it again."

—Jean Renoir

"To be an artist means to search, to find and look at these realities. To be an artist means never look away."

—Akira Kurosawa
(1910–1998)
one of the pre-eminent directors in film history, made Japanese movies into a powerful artistic force.

S ome people in the film industry, usually actors, take movies much less seriously than others. In turn, filmmakers are sometimes contemptuous of actors, feeling, no doubt, that movies would be fine if actors didn't have to be involved. Actors and directors unite in their denigration of the struggling screenwriter, who feels that he is the key to the entire process and wishes his pay would reflect that. Depending on whom you're talking to about the movies, you can drop one of the following lines.

"Acting: An art which consists of keeping the audience from coughing."

—RALPH RICHARDSON

"The length of a film should be directly related to the endurance of the human bladder."

—ALFRED HITCHCOCK

"What I've learned is that life is too short and movies are too long."

—DENIS LEARY

"I don't take the movies seriously, and anyone who does is in for a headache."

—BETTE DAVIS

"I never enjoyed working in a film."

—MARLENE DIETRICH
(1901–1992)
became the embodiment of sexy and sultry in such movies as *Shanghai Express* and *The Scarlet Empress*.

"I've made so many movies playing a hooker that they don't pay me in the regular way anymore. They leave it on the dresser."

—SHIRLEY MACLAINE

"The close-up says everything."

—MARLON BRANDO

"If you are directing, you have the opportunity to put your signature on the bottom of the frame. You have the opportunity to say, 'This is what I believe. That is my credo. That is what I wish to state.'"

—RICHARD ATTENBOROUGH

"At the end of the game, it's the director who will attract the actors and it's the script that will attract the director. It all starts with the screenplay."

—DAVID BROWN

"For me, movies should be visual. If you want dialogue, you should read a book."

—VILMOS ZSIGMOND (1930–)
an award-winning cinematographer, has worked on such movies as *McCabe and Mrs. Miller* (1971) and *Deliverance* (1972).

"Anybody can direct, but there are only eleven good writers."

—MEL BROOKS

"Being a screenwriter is not enough for a full creative life."

—WILLIAM GOLDMAN

"Having your book turned into a movie is like seeing your oxen turned into bouillon cubes."

—JOHN LECARRE (1931–)
is the pseudonym of David Cornwell, a British writer of spy thrillers such as *Tinker, Tailor, Soldier, Spy* and *The Russia House*.

"Never judge a book by its movie."

—J. W. EAGAN

"There are three kinds of people: men, women, and actors."

—D. A. DORAN

"Movies are not scripts, movies are films; they're not books, they're not the theatre."

—NICOLAS ROEG

"I don't think you should feel about a film. You should feel about a woman, not a movie. You can't kiss a movie."

—JEAN-LUC GODARD

"The only really good thing about acting in movies is there's no heavy lifting."

—CARY GRANT (1904–1986) born Archibald Leach, became the embodiment of the sophisticated, suave leading man in such movies as *The Philadelphia Story*.

"You know, when I first went into the movies Lionel Barrymore played my grandfather. Later he played my father and finally he played my husband. If he had lived I'm sure I would have played his mother. That's the way it is in Hollywood. The men get younger and the women get older."

—LILLIAN GISH

"Never treat your audience as customers, always as partners."

—JIMMY STEWART

"There are only three ages for women in Hollywood—Babe, District Attorney, and Driving Miss Daisy."

—GOLDIE HAWN

"Being a movie star is a rare job. Nobody gives you any guarantees that you'll get to do it forever. It's a very lucky and privileged position to be in."

—DIANE KEATON

"The dance that happens between an actor and a director is a very delicate thing . . . it's why people tend to work together on many films over and over."

—SYDNEY POLLACK (1934–2008) was the director of *The Way We Were, Three Days of the Condor,* and *Out of Africa*.

"Studio executives are intelligent, brutally overworked men and women who share one thing in common with baseball managers: they wake up every morning of the world with the knowledge that sooner or later they're going to get fired."

—WILLIAM GOLDMAN

"You're only as good as your last picture."

—MARIE DRESSLER

S ome people believe that the function of movies is to teach the audience. Others are of the opinion that if the movie doesn't bore anyone to death it's worked pretty well. Wherever you stand on the issue, in any gathering in southern California there's sure to be at least one person in your vicinity with the opposite view. Twit their sensibilities with one of these quotations.

"Every time I go to a movie, it's magic, no matter what the movie's about."
—STEVEN SPIELBERG

"A good film is when the price of the dinner, the theatre admission and the babysitter were worth it."
—ALFRED HITCHCOCK

"If my film makes one more person miserable, I've done my job."
—WOODY ALLEN (1935–)
has been hailed as one of America's foremost film directors for movies such as *Annie Hall* and *Hannah and Her Sisters.*

"It's movies that have really been running things in America ever since they were invented. They show you what to do, how to do it, when to do it, how to feel about it, and how to look how you feel about it."
—ANDY WARHOL

"We learn how to kiss or to drink, talk to our buddies—all the things that you can't really teach in social studies or history—we all learn them at the movies."
—JACK NICHOLSON

Over the years, directors, actors, and executives have adapted movies to the changing tastes of the public and the developing technology of the industry. Not that they've always been pleased about it. The following quotes will help you sound like you fit in with the glitterati who rove up and down Hollywood Boulevard.

"Adding sound to movies would be like putting lipstick on the Venus de Milo."

—MARY PICKFORD

"A wide screen just makes a bad film twice as bad."

—SAMUEL GOLDWYN

"Cinema is the most beautiful fraud in the world."

—JEAN-LUC GODARD (1930–) is representative of the French New Wave movement in cinema with movies such as *À bout de souffle*, *Le Vent d'est*, and *Prénom Carmen*.

"Everybody's a filmmaker today."

—JOHN MILIUS

"I think cinema, movies, and magic have always been closely associated. The very earliest people who made film were magicians."

—FRANCIS FORD COPPOLA

"A story should have a beginning, a middle, and an end . . . but not necessarily in that order."

—JEAN-LUC GODARD

Nothing condemns a movie more to intellectual ridicule than success. If a lot of people like it and are willing to pay money to go see it, the thinking goes, it can't be much good. Occasionally, a movie critics hailed upon its release will become popular, at which point the same critics will find numerous flaws in the film they overlooked the first time ("The love scenes are *so* forced and predictable!") and denounce it as pandering to popular taste. From the standpoint of movie critics (especially those from the *New York Times* and the *New Yorker*), the best films are made by unknown Malaysian directors, filmed in Spanish on location in Guatemala, and released in only three theaters in the United States, two of which happen to be located on the Lower East Side of Manhattan and seat fifteen people each. If you want to sound sophisticated and knowledgeable when you're around movie people, quote one of these sentiments.

> "If my films don't show a profit, I know I'm doing something right."
>
> —WOODY ALLEN

"If you don't like my movies, don't watch them."

—DARIO ARGENTO

"Even if I set out to make a film about a filet of sole, it would be about me."

—FEDERICO FELLINI

"Shoot a few scenes out of focus. I want to win the foreign film award."

—BILLY WILDER (1906–2002) was an American director who specialized in screwball comedies such as *Ninotchka* and *Some Like It Hot.*

The cinema continues to fascinate and entertain us. And since everyone's always talking about the last movie they saw, the great special effects shot in the last scene, the wonderful acting job the star almost did . . . feel free to throw in some comments along the following lines.

"In feature films, the director is God; in documentary films, God is the director."

—ALFRED HITCHCOCK

"Film spectators are quiet vampires."

—JIM MORRISON

"A film is a petrified fountain of thought."

—JEAN COCTEAU (1889–1963) was one of a number of French film directors in the mid-twentieth century who were deeply influenced by surrealism, as evidenced by such films as *Orphée* and *Les parents terribles.*

"Cinema is a matter of what's in the frame and what's out."

—MARTIN SCORSESE

"The secret to film is that it's an illusion."

—GEORGE LUCAS

"There's only one thing that can kill the movies, and that's education."

—WILL ROGERS

"When you're making a movie, you can't think anybody will ever see it. You've just got to make a movie for the values it has. The greatest films were made because someone really wanted to make them."

—CLINT EASTWOOD

"A movie doesn't have to do everything. A movie just has to do a couple of things. If it does those things well and gives you a cool night at the movies, an emotion, that's good enough."

—QUENTIN TARANTINO (1963–) has been noted throughout his directorial career for his use of nonlinear storylines and ultraviolent scripts.

We'll let one of America's great comic talents have the last word:

"You know what your problem is, it's that you haven't seen enough movies, all of life's riddles are answered in the movies."

—STEVE MARTIN

PART II

LITERATURE

"Books are humanity in print."

—BARBARA TUCHMAN

THE NOVEL

Since the first novels were written in the eighteenth century, intellectuals have been proclaiming the death of the novel. Part of the reason for this, of course, is that it's much more exciting to announce the death or destruction of something than to celebrate its continuation. ("This year, novelists kept on writing novels. Way to go, guys!") As a matter of fact, today more novels than ever are churned out. Snooty intellectuals are therefore reduced to complaining about both the quality and the quantity of these productions, pointing out that the novels they like to read are hardly read by anyone—proving their worth. If you're caught in a discussion, sometime, about whether the novel is really dead, trot out something like this.

"If I were a writer, how I would enjoy being told the novel is dead. How liberating to work in the margins, outside a central perception."

—DON DELILLO

"Novels so often provide an anodyne and not an antidote, glide one into torpid slumbers instead of rousing one with a burning brand."

—VIRGINIA WOOLF (1882–1941)
was an English novelist and diarist as well as a central part of the Bloomsbury Group.

"The novel is always pop art, and the novel is always dying. That's the only way it stays alive. It does really die."

—LESLIE FIEDLER

"I find in most novels no imagination at all. They seem to think the highest form of the novel is to write about marriage, because that's the most important thing there is for middle-class people."

—GORE VIDAL

"Every author really wants to have letters printed in the papers. Unable to make the grade, he drops down a rung of the ladder and writes novels."

—P. G. WODEHOUSE

"The last time I was in Spain I got through six Jeffrey Archer novels. I must remember to take enough toilet paper next time."

—BOB MONKHOUSE

"Novels as dull as dishwater, with the grease of random sentiments floating on top."

—ITALO CALVINO (1923–1985)
wrote such novels is *Invisible Cities* and *The Baron of the Trees*.

"A person, be it gentleman or lady, who has not pleasure in a good novel, must be intolerably stupid."

—JANE AUSTEN

"People think that because a novel's invented, it isn't true. Exactly the reverse is the case. Biography and memoirs can never be wholly true, since they cannot include every conceivable circumstance of what happened. The novel can do that."

—ANTHONY POWELL

"Nothing induces me to read a novel except when I have to make money by writing about it. I detest them."

—VIRGINIA WOOLF

W riters are quick to explain that although the novel may be dead, dying, or decomposing, their novel will revive the discredited genre and instantly elevate them to the post of Recognized Genius. The chief enemies of such genius are the Critics, who are universally derided in all creative spheres. To ingratiate yourself at any gathering in which authors are present, savage critics by quoting something like the following.

"Any reviewer who expresses rage and loathing for a novel is preposterous. He or she is like a person who has put on full armor and attacked a hot fudge sundae."

—KURT VONNEGUT (1922–2007)
wrote novels that include *Slaughterhouse-Five*, *Cat's Cradle*, and *Breakfast of Champions*.

"I cringe when critics say I'm a master of the popular novel. What's an unpopular novel?"

—IRWIN SHAW

"Whatever I do is done out of sheer joy; I drop my fruits like a ripe tree. What the general reader or the critic makes of them is not my concern."

—HENRY MILLER

"It's with bad sentiments that one makes good novels."

—ALDOUS HUXLEY

"A novel that does not uncover a hitherto unknown segment of existence is immoral. Knowledge is the novel's only morality."

—MILAN KUNDERA (1929–)
a Czech writer who is best known for his novel *The Unbearable Lightness of Being*.

"They say great themes make great novels . . . but what these young writers don't understand is that there is no greater theme than men and women."

—JOHN O'HARA

"When writing a novel a writer should create living people; people not characters. A character is a caricature."

—ERNEST HEMINGWAY

"A good novel tells us the truth about its hero; but a bad novel tells us the truth about its author."

—G. K. CHESTERTON

"It's not a good idea to put your wife into a novel; not your latest wife, anyway."

—NORMAN MAILER (1923–2007)
an American novelist and journalist who blended reportage with opinion and personal experience.

"Great, big, serious novels always get awards. If it's a battle between a great, big, serious novel and a funny novel, the funny novel is always doomed."

—NEIL GAIMAN

"There are no laws for the novel. There never have been, nor can there ever be."

—DORIS LESSING

"The only reason for the existence of a novel is that it does attempt to represent life."

—HENRY JAMES

"What I couldn't help noticing was that I learned more about the novel in a morning by trying to write a page of one than I'd learned in seven years or so of trying to write criticism."

—PHILIP PULLMAN (1946–)
is best known for the trilogy *His Dark Materials*.

"Novel writing is far and away the most exhausting work I know."

—C. S. FORESTER

Novel writers and critics alike struggle to explain exactly what should and shouldn't go into a novel—no easy task, since they usually disagree on whether writing novels is even a worthwhile pursuit. One thing they do agree on is that writing a novel is beyond the poor abilities of most people and they shouldn't be encouraged to try. "It takes a lot of energy and a lot of neurosis to write a novel," said novelist Laurence Durrell. "If you were really sensible, you'd do something else." When a novelist starts complaining about the agonies of writing within your earshot, you can endear yourself to her or him by one of these quotations.

"Any fool can write a novel, but it takes real genius to sell it."

—J. G. BALLARD

"The great American novel has not only already been written, it has already been rejected."

—W. SOMERSET MAUGHAM
(1874–1965)

was known for his sarcastic sense of humor, and his novels such as *Of Human Bondage* became widely popular before World War II.

"There's no reason you should write any novel quickly."

—JOHN IRVING

"A good novel is worth more than the best scientific study."

—SAUL BELLOW

"Writing a novel is like making love, but it's also like having a tooth pulled. Pleasure and pain. Sometimes it's like making love while having a tooth pulled."

—DEAN KOONTZ

"Writing a novel is a terrible experience, during which the hair often falls out and the teeth decay."

—FLANNERY O'CONNOR

"A novel must be exceptionally good to live as long as the average cat."

—LORD CHESTERFIELD
(1694–1773)
a wealthy and politically powerful member of the British aristocracy, was noted for his witty epigrams.

"I can't understand why a person will take a year to write a novel when he can easily buy one for a few dollars."

—FRED ALLEN

"The really great novels tends to be the exact negative of its author's life."

—ANDRÉ MAUROIS (1885–1967)
composed biographies of prominent British figures such as Disraeli, Shelley, and Byron.

"Only in a novel are all things given full play."

—D. H. LAWRENCE

"It is the test of a novel writer's art that he conceal his snake-in-the-grass; but the reader may be sure that it is always there."

—ANTHONY TROLLOPE

"The first sentence of every novel should be: Trust me, this will take time but there is order here, very faint, very human."

—MICHAEL ONDAATJE

In the end, writers agree, they are at least as interesting as their novels. Hence the popularity of that peculiar book, the literary biography. In essence it is a long book written about someone who spent a long time writing books. But it gives writers—and you—a chance to comment extensively on their writing.

"Writing a story or a novel is one way of discovering sequence in experience, of stumbling upon cause and effect in the happenings of a writer's own life."

—EUDORA WELTY (1909–2001)
wrote short stories and novels about the American South that group her with William Faulkner as one of the great writers of Southern Gothic.

"The suspense of a novel is not only in the reader, but in the novelist, who is intensely curious about what will happen to the hero."

—MARY MCCARTHY

"My first novel took twelve years to complete because life got in my way."

—Donald McKay

"A novel has to have shape, and life doesn't have any."

—Jean Rhys (1890–1979) Dominican novelist, wrote *Wide Sargasso Sea*, a "prequel" to Charlotte Brontë's Jane Eyre.

"A novel, in the end, is a container, a shape which you are trying to pour your story into."

—Helen Dunmore

"I had a romance novel inside me, but I paid three sailors to beat it out of me with steel pipes."

—Patton Oswalt

"The fundamental purpose of a novel like Count Julian is to achieve the unity of object and means of representation, the fusion of treason as scheme and treason as language."

—Juan Goytisolo (1931–) is a Spanish poet and novelist who lives in Marrakech. His novels include *The Young Assassins*, *Count Julian*, and *Juan the Landless*.

"The novel is the highest form of human expression so far attained. Why? Because it is so incapable of the absolute."

—D. H. Lawrence

"A book is sent out into the world, and there is no way of fully anticipating the responses it will elicit."

—Chaim Potok (1929–2002) was born to immigrant parents in Brooklyn, New York. His best-known book is *The Chosen*, published in 1967.

A nd a final word on the subject:

"Every journalist has a novel in him, which is an excellent place for it."

—Russell Lynes

POETRY

"Never leave me alone with the poets," *New Yorker* editor Harold Ross begged his staff. His sentiment is understandable: poetry is among the most confusing of arts. At least with novels it's a reasonably sure bet that you can hazard a guess at what the author meant. But poetry seems to take us into a new and dreadful world in which meanings are turned upside down, words and their definitions part ways, and every phrase seems to allude back to something else, only half glimpsed.

Poets themselves are not only aware of this ambiguity; they revel in it. Now you can revel with them (even if you don't understand them) by quoting one of the following.

"Most people ignore most poetry because most poetry ignores most people."

—ADRIAN MITCHELL

"It's easier to quote poets than to read them."

—ALLISON BARROWS

"A poem is no place for an idea."

—EDGAR WATSON HOWE

"Poetry is the deification of reality."

—EDITH SITWELL (1887–1964) shocked her aristocratic parents by her determination to shun their privileged lifestyle and become a poet.

"All slang is a metaphor, and all metaphor is poetry."

—G. K. CHESTERTON

"Poetry often enters through the window of irrelevance."

—M. C. RICHARDS

"Poetry is what gets lost in translation."

—ROBERT FROST (1874–1963) was an American poet, most often associated with New England, where many of his poems are set.

"Poetry is the journal of the sea animal living on land, wanting to fly in the air. Poetry is a search for syllables to shoot at the barriers of the unknown and the unknowable. Poetry is a phantom script telling how rainbows are made and why they go away."

—CARL SANDBURG

"Even when poetry has a meaning, as it usually has, it may be inadvisable to draw it out . . . . Perfect understanding will sometimes almost extinguish pleasure."

—A. E. HOUSMAN

"Poetry is a mirror which makes beautiful that which is distorted."

—PERCY SHELLEY

It's worth noting that Plato banished poets from his ideal Republic since they were purveyors of creative truth—not a welcome commodity in the kind of semi-totalitarian state he had in mind. Poets generally have been viewed in the same way Lady Caroline Lamb saw Lord Byron: "Mad, bad, and dangerous to know." The nicest thing you can say to a poet is, "You disturb me." If you want something a bit more eloquent to make them feel good, try one of the following.

"The worst tragedy for a poet is to be admired through being misunderstood."

—JEAN COCTEAU

"Poetry is nearer to vital truth than history."

—PLATO

"Poets are the unacknowledged. A poet is an unhappy being whose heart is torn by secret sufferings, but whose lips are so strangely formed that when the sighs and the cries escape them, they sound like beautiful music . . . ."

—SOREN KIERKEGAARD
(1813–1855)
wrote extensively in critique of the dominant Hegelian philosophy of his day and in support of Christianity.

"You don't have to suffer to be a poet; adolescence is enough suffering for anyone."

—JOHN CIARDI

"In science one tries to tell people, in such a way as to be understood by everyone, something that no one ever knew before. But in poetry, it's the exact opposite."

—PAUL DIRAC

"Poetry is man's rebellion against being what he is."

—JAMES BRANCH CABELL
(1879–1958)
an American fantasist and essayist, reached the height of his popularity in the 1920s.

"If Galileo had said in verse that the world moved, the Inquisition might have let him alone."

—THOMAS HARDY

"A poet's work is to name the unnameable, to point at frauds, to take sides, start arguments, shape the world, and stop it going to sleep."

—SALMAN RUSHDIE

"The poet doesn't invent. He listens."

—JEAN COCTEAU

"A poet is, before anything else, a person who is passionately in love with language."

—W. H. AUDEN

"All bad poetry springs from genuine feeling."

—OSCAR WILDE

"A poet's autobiography is his poetry. Anything else is just a footnote."

—YEVGENY YEVTUSHENKO (1933–)
was a Russian poet and novelist, often grouped with dissidents during the height of Soviet repression of artistic figures.

"A poet looks at the world the way a man looks at a woman."

—WALLACE STEVENS

"God is the perfect poet."

—ROBERT BROWNING

A nd how does a poet make poetry? Well, you can always ask. They're happy to tell you. And once you get some answers from them, such as the following, you can use them to impress others.

"Poetry is plucking at the heartstrings, and making music with them."

—DENNIS GABOR

"Poetry is the art of uniting pleasure with truth."

—SAMUEL JOHNSON

"Poetry is the rhythmical creation of beauty in words."

—EDGAR ALLAN POE

"A poem is never finished, only abandoned."

—PAUL VALÉRY (1871–1945)
was a French poet and essayist, was influential in the development of French belle letters prior to World War II.

"I was working on the proof of one of my poems all the morning and took out a comma. In the afternoon I put it back again."

—OSCAR WILDE

"Poetry is not a turning loose of emotion, but an escape from emotion; it is not the expression of personality, but an escape from personality. But, of course, only those who have personality and emotions know what it means to want to escape from these things."

—T. S. ELIOT

"Poetry: the best words in the best order."

—SAMUEL TAYLOR COLERIDGE

I hope that clarifies things. But no matter how a poem comes to light, the most important point about poetry—at least according to the poets—is that it is superior to prose, and thus poets occupied a rarified sphere at the apex of the literary pantheon. You can pay them appropriate homage by dropping one of the following gems.

"One merit of poetry few persons will deny: it says more and in fewer words than prose."

—VOLTAIRE (1694–1778) born François-Marie Arouet, is the chief representative of the French Enlightenment of the eighteenth century.

"Poetry is all that is worth remembering in life."

—WILLIAM HAZLITT

"It is the job of poetry to clean up our word-clogged reality by creating silences around things."

—STEPHEN MALLARMÉ

"Poetry is just the evidence of life. If your life is burning well, poetry is just the ash."

—LEONARD COHEN

"Poetry is a deal of joy and pain and wonder, with a dash of the dictionary."

—KAHLIL GIBRAN

"There's no money in poetry, but then there's no poetry in money, either."

—ROBERT GRAVES (1895–1985) is primarily known for his autobiography, *Goodbye to All That*, and for his novel *I, Claudius*.

"Out of the quarrel with others we make rhetoric; out of the quarrel with ourselves we make poetry."

—WILLIAM BUTLER YEATS

"There exist only three beings worthy of respect: the priest, the soldier, the poet. To know, to kill, to create."

—CHARLES BAUDELAIRE

In the event of a discussion of poetry becoming too exotic, always remember Oscar Wilde's wry observation.

"A poet can survive everything but a misprint."

—OSCAR WILDE

DRAMA

"Drama," said the playwright Eugene Ionesco, "lies in the extreme exaggeration of the feelings, an exaggeration that dislocates flat everyday reality." Well, he'd know. Ionesco was one of the creators of the Theater of the Absurd, which has had a profound impact on modern drama. And it certainly exaggerates the hell out of reality (if you don't believe me, watch a production of *Rhinoceros* sometime). If conversation turns to the state of theater in the modern world, drop a few quotes to show how sophisticated you are.

"Theater is, of course, a reflection of life. Maybe we have to improve life before we can hope to improve theater."

—W. R. INGE

"The theater is so endlessly fascinating because it's so accidental. It's so much like life."

—ARTHUR MILLER (1915–2005) was one of the preeminent American dramatists of the latter half of the twentieth century, with such masterpieces as *Death of a Salesman.*

"No theater could sanely flourish until there was an umbilical connection between what was happening on the stage and what was happening in the world."

—KENNETH TYNAN

"There are lots of young vital playwrights who are experimenting, and these are the plays that people who are interested in the theatre should see. They should go off Broadway. They should go to the cafe theatres and see the experiments that are being made."

—EDWARD ALBEE

"I think theater ought to be theatrical . . . you know, shuffling the pack in different ways so that it's—there's always some kind of ambush involved in the experience. You're being ambushed by an unexpected word, or by an elephant falling out of the cupboard, whatever it is."

—TOM STOPPARD

"The perfection in theater is that it's over the second it's done."

—WILLIAM HURT

"Thank God for the theater."

—RAUL JULIA

The theater is one of those things like God, art, or the Republican Party that intellectuals are always declaring dead. Despite this, every season, the theater gets out of its grave and walks down 42nd Street in New York. Still, if you want to appear hip and cool, quote something like these.

"I'm the end of the line; absurd and appalling as it may seem, serious New York theater has died in my lifetime."

—ARTHUR MILLER

"Theater people are always pining and agonizing because they're afraid that they'll be forgotten. And in America they're quite right. They will be."

—AGNES DE MILLE

"I think theater is powerful. The best experiences I had in the theater are more powerful than the best experiences I had in the movies."

—WILLIAM H. MACY

"The theater is the only branch of art much cared for by people of wealth; like canasta, it does away with the bother of talk after dinner."

—MARY MCCARTHY (1912–1989)
critic and essayist, was deeply involved in the political left during and after World War II.

The biggest challenge to live theater is that it's, well, live. It's played in front of an audience who are impudent enough to have opinions about what they're watching. Just as it would be easier to publish books if they didn't have to be written by authors, so many actors and directors feel that if we could abolish audiences, drama would flourish. Show them you agree and are no mere spectator by quoting from the following.

"I write for an audience that likes what I like, reads what I read, thinks about the things I think about. In many ways, this puts me in opposition to the people who go to the theater generally."
—ERIC BOGOSIAN

"People wear shorts to the Broadway theater. There should be a law against that."
—STANLEY TUCCI

"You need three things in the theater—the play, the actors, and the audience—and each must give something."

—KENNETH HAIGH (1931–)
British actor, has been widely praised for his performance in John Osborne's play *Look Back in Anger* in 1956.

"It is a hopeless endeavour to attract people to a theatre unless they can be first brought to believe that they will never get in."

—CHARLES DICKENS

"If you really want to help the American theater, don't be an actress, dahling. Be an audience."

—TALLULAH BANKHEAD

"One of the things I love about theater, one of the reasons I'll never give it up, is that it's fifty percent the audience's responsibility."

—WILLIAM PETERSEN

"In theater, the wellspring of the character comes from the doing of it, like a trial by fire, but in front of an audience."

—ESTELLE PARSONS (1927–)
acted both on Broadway and in film and won an Oscar for a supporting role in *Bonnie and Clyde*.

"I made mistakes in drama. I thought drama was when the actors cried. But drama is when the audience cries."

—FRANK CAPRA

"As long as more people will pay admission to a theater to see a naked body than to see a naked brain, the drama will languish."

—GEORGE BERNARD SHAW

"The adrenaline of a live performance is unlike anything in film or theater. I can see why it's so addictive."

—GWYNETH PALTROW

S till, it can't be denied that Gwyneth Paltrow is right: there's something addictive about live theater. It brings together writing, acting, emotion, and immediacy. Sometimes it conveys a profound intellectual experience; other times it's just fun.

"When you come into the theater, you have to be willing to say, 'We're all here to undergo a communion, to find out what the hell is going on in this world.' If you're not willing to say that, what you get is entertainment instead of art, and poor entertainment at that."

—DAVID MAMET (1947–)
is a prominent American playwright whose plays include the award-winning *Glengarry Glen Ross* and *Speed-the-Plow*.

"A theatre, a literature, an artistic expression that does not speak for its own time has no relevance."

—DARIO FO

"From the start it has been the theater's business to entertain people . . . it needs no other passport than fun."

—BERTOLT BRECHT

"I want to give the audience a hint of a scene. No more than that. Give them too much and they won't contribute anything themselves. Give them just a suggestion and you get them working with you. That's what gives the theater meaning: when it becomes a social act."

—ORSON WELLES

"What people really want in the theater is fantasy involvement and not reality involvement."

—EDWARD ALBEE (1928–)
is best known for his plays
Who's Afraid of Virginia Woolf,
The Zoo Story, and *A Delicate Balance.*

"The drama may be called that part of theatrical art which lends itself most readily to intellectual discussion; what is left is theater."

—ROBERTSON DAVIES

"I think the cinema you like has more to do with silence, and the theater you like has more to do with language."

—BEN KINGSLEY

"God comes to us in theater in the way we communicate with each other, whether it be a symphony orchestra, or a wonderful ballet, or a beautiful painting, or a play. It's a way of expressing our humanity."

—JULIE HARRIS

"It's hard enough to write a good drama, it's much harder to write a good comedy, and it's hardest of all to write a drama with comedy. Which is what life is."

—JACK LEMMON

"Failure in the theater is more dramatic and uglier than any other form of writing. It costs so much, you feel so guilty."

—LILLIAN HELLMAN
(1905–1984)
wrote such plays as *The Children's Hour* and
The Little Foxes.

"A talent for drama is not a talent for writing but is an ability to articulate human relationships."

—GORE VIDAL

"The atmosphere of the theater is my oxygen."

—PLÁCIDO DOMINGO

LANGUAGE

Language is the meat and drink of intellectuals. They are—rightly—fascinated by its endless permutations and its amazing ability to convey thoughts over the span of thousands of years and tens of thousands of miles. Language holds the power of beauty, of anger, of inspiration, of hatred, and of knowledge. There's no better entry into the world of intellect than through the careful use of and appreciation for language.

"Language is the armory of the human mind, and at once contains the trophies of its past and the weapons of its future conquests."

—SAMUEL TAYLOR COLERIDGE

"Language is the soul of intellect, and reading is the essential process by which that intellect is cultivated beyond the commonplace experiences of everyday life."

—CHARLES SCRIBNER
(1854–1930)
joined his father's publishing firm after leaving college and continued to build it, making it one of the chief publishing houses in America.

"Language is the archives of history."

—RALPH WALDO EMERSON

"Language is not an abstract construction of the learned or of dictionary markers but is something arising out of the work, needs, ties, joys, affections, tastes, of long generations of humanity."

—NOAH WEBSTER

"Language is a cracked kettle on which we beat out tunes for bears to dance to, while all the time we long to move the stars to pity."

—GUSTAVE FLAUBERT

"Language is the light of the mind."

—JOHN STUART MILL

"Language is the dress of thought."

—SAMUEL JOHNSON
(1709–1784)
was an English author and lexicographer, known for his compilation of the first major English-language dictionary.

"The tongue is but three inches long yet it can kill a man six feet high."

—JAPANESE PROVERB

"I personally think we developed language because of our deep need to complain."

—LILY TOMLIN

"Language is a skin: I rub my language against the other. It is as if I had words instead of fingers, or fingers at the tip of my words. My language trembles with desire."

—ROLAND BARTHES

"Language is a virus from outer space."

—WILLIAM S. BURROUGHS
(1914–1997)
was a voice of the Beat Generation of writers and poets in the late 1950s and early 1960s, along with Ken Kesey and Jack Kerouac.

"Language is wine upon the lips."

—VIRGINIA WOOLF

P art of the fasci-
nation with lan-
guage is that there
are so many of them,
and that they differ
so widely from one
another. The ideal
intellectual speaks at
least five languages and
has a certain measure
of contempt for any-
one speaking fewer. If
you don't speak that
many—or any—you
can at least let drop
these pearls of wisdom.

"Those who know nothing of foreign languages know nothing of
their own."

—JOHANN WOLFGANG VON
GOETHE

"It is difficult for a woman to
define her feelings in a language
which is chiefly made by men to
express theirs."

—THOMAS HARDY

"The only language men ever
speak perfectly is the one they
learn in babyhood when no one
can teach them anything."

—MARIA MONTESSORI

"We are tied down to a language
which makes up in obscurity
what it lacks in style."

—TOM STOPPARD (1937–)
is the author of such plays as
Rosencrantz and Guildenstern Are Dead,
The Coast of Utopia, and *Arcadia*.

"Language is the tool of my trade,
and I use them all—all the Eng-
lishes I grew up with."

—AMY TAN

"That woman
speaks eight
languages
and can't say
no in any of
them."

—DOROTHY PARKER

"Americans who travel abroad for the first time are often shocked to discover that, despite all the progress that has been made in the last thirty years, many foreign people still speak in foreign languages."

—DAVE BARRY

"I am very sorry, but I cannot learn languages. I have tried hard, only to find that men of ordinary capacity can learn Sanskrit in less time than it takes me to buy a German dictionary."

—GEORGE BERNARD SHAW

"The quantity of consonants in the English language is constant. If omitted in one place, they turn up in another. When a Bostonian 'pahks' his 'cah,' the lost r's migrate southwest, causing a Texan to 'warsh' his car and invest in 'erl wells.'"

—ANONYMOUS

"In general, every country has the language it deserves."

—JORGE LUIS BORGES
(1899–1996)
one of the most influential writers of the latter half of the twentieth century, was an Argentinian essayist and poet.

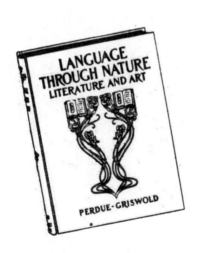

It may not be possible for you to learn a variety of other languages, but pretty much everyone knows slang—which sometimes seems another language, especially to anyone over the age of fifty. Opinion on slang is divided. America has no institution such as the French Academy to man our linguistic ramparts, repelling new words. That's probably just as well, but with the onset of Textish (the peculiar shorthand associated with text messaging), one can't help feeling we've gone too far. Here are some thoughts that you can share on the subject of slang, profanity, and the misuse of language.

"It's a strange world of language in which skating on thin ice can get you into hot water."

—FRANKLIN P. JONES

"Slang is a language that rolls up its sleeves, spits on its hands, and goes to work."

—CARL SANDBURG

"Ours is a precarious language, as every writer knows, in which the merest shadow line often separates affirmation from negation, sense from nonsense, and one sex from the other."

—JAMES THURBER (1894–1961) was a major figure in American humor of the twentieth century, through his short stories and drawings.

"In certain trying circumstances, urgent circumstances, desperate circumstances, profanity furnishes a relief denied even to prayer."

—MARK TWAIN

"Swearing was invented as a compromise between running away and fighting."

—PETER FINLEY DUNNE

"By such innovations are languages enriched, when the words are adopted by the multitude and naturalized by custom."

—MIGUEL DE CERVANTES

"Man does not live by words alone, despite the fact that sometimes he has to eat them."

—ADLAI E. STEVENSON

"England and America are two countries separated by the same language."

—GEORGE BERNARD SHAW

"But if thought corrupts language, language can also corrupt thought."

—GEORGE ORWELL (1903–1950) was the pen name of Eric Blair, a novelist and critic, famous today for his novels *Animal Farm* and the dystopic *1984*.

"As societies grow decadent, the language grows decadent, too. Words are used to disguise, not to illuminate, action: you liberate a city by destroying it. Words are to confuse, so that at election time people will solemnly vote against their own interests."

—GORE VIDAL

"The great enemy of clear language is insincerity. When there is a gap between one's real and one's declared aims, one turns, as it were, instinctively to long words and exhausted idioms, like a cuttlefish squirting out ink."

—GEORGE ORWELL

"If names are not correct, language will not be in accordance with the truth of things."

—CONFUCIUS

Language remains our most basic means of communication, and one has to say that, after evolving for millions of years, it's doing pretty well. At least, no one's come up with anything better. And intellectuals have excelled in pushing it to the limits. You can show your sophistication and your appreciation of their efforts by effortlessly dropping one of the following into a pregnant pause at dinner.

"I've always loved the flirtatious tango of consonants and vowels, the sturdy dependability of nouns and capricious whimsy of verbs, the strutting pageantry of the adjective and the flitting evanescence of the adverb, all kept safe and orderly by those reliable little policemen, punctuation marks. Wow! Think I got my ass kicked in high school?"

—DENNIS MILLER

"Dictionaries are like watches; the worst is better than none, and the best cannot be expected to go quite true."

—SAMUEL JOHNSON

"A definition is the enclosing a wilderness of idea within a wall of words."

—SAMUEL BUTLER (1835–1902) was a Victorian novelist, known for his works *The Way of All Flesh* and *Erewhon* (a syllabic reverse spelling of "nowhere").

"The finest language is mostly made up of simple unimposing words."

—GEORGE ELIOT

"Language is the most imperfect and expensive means yet discovered for communicating thought."

—WILLIAM JAMES

PART III
MUSIC

"Without music,

life would be a mistake."

—FRIEDRICH NIETZSCHE

CLASSICAL MUSIC AND COMPOSERS

"If music be the food of love, play on!" says Duke Orsino in William Shake-speare's *Twelfth Night*. And what indeed would life be without music? For intellectuals, music should be approached cerebrally as well as emotion-ally and never confused with popular tunes. Dan Rather put it nicely: "An intellectual snob is someone who can listen to the *William Tell Overture* and not think of the Lone Ranger." The best musicians, therefore, are dead ones, who can't argue back against the interpretation of their works by critics. Classical music fits the bill very well for this sort of thing, with its pantheon of composers safely underground. If you want to quote musi-cians or about musicians—and you certainly should, since it shows you to be a person of taste and erudition—try one of these.

"If I should ever die, God forbid, let this be my epitaph:

The only proof he needed

For the existence of God

Was music."

—KURT VONNEGUT

"After silence, that which comes nearest to expressing the inex-pressible is music."

—ALDOUS HUXLEY

"Music expresses that which can-not be put into words and that which cannot remain silent."

—VICTOR HUGO (1802–1885)
author of *Les Misérables*, became to many Frenchmen the embodiment of liberalism in the mid-nineteenth century.

"Music gives soul to the universe

Wings to the mind

Flight to the imagination

And life to everything"

—PLATO

"Music is the art of thinking with sounds."

—JULES COMBARIEU

"I think I should have no other mortal wants, if I could always have plenty of music. It seems to infuse strength into my limbs, and ideas into my brain. Life seems to go on without effort, when I am filled with music."

—George Eliot

"Music is a discipline and a mistress of order and good manners. She makes the people milder and gentler, more moral and more reasonable."

—Martin Luther

"There's music in the sighing of a reed

There's music in the gushing of a rill

There's music in all things, if men had ears

Their earth is but an echo of the spheres."

—Lord Byron (1788–1824)
was a poet who commanded a rock-star following in nineteenth-century Europe with such poems as "Don Juan."

"Take a music bath once or twice a week for a few seasons, and you will find that it is to the soul what the water bath is to the body."

—Oliver Wendell Holmes

It's true that some have taken a somewhat less elevated view of music and of musical instruments. The bagpipes in particular come in for some nasty hits for some reason. And some people's souls just aren't touched by beautiful harmonies.

"Music makes one feel so romantic. At least it always gets on one's nerves, which is the same thing nowadays."

—Oscar Wilde

"There are some experiences in life which should not be demanded twice from any man, and one of them is listening to the Brahms Requiem."

—George Bernard Shaw
(1856–1950)
a playwright, known for his biting satire as well as for his fierce convictions and for his vegetarianism, wrote *Pygmalion*.

"Anything that is too stupid to be spoken is sung."

—Voltaire

"Musical people always want one to be perfectly dumb at the very moment when one is longing to be perfectly deaf."

—OSCAR WILDE

"I don't know anything about music. In my line, you don't have to."

—ELVIS PRESLEY

"The Irish gave the bagpipes to the Scots as a joke. Unfortunately, the Scots haven't seen the joke yet."

—OLIVER HERFORD

"Give the piper a penny to play and two pence to leave."

—ENGLISH PROVERB

"I understand the inventor of the bagpipes was inspired when he saw a man carrying an indignant, asthmatic pig under his arm. Unfortunately, the manmade sound never equaled the purity of the sound achieved by the pig."

—ALFRED HITCHCOCK

Before the magnificent array of great composers—Brahms, Beethoven, Bach, Handel, Mozart—intellectuals stand in awe. However, musicians themselves are notoriously insecure. Remember that it's all right to quote something nice about a composer to another musician—but only if the person you're quoting is dead.

"[Bach is] the immortal god of harmony."

—LUDWIG VAN BEETHOVEN
(1770–1827)
the pre-eminent composer of the early nineteenth century and was a major figure in the musical Romantic movement.

"Everything will pass, and the world will perish but the Ninth Symphony will remain."

—MIKHAIL BAKUNIN

"After playing Chopin, I feel as if I had been weeping over sins that I had never committed, and mourning over tragedies that were not my own."

—OSCAR WILDE

"Handel is so great and so simple that no one but a professional musician is unable to understand him."

—SAMUEL BUTLER

"Handel was the Jupiter of music . . . his hallelujahs open the heavens. He utters the word 'Wonderful' as if all their trumpets spoke together. And then, when he comes to earth, to make love admidst nymphs and shepherds (for the beauties of all religions find room within his breast), his strains drip milk and honey, and his love is the youthfulness of the Golden Age."

—LEIGH HUNT

"O Mozart, immortal Mozart, how many, how infinitely many inspiring suggestions of a finer, better life have you left in our souls!"

—FRANZ SCHUBERT
(1797–1828)
Austrian composer, wrote a number of *lieder* (songs) and nine symphonies.

"Mozart should have composed *Faust*."

—JOHANN WOLFGANG VON
GOETHE

"Bach almost persuades me to be a Christian."

—ROGER FRY

"You play Bach your way and I'll play him his way."

—WANDA LANDOWSKA

"[Beethoven] reminds me of a man driving the car with the handbrake on, but stubbornly refusing to stop, even though there is a strong smell of burning rubber."

—COLIN WILSON

"[Mozart] roused my admiration when I was young; he caused me to despair when I reached maturity; he is now the comfort of my old age."

—GIOACHINO ROSSINI
(1792–1868)
composed primarily operatic music, including, most famously, *The Barber of Seville*.

"Mozart is sunshine."

—ANTONIN DVORÁK

"I'm a revolutionary, money means nothing to me."

—FRÉDÉRIC CHOPIN
(1810–1849)
composed numerous symphonies and shorter pieces, mostly in the Romantic style then prevalent in Europe.

"I shall seize Fate by the throat; it shall certainly not bend and crush me completely.

—Ludwig van Beethoven

Mozart began composing when he was five years old and wrote his first symphony when he was seven. He can therefore serve as a useful reminder of the mediocrity of our own accomplishments. If you know someone who's getting above themselves, bring them down to Earth by saying:

"It is a sobering thought that when Mozart was my age he had been dead for three years."
—Tom Lehrer

Opera

Opera might have been specially made for appreciation by intellectuals and the snobbishly elite. It's certainly beyond the comprehension of most ordinary people, since in its essence it consists of people singing about a story that no one in the audience cares about in a language that none of the onlookers understand. For this reason, people love to put on formal-wear and attend the opera, sipping champagne between acts and comparing this year's soprano in *Lucia del Lammermore* with the singer they saw two years ago at La Scala in Rome.

"At these concerts," George Bernard Shaw famously observed, "you will find rows of weary people who are there not because they really like classical music, but because they think they ought to like it." Despite the fact that no one understands the opera, (and that most don't like it) everyone still loves to talk about it. Join the conversation with the following quotes:

"Grand opera is the most powerful of stage appeals, and that almost entirely through the beauty of music."

—JOHN PHILIP SOUSA

"An opera begins long before the curtain goes up and ends long after it has come down. It starts in my imagination, it becomes my life, and it stays part of my life long after I've left the opera house."

—MARIA CALLAS (1923–1977) was among the most acclaimed opera singers of the past century. She was also, as *Opera News* puts it, "the definition of the diva as artist."

"I have always believed that opera is a planet where the muses work together, join hands and celebrate all the arts."

—FRANCO ZEFFIRELLI

"Staid middle age loves the hurricane passions of opera."

—MASON COOLEY

"Any subject is good for opera if the composer feels it so intently he must sing it out."

—GIAN CARLO MENOTTI

"Because, in opera, I have to sing for people that are very far from me, instead of when I sing a song, I try to imagine to sing like in an ear of a child."

—ANDREA BOCELLI (1958–)
has tried to turn opera music into a popular art form, recording music with such stars as Sarah Brightman and Celine Dion.

"But nevertheless, it's music ultimately that matters in opera, and opera is a piece of music reaching out as a vision in sound reaching out to the world."

—JOHN EATON

"I would just like to say that opera is no longer about fat people in breastplates shattering wine glasses."

—LESLEY GARRETT

All that said, a surprisingly large number of people have found bitter things to say about the opera. It's curious, really, because not many people have actually attended an operatic performance, and even fewer seem inclined to give the experience a try. If you want to find something a bit more pointed to say about opera than "Turn off that damn screaming," try one of the following.

"Going to the opera, like getting drunk, is a sin that carries its own punishment with it."

—HANNAH MORE

"I don't mind what language an opera is sung in so long as it is a language I don't understand."

—EDWARD APPLETON

"No good opera plot can be sensible, for people do not sing when they are feeling sensible."

—W. H. AUDEN

"In opera, there is always too much singing."

—CLAUDE DEBUSSY (1862–1918) was a composer whose works are widely associated with the Impressionist school of music.

"I don't think an opera house is ever a place that can make you entirely happy."

—BERNARD HAITINK

"Of all the noises known to man, opera is the most expensive."

—MOLIÈRE

"Opera happens because a large number of things amazingly fail to go wrong."

—TERRY PRATCHETT

"Opera in English is, in the main, just about as sensible as baseball in Italian."

—H. L. MENCKEN

"Opera, next to Gothic architecture, is one of the strangest inventions of Western man. It could not have been foreseen by any logical process."

—KENNETH CLARK

"Opera? Just what the world needs: more fat women screaming."

—PETER BOYLE

"People are wrong when they say opera is not what it used to be. It is what it used to be. That is what's wrong with it."

—NOEL COWARD (1899–1973) playwright, composer, and wit, was known for his light banter and charm, on display in his comic play *Private Lives*.

"The taxpayers cannot be relied upon to support performing arts such as opera. As a taxpayer, I am forced to admit that I would rather undergo a vasectomy via Weed Whacker than attend an opera."

—DAVE BARRY

"I wouldn't mind seeing opera die. Ever since I was a boy, I regarded opera as a ponderous anachronism, almost the equivalent of smoking."

—FRANK LLOYD WRIGHT

"Sleep is an excellent way of listening to an opera."

—JAMES STEPHENS

"The opera is like a husband with a foreign title, expensive to support, hard to understand, and therefore a supreme social challenge."

—CLEVELAND AMORY

"When an opera star sings her head off, she usually improves her appearance."

—VICTOR BORGE (1909–2000) was an accomplished pianist who turned his talents to comedy, making classical music both accessible and hilarious.

"Opera is where a guy gets stabbed in the back, and instead of dying, he sings."

—ROBERT BENCHLEY

Of all operatic words, those of Richard Wagner are probably the most widely known and the most extensively excoriated. This isn't too surprising, of course. Wagner was a notorious anti-Semite, much beloved by Adolph Hitler and the Nazis. His music is ponderous, and his masterpiece, *The Ring Cycle*, takes a week to perform. Indeed, for most Americans the name Wagner probably means Elmer Fudd singing "Kill the wabbit! Kill the wabbit! Kill the wabbit!" When the subject of Wagner's music comes up, you can hold your own with these comments.

"One can't judge Wagner's opera *Lohengrin* after a first hearing, and I certainly don't intend to hear it a second time."

—GIOACHINO ROSSINI

"I have witnessed and greatly enjoyed the first act of everything which Wagner created, but the effect on me has always been so powerful that one act was quite sufficient; whenever I have witnessed two acts I have gone away physically exhausted; and whenever I have ventured an entire opera the result has been the next thing to suicide."

—MARK TWAIN

"Is Wagner a human being at all? Is he not rather a disease? He contaminates everything he touches—he has made music sick."

—FRIEDRICH NIETZSCHE
(1844–1900)
a nineteenth-century philosopher, wrote about subjects such as the decline of religion and the rise of power.

"Wagner has lovely moments but awful quarters of an hour."

—GIOACHINO ROSSINI

"I have been told that Wagner's music is better than it sounds."

—MARK TWAIN

PART IV

SCIENCE

"If it's green or wriggles, it's biology.

If it stinks, it's chemistry.

If it doesn't work, it's physics."

—*Handy Guide to Science*

General Science

The sciences seem to have been in competition for quite some time to see which one is the scariest. Before 1945, chemistry was frightening because it was chemists who developed gas warfare in World War I and World War II. Then the atomic bomb was dropped on Hiroshima and Nagasaki, and the physicists became science's boogymen. Not only did they invent really powerful bombs, but as we learned from our local movie theaters, they created atomic radiation, which did things like revive corpses and turn them into zombies and mutate spiders into giant killing machines that destroyed Cleveland.

Nowadays, physics is still pretty nerve-wracking (so is Cleveland!). But before we turn to it, here are some general thoughts about science—its promises and limitations.

"Equipped with his five senses, man explores the universe around him and calls the adventure Science."

—EDWIN POWELL HUBBLE

"Science is the great antidote to the poison of enthusiasm and superstition."

—ADAM SMITH

"Science does not know its debt to imagination."

—RALPH WALDO EMERSON

"There is something fascinating about science. One gets such wholesale returns of conjecture out of such a trifling investment of fact."

—MARK TWAIN

"The important thing in science is not so much to obtain new facts as to discover new ways of thinking about them."

—WILLIAM LAWRENCE BRAGG
(1890–1971)

was the director of the prestigious Cavendish Laboratory at Cambridge University.

"Science has made us gods even before we are worthy of being men."

—JEAN ROSTAND

"The saddest aspect of life right now is that science gathers knowledge faster than society gathers wisdom."

—ISAAC ASIMOV

"Science is simply common sense at its best."

—THOMAS HUXLEY (1825–1895)
a popularizer of Victorian science, was sometimes called "Darwin's bulldog" because of his fierce defense of the theory of evolution.

Science builds off theories and hypotheses, and, despite the cautions of others, scientists tend to become attached to theories. If you feel a scientist is becoming a bit dogmatic, you can always tell her something along the following lines.

"A fact is a simple statement that everyone believes. It is innocent, unless found guilty. A hypothesis is a novel suggestion that no one wants to believe. It is guilty, until found effective."

—EDWARD TELLER

"Great scientific discoveries have been made by men seeking to verify quite erroneous theories about the nature of things."

—ALDOUS HUXLEY

"The doubter is a true man of science; he doubts only himself and his interpretations, but he believes in science."

—CLAUDE BERNARD

"I have had my results for a long time, but I do not yet know how I am to arrive at them."

—KARL FRIEDRICH GAUSS (1777–1855)
was a mathematician who contributed to numbers theory, statistics, and differential geometry, among other fields.

"Theory helps us bear our ignorance of facts."

—GEORGE SANTAYANA

"For every fact there is an infinity of hypotheses."

—ROBERT M. PIRSIG

"Science commits suicide when it adopts a creed."

—THOMAS HENRY HUXLEY

"In all science, error precedes the truth, and it is better it should go first than last."

—HUGH WALPOLE

Physics

Physics is among the most intimidating of the sciences because it seems to deal with the very big—the way the universe works—on a macro scale. Fortunately, at least some scientists have tried to keep all this in perspective. It's hard to do this when they have to constantly remind the uninitiated that there are a billion stars in a galaxy and billions upon billions of galaxies in the know universe (not to mention the possibility of an infinity of universes—a statement that causes many listeners' eyes to briefly roll up into their heads before they stagger over to the bar and order another double Scotch). You can hold your own with physicists with something along the following lines:

"In science it often happens that scientists say, 'You know that's a really good argument; my position is mistaken,' and then they actually change their minds and you never hear that old view from them again. They really do it. It doesn't happen as often as it should, because scientists are human and change is sometimes painful. But it happens every day. I cannot recall the last time something like that happened in politics or religion."

—CARL SAGAN (1934–1996)
became known to millions of Americans through his award-winning miniseries *Cosmos*.

"Physics isn't a religion. If it were, we'd have a much easier time raising money."

—LEON LEDERMAN

"It should be possible to explain the laws of physics to a barmaid."

—ALBERT EINSTEIN
(1879–1955)
among the most important scientists who ever lived, revolutionized modern physics with his theories of special and general relativity.

"Physics is, hopefully, simple. Physicists are not."

—Edward Teller

"In physics your solution should convince a reasonable person . . . . Ultimately in physics you're hoping to convince Nature. And I've found Nature to be pretty reasonable."

—Frank Wilczek

"All of my life I have been fascinated by the big questions that face us and have tried to find scientific answers to them. Perhaps that is why I have sold more books on physics than Madonna has on sex."

—Stephen Hawking (1942–)
has been hailed as the most important physicist since Einstein.

All of this helps to place physics at the center of science. When talking to physicists, feel free to toss out something inspirational and uplifting, always remembering that physics started with the ancient Greeks.

"Give me a level long enough and a fulcrum on which to place it, and I shall move the world."

—Archimedes

"Not only is the universe stranger than we imagine, it is stranger than we can imagine."

—Sir Arthur Eddington

"The effort to understand the universe is one of the very few things that lifts human life a little above the level of farce and gives it some of the grace of tragedy."

—Steven Weinberg

"Magnetism, you recall from physics class, is a powerful force that causes certain items to be attracted to refrigerators."

—Dave Barry

"Physics is mathematical not because we know so much about the physical world, but because we know so little; it is only its mathematical properties that we can discover."

—BERTRAND RUSSELL
(1872–1970)
descended from an aristocratic and politically influential English family, became a mathematician and philosopher.

"In physics, you don't have to go around making trouble for yourself, nature does it for you."

—FRANK WILCZEK

"Physics is geometric proof on steroids."

—S. A. SACHS

"It would be a poor thing to be an atom in a universe without physicists, and physicists are made of atoms. A physicist is an atom's way of knowing about atoms."

—GEORGE WALD

"The whole history of physics proves that a new discovery is quite likely lurking at the next decimal place."

—F. K. RICHTMEYER

.

"The radical novelty of modern science lies precisely in the rejection of the belief, which is at the heart of all popular religion, that the forces which move the stars and atoms are contingent upon the preferences of the human heart."

—WALTER LIPPMANN
(1889–1974)
was an American journalist and commentator who had an immense political and social influence through his syndicated newspaper column.

"Physics is imagination in a straight jacket."

—JOHN MOFFAT

"The most exciting phrase to hear in science, the one that heralds the most discoveries, is not 'Eureka!' (I found it!) but 'That's funny . . . .'"

—ISAAC ASIMOV

BIOLOGY

For many years, biology was the unassuming wallflower sister of physics, patiently waiting in the wings, hoping that someone would ask her to dance. Charles Darwin ended that in 1858 when he published his book on the theory of natural selection in 1858. From that point on, biology has been a keen participant in scientific debate, provoking controversy that exploded in America in the Scopes trial of 1926 over whether Darwin's theory should be taught in high schools. More recently this argument has been reframed in the controversy over the teaching of "intelligent design."

Here are some thoughts to toss out if the discussion around your dinner table turns to the biological sciences.

"What can be more curious than that the hand of a man, formed for grasping, that of a mole for digging, the leg of a horse, the paddle of a porpoise, and the wing of a bat should all be constructed on the same pattern and should include similar bones, and in the same relative positions?"

—CHARLES DARWIN
(1809–1882)
was the originator (along with Alfred Russell Wallace) of the theory of evolution by natural selection.

"Biology is the science. Evolution is the concept that makes biology unique."

—JARED DIAMOND

"The essence of life is statistical improbability on a colossal scale."

—RICHARD DAWKINS

"Imagination reaches out repeatedly trying to achieve some higher level of understanding, until suddenly I find myself momentarily alone before one new corner of nature's pattern of beauty and true majesty revealed."

—RICHARD P. FEYNMAN

"To produce a really good biological theory one must try to see through the clutter produced by evolution to the basic mechanisms lying beneath them . . . ."

—FRANCIS CRICK (1916–2004)
together with James D. Watson, discovered the structure of the DNA molecule in 1953.

"Culture is how biology responds and makes its living conditions better."

—C. J. CHERRYH

"The fact of evolution is the backbone of biology, and biology is thus in the peculiar position of being a science founded on an improved theory."

—CHARLES DARWIN

"The capacity to blunder slightly is the real marvel of DNA. Without this special attribute, we would still be anaerobic bacteria and there would be no music."

—LEWIS THOMAS

"Nothing in biology makes sense except in the light of evolution."

—THEODOSIUS DOBZHANSKY

"[Natural selection] has no vision, no foresight, no sight at all. If it can be said to play the role of a watchmaker in nature, it is the blind watchmaker."

—RICHARD DAWKINS

"Creationist critics often charge that evolution cannot be tested and therefore cannot be viewed as a properly scientific subject at all. This claim is rhetorical nonsense."

—STEPHEN JAY GOULD

"The fundamentalists deny that evolution has taken place; they deny that the earth and the universe as a whole are more than a few thousand years old, and so on. There is ample scientific evidence that the fundamentalists are wrong in these matters, and that their notions of cosmogony have about as much basis in fact as the Tooth Fairy has."

—ISAAC ASIMOV (1920–1992)
wrote or edited some 500 books, including annotations of Byron and the Bible and the science fiction classic *Foundation* trilogy.

"Science has proof without any certainty. Creationists have certainty without any proof."

—ASHLEY MONTAGU

"Today, the theory of evolution is an accepted fact for everyone but a fundamentalist minority, whose objections are based not on reasoning but on doctrinaire adherence to religious principles."

—JAMES D. WATSON

"Evolution is not a force but a process. Not a cause but a law."

—JOHN MORLEY

"Today the theory of evolution is about as much open to doubt as the theory that the earth goes round the sun."

—RICHARD DAWKINS

"The proof of evolution lies in those adaptations that arise from improbable foundations."

—STEPHEN JAY GOULD
(1941–2002)
was an evolutionary biologist, best known for his theory of "punctuated equilibrium," a refinement of Darwin's theory.

"All the ills from which America suffers can be traced to the teaching of evolution."

—WILLIAM JENNINGS BRYAN

"A curious aspect of the theory of evolution is that everybody thinks he understands it."

—JACQUES MONOD

"Biology has at least fifty more interesting years."

—JAMES D. WATSON

MATHEMATICS

Math is a subject in which a person does either very well or very badly. Of all the subjects we study in elementary school and high school, it's probably the only one to give us anxiety attacks—apart from gym class. Perhaps the most perceptive comment was made by the German philosopher and poet Johann von Goethe (who was, himself, adept in mathematics), "Mathematicians are like Frenchman: Whatever you say to them, they translate it into their own language and forthwith it means something entire different." Or, as an anonymous commentator once observed, "Math is like love. A simple idea, but it can get complicated." Even if you failed basic geometry in high school, you can still hold your own by quoting from these words of wisdom:

"If people do not believe that mathematics is simple, it is only because they do not realize how complicated life is."

—JOHN LOUIS VON NEUMANN

"Mathematics are well and good but nature keeps dragging us around by the nose."

—ALBERT EINSTEIN

"I never did very well in math—I could never seem to persuade the teacher that I hadn't meant my answers literally."

—CALVIN TRILLIN (1935–)
served on the staff of the *New Yorker,* as well as writing for *The Nation*. His subjects have included politics, travel, and food.

"Arithmetic is where numbers fly like pigeons in and out of your head."

—CARL SANDBURG

"So if a man's wit be wandering, let him study the mathematics; for in demonstrations, if his wit be called away never so little, he must begin again."

—FRANCIS BACON

"The essence of mathematics is not to make simple things complicated, but to make complicated things simple."

—S. GUDDER

"Let us grant that the pursuit of mathematics is a divine madness of the human spirit, a refuge from the goading urgency of contingent happenings."
—ALFRED NORTH WHITEHEAD

"Music is the pleasure the human mind experiences from counting without being aware that it is counting."
—GOTTFRIED LEIBNIZ
(1646–1716)
is credited with the invention of the differential calculus at the same time as Isaac Newton, as well as other mathematical innovations.

"Anyone who cannot cope with mathematics is not fully human. At best he is a tolerable subhuman who has learned to wear shoes, bathe, and not make messes in the house."
—ROBERT HEINLEIN

"We could use up two Eternities in learning all that is to be learned about our own world and the thousands of nations that have arisen and flourished and vanished from it. Mathematics alone would occupy me eight million years."
—MARK TWAIN

"With my full philosophical rucksack I can only climb slowly up the mountain of mathematics."

—LUDWIG WITTGENSTEIN

Mathematics is one of the few sciences that keeps asking if its results mean anything. In a scintillating flight across the cloudless skies of the higher calculus, mathematicians are apt to lose themselves in the sheer aesthetic joy of their constructs, only to come to Earth later and start wondering if their equations have anything to do with reality. Should you come upon a mathematician sitting alone in a corner, white-knuckled hands wrapped tightly around a glass of campari and lemon juice, you can comfort her by quoting from the following:

"Mathematics is the supreme judge; from its decisions there is no appeal."

—TOBIAS DANTZIG

"The laws of nature are but the mathematical thoughts of God."

—EUCLID

"I used to love mathematics for its own sake, and I still do, because it allows for no hypocrisy and no vagueness . . . ."

—STENDHAL (1783–1842)
was the pen name of writer Marie-Henri Beyle, whose masterpiece is *The Red and the Black*.

"As far as the laws of mathematics refer to reality, they are not certain; and as far as they are certain, they do not refer to reality."

—ALBERT EINSTEIN

"I like mathematics because it is not human and has nothing particular to do with this planet or with the whole accidental universe— because like Spinoza's God, it won't love us in return."

—BERTRAND RUSSELL

"Pure mathematics is, in its way, the poetry of logical ideas."

—ALBERT EINSTEIN

"Mathematics is the only science where one never knows what one is talking about nor whether what is said is true."

—BERTRAND RUSSELL

"In mathematics, you don't understand things. You just get used to them."

—JOHANN VON NEUMANN

All in all, economics may be stuck with the title of the Dismal Science, but mathematics is a close runner-up. That is, unless you talk for a few minutes to mathematicians, who are perpetually fascinated by the transcendent beauty of differential calculus and the joys of prime integers. Even if you can't make head or tail of what they're talking about, you can always impress them—to say nothing of other non-mathematically gifted folk—with one of the following quotes:

"Mathematics is the queen of sciences, and arithmetic is the queen of mathematics."
—KARL FRIEDRICH GAUSS

"What would life be without arithmetic but a scene of horrors."
—SYDNEY SMITH

"God does not care about our mathematical difficulties; He integrates empirically."
—ALBERT EINSTEIN

"For the things of this world cannot be made known without a knowledge of mathematics."
—ROGER BACON (1214–1294)
English monk and philosopher, was one of the founders of Empiricism, which holds that the foundation of knowledge is experience.

"The union of the mathematician with the poet, fervor with measure, passion with correctness, this is surely the ideal."
—WILLIAM JAMES

"The mathematical sciences particularly exhibit order, symmetry, and limitation; and these are the greatest forms of the beautiful."
—ARISTOTLE

"Why do we believe that in all matters the odd numbers are more powerful?"

—PLINY THE ELDER

"Uneven numbers are the gods' delight."

—VIRGIL (70 BCE–19 BCE)
a Roman poet, exemplar of the Golden Age of classical Latin, was author of *The Aeneid*.

"One of the endlessly alluring aspects of mathematics is that its thorniest paradoxes have a way of blooming into beautiful theories."

—PHILIP J. DAVIS

"Pure mathematics is the world's best game. It is more absorbing than chess, more of a gamble than poker, and lasts longer than Monopoly. It's free. It can be played anywhere—Archimedes did it in a bathtub."

—RICHARD J. TRUDEAU

"Twice two makes four seems to me simply a piece of insolence. Twice two makes four is a pert coxcomb who stands with arms akimbo barring your path and spitting. I admit that twice two makes four is an excellent thing, but if we are to give everything its due, twice two makes five is sometimes a very charming thing too."

—FYODOR DOSTOEVSKY

"I don't believe in mathematics."

—ALBERT EINSTEIN

PART V

POLITICS, HISTORY, AND GOVERNMENT

"Man is by nature a political animal."

—ARISTOTLE

POLITICS AND GOVERNMENT

One January afternoon in the tumultuous and gloomy year of 1933, someone stepped into the dining room at the Algonquin Hotel in New York City and announced to those gathered around its famous Round Table, "Well, Calvin Coolidge is dead."

There was silence for a few moments, and then Dorothy Parker lifted her lovely dark eyes and soft, innocent face.

"How can you tell?" she asked.

Americans have always had a touch and go relationship with their politicians. Political complaint is one of the chief forms of American entertainment, and there's no sign of it losing its popularity. ("A statesman is a dead politician," opined cartoonist Berkley Breathed. "Lord knows, we need more statesmen!") After all, as we look at the array of political lunatics infesting Washington and the various state capitals, we can remind ourselves that it's always nice to have someone to feel superior to.

When dinner table talk turns to politics, throw out something like the following:

"A politician needs the ability to foretell what is going to happen tomorrow, next week, next month, and next year. And to have the ability afterwards to explain why it didn't happen."

—WINSTON CHURCHILL

"Too bad that all the people who really know how to run the country are busy driving taxi cabs and cutting hair."

—GEORGE BURNS

"I have come to the conclusion that politics are too serious a matter to be left to the politicians."

—Charles de Gaulle

"Nothing is so admirable in politics as a short memory."

—John Kenneth Galbraith
(1908–2006)
was leading figure in American Keynesian economics and an advisor to President John F. Kennedy.

"Politics is the art of the possible."

—Otto von Bismarck

"Politics is supposed to be the second-oldest profession. I have come to realize that it bears a very close resemblance to the first."

—Ronald Reagan

"A politician is a fellow who will lay down your life for his country."

—Texas Guinan

"A politician is a statesman who approaches every question with an open mouth."

—Adlai Stevenson

"Politics is the art of looking for trouble, finding it everywhere, diagnosing it incorrectly, and applying the wrong remedies.

—GROUCHO MARX (1890–1977) together with his brothers Harpo and Chico, created sparkling gems of American humor in films such as *Duck Soup* and *Night at the Opera*.

"Truthfulness has never been counted among the political virtues, and lies have always been regarded as justifiable tools in political dealings."

—HANNAH ARENDT

"Politics, n. A strife of interests masquerading as a contest of principles. The conduct of public affairs for private advantage."

—AMBROSE BIERCE

"Ninety-eight percent of the adults in this country are decent, hardworking, honest Americans. It's the other lousy two percent that get all the publicity. But then, we elected them."

—LILY TOMLIN (1939–) is a comedic actress with a long career behind her, both in the movies and on stage.

"When I entered politics, I took the only downward turn you could take from journalism."

—JIM HIGHTOWER

A big part of the problem with politics is that we keep electing politicians. And since the day that the first Neanderthal politician lumbered forth from his cave to offer his fellow cavemen extra pelts if they'd vote him in as Chief Mastodon Basher, politicians have been on the take. Should anyone lose sight of that—though it's hard to forget—remind them by quoting something like these:

"Wherefore being all of one mind, we do highly resolve that government of the grafted by the grafter for the grafter shall not perish from the earth."

—MARK TWAIN

"Politicians are the same all over. They promise to build a bridge even where there is no river."

—NIKITA KRUSHCHEV

"A politician is a man who will double cross that bridge when he comes to it."

—OSCAR LEVANT

"We hang the petty thieves and appoint the great ones to public office."

—AESOP (CA. 620 BCE–564 BCE) compiled a collection of fables, few of which he probably wrote.

"There is one safeguard known generally to the wise, which is an advantage and security to all, but especially to democracies as against despots. What is it? Distrust."

—DEMOSTHENES

"The work of the political activist inevitably involves a certain tension between the requirement that position be taken on current issues as they arise and the desire that one's contributions will somehow survive the ravages of time."

—ANGELA DAVIS

"Democracy means simply the bludgeoning of the people by the people for the people."

—OSCAR WILDE (1854–1900) was known for his flamboyant lifestyle as well as for his clever epigrams, satirizing the Victorian age.

I'm not saying that there isn't still some idealism left in the political arena. If you're afraid of being too cynical (although when it comes to politics, cynicism is the default mode of most intellectuals), try one of these quotes to soften the mood.

"Public sentiment is everything. With public sentiment nothing can fail; without it nothing can succeed. He who molds public sentiment goes deeper than he who enacts statutes or decisions possible or impossible to execute."

—ABRAHAM LINCOLN

"The true test of the American ideal is whether we're able to recognize our failings and then rise together to meet the challenges of our time. Whether we allow ourselves to be shaped by events and history, or whether we act to shape them."

—BARACK OBAMA

"Ideas are great arrows, but there has to be a bow. And politics is the bow of idealism."

—BILL MOYERS

"To put the world right in order, we must first put the nation in order; to put the nation in order, we must first put the family in order; to put the family in order, we must first cultivate our personal life; we must first set our hearts right."

—CONFUCIUS

"In politics, an organized minority is a political majority."

—JESSE JACKSON (1941–)
is an African-American activist.

"The sad duty of politics is to establish justice in a sinful world."

—JIMMY CARTER

"There are times in politics when you must be on the right side and lose."

—JOHN KENNETH GALBRAITH

"Political convulsions, like geological upheavings, usher in new epochs of the world's progress."
—WENDELL PHILLIPS

"The price of apathy towards public affairs is to be ruled by evil men."

—PLATO (428 BCE–348 BCE)
perhaps, the most influential philosopher who ever lived, founded the Academy.

It's during election season when politics is at its most depressing—or entertaining, depending on your viewpoint. If you want to show your interest in and detachment from the prevailing political winds, quote something along these lines:

"If God wanted us to vote, he would have given us candidates."
—JAY LENO

"Whenever a man has cast a longing eye on offices, a rottenness begins in his conduct."
—THOMAS JEFFERSON

"A politician should have three hats. One for throwing into the ring, one for talking through, and one for pulling rabbits out of if elected."
—CARL SANDBURG (1878–1967)
was a poet who attempted to distill the American spirit and experience in such poems as "Chicago."

"In war you can only be killed once, but in politics many times."
—WINSTON CHURCHILL

"Anyone that wants the presidency so much that he'll spend two years organizing and campaigning for it is not to be trusted with the office."

—DAVID BRODER

"An election is coming. Universal peace is declared, and the foxes have a sincere interest in prolonging the lives of the poultry."

—GEORGE ELIOT (1819–1880)
is the pseudonym of Mary Anne Evans, a novelist who wrote books such as *Middlemarch*.

"A national political campaign is better than the best circus ever heard of, with a mass baptism and a couple of hangings thrown in."

—H. L. MENCKEN

"Good thing we've still got politics in Texas—finest form of free entertainment ever invented."

—MOLLY IVINS

"In our brief national history we have shot four of our presidents, worried five of them to death, impeached one, and hounded another out of office. And when all else fails, we hold an election and assassinate their character."

—P. J. O'ROURKE

S ooner or later any political discussion, particularly one fueled by cocktails, is going to divide into a minimum of two camps: Democrats and Republicans. You can stand above the fray by throwing out observations about both parties.

"The Democrats are the party that says government will make you smarter, taller, richer, and remove the crabgrass on your lawn. The Republicans are the party that says government doesn't work and then they get elected and prove it."

—P. J. O'ROURKE (1947–)
is a humorist and journalist, distinguished by his libertarianism and economic conservatism.

"I recognize the Republican Party as the sheet anchor of the colored man's political hopes and the ark of his safety."

—FREDERICK DOUGLASS

"A conservative is one who admires radicals centuries after they're dead."

—LEO ROSTEN

"The Democrats seem to be basically nicer people, but they have demonstrated time and again that they have the management skills of celery. They're the kind of people who'd stop to help you change a flat, but would somehow manage to set your car on fire. I would be reluctant to entrust them with a Cuisinart, let alone the economy. The Republicans, on the other hand, would know how to fix your tire, but they wouldn't bother to stop because they'd want to be on time for Ugly Pants Night at the country club."

—DAVE BARRY

"Thinking about profound social change, conservatives always expect disaster, while revolutionaries confidentially expect utopia. Both are wrong."

—CAROLYN HEILBRUN
(1926–2003)
was a scholar and professor at New York University, as well as author of a series of mystery novels under the pseudonym Amanda Cross.

P olitics is an inevitable part of American life. It's also free entertainment, not to mention a determining factor in shaping the life of the nation for the future. Though it's most fun to indulge in politics around election time, it's a subject that's also been known at any time of the year to bring congenial dinner parties to crashing conclusions, as the room separates into liberals and conservatives (with libertarians exiled to the balcony by both sides). If you want to lighten the mood under such circumstances, try tossing out a quote or two.

"In our age there is no such thing as 'keeping out of politics.' All issues are political issues, and politics itself is a mass of lies, evasions, folly, hatred, and schizophrenia."

—GEORGE ORWELL

"You can't ignore politics, no matter how much you'd like to."

—MOLLY IVINS

WAR

"War," the German military theoretician Karl von Clauswitz observed, "is politics by other means." And while almost all politicians can be counted upon to denounce war, none seem to have found a method of preventing it. In fact, some have spent a lot of time figuring out how to present it in the most favorable light. The most naked statement of this was made by Adolph Hitler's comrade Hermann Goering:

"Naturally the common people don't want war; neither in Russia, nor in England, nor in America, nor in Germany. That is understood. But after all, it is the leaders of the country who determine policy, and it is always a simple matter to drag the people along, whether it is a democracy, or a fascist dictatorship, or a parliament, or a communist dictatorship. Voice or no voice, the people can always be brought to the bidding of the leaders. That is easy. All you have to do is to tell them they are being attacked, and denounce the pacifists for lack of patriotism and exposing the country to danger. It works the same in any country."

Contrary to Goering's pronouncement, the leaders of most other countries have vigorously denounced international conflict and, at least in some cases, done their best to prevent it.

"Every gun that is made, every warship launched, every rocket fired, signifies, in the final sense, a theft from those who hunger and are not fed, those who are cold and are not clothed."
—DWIGHT D. EISENHOWER

"I have seen war. I have seen war on land and sea. I have seen blood running from the wounded. I have seen the dead in the mud. I have seen cities destroyed. I have seen children starving. I have seen the agony of mothers and wives. I hate war."
—FRANKLIN DELANO
ROOSEVELT

"War is a series of catastrophes that results in victory."
—GEORGES CLEMENCEAU
(1841–1929)
was Prime minister of France
during World War I.

"There never was a good war or a bad peace."

—BENJAMIN FRANKLIN

"I know war as few other men now living know it, and nothing to me is more revolting. I have long advocated its complete abolition, as its very destructiveness on both friend and foe has rendered it useless as a method of settling international disputes."
—DOUGLAS MACARTHUR

"War would end if the dead could return."

—STANLEY BALDWIN

Nonetheless, many have argued that war is often a necessary prelude to peace. Others contend that the way to peace is to stop war. Depending on which side of this argument you come down on, the following will be of service.

"The purpose of all wars . . . is peace."

—St. Augustine

"War is a poor chisel to carve out tomorrow."

—Martin Luther King Jr.

"You are not going to get peace with millions of armed men. The chariot of peace cannot advance over a road littered with cannon."

—David Lloyd George

"War is an ugly thing but not the ugliest of things. The decayed and degraded state of moral and patriotic feeling which thinks that nothing is worth war is much worse."

—John Stuart Mill

"What difference does it make to the dead, the orphans, and the homeless whether the mad destruction is wrought under the name of totalitarianism or the holy name of liberty or democracy?"

—Mohandas Gandhi

"War may sometimes be a necessary evil. But no matter how necessary, it is always an evil, never a good."

—Jimmy Carter

"You cannot simultaneously prevent and prepare for war."

—Albert Einstein

"It is an unfortunate fact that we can secure peace only by preparing for war."

—John F. Kennedy
(1917–1963)
was thirty-fifth president of the United States. He was assassinated on November 22, 1963.

"There is nothing so likely to produce peace as to be well prepared to meet the enemy."

—George Washington

"We make war that we may live in peace."

—Aristotle

The twentieth century ushered in an age in which, for the first time in human history, questions of war and peace became literally questions about the survival of the human race. This has given a new urgency to the problem of war, but sadly we seem as far as ever from a solution. However, you can make others aware of the wisdom of our elders regarding the subject by citing to them some of these quotations:

"Ours is a world of nuclear giants and ethical infants. We know more about war than we know about peace, more about killing than we know about living. We have grasped the mystery of the atom and rejected the Sermon on the Mount."

—OMAR BRADLEY

"I know not with what weapons World War III will be fought, but World War IV will be fought with sticks and stones."

—ALBERT EINSTEIN

"War does not determine who is right—only who is left."

—BERTRAND RUSSELL

"Only the dead have seen the end of war."

—GEORGE SANTAYANA

"War, in one form or another, appeared with the first man. At the dawn of history, its morality was not questioned; it was simply a fact, like drought or disease— the manner in which tribes and then civilizations sought power and settled their differences."

—BARACK OBAMA

"You can no more win a war than you can win an earthquake."

—JEANETTE RANKIN
(1880–1973)
was the first woman elected to Congress. Out of her pacifist convictions, she opposed U.S. entry into both world wars.

"War is a cowardly escape from the problems of peace."

—THOMAS MANN

Concerning the conduct of war itself, we have long passed the point where we can talk about a "civilized" way to conduct war. Modern wars are anything but civilized, so feel free to let this fact be known.

"In war, truth is the first casualty."

—AESCHYLUS

"In time of war the loudest patriots are the greatest profiteers."

—AUGUST BEBEL

"The object of war is not to die for your country, but to make the other bastard die for his."

—GEORGE PATTON (1885–1945) commanded the U.S. Third Army during the invasion of France in 1944 and was hailed as a war hero.

"It is well that war is so terrible, or we should grow too fond of it."

—ROBERT E. LEE

"War is hell!"

—WILLIAM TECUMSEH SHERMAN

"The art of war is simple enough. Find out where your enemy is. Get at him as soon as you can. Strike him as hard as you can, and keep moving on."

—ULYSSES S. GRANT

"In peace the sons bury their fathers, but in war the fathers bury their sons."

—CROESUS

"War is too serious a matter to entrust to military men."

—GEORGES CLEMENCEAU

In some distant future, perhaps humankind will have learned a better way of settling disputes aside from killing one another. Citizens of that age will look back in wonder at their barbaric past. You can raise a glass to that bloodless future and quote one of these.

"Peace is not the absence of war; it is a virtue, a state of mind, a disposition for benevolence, confidence, and justice."

—BARUCH SPINOZA (1632–1677) precursor of the Enlightenment, is noted as much for his scientific as for his philosophic investigations.

"In such a world of conflict, a world of victims and executioners, it is the job of thinking people not to be on the side of the executioners."

—ALBERT CAMUS

"Can anything be stupider than that a man has the right to kill me because he lives on the other side of the river and his ruler has a quarrel with mine, though I have not quarreled with him?"

—BLAISE PASCAL

"Sometime they'll give a war and nobody will come."

—CARL SANDBURG

HISTORY

Intellectuals are generally divided on the subject of history. Some argue that we can learn everything from it; others claim that it teaches us nothing. You don't necessarily have to choose sides in this argument, but you should have some ammunition to throw out to both camps.

"History is a guide to navigation in perilous times. History is who we are and why we are the way we are."

—DAVID C. MCCULLOUGH

"We learn from history that we learn nothing from history."

—GEORGE BERNARD SHAW

"What experience and history teach is this—that people and governments never have learned anything from history, or acted on principles."

—GEORG WILHELM FRIEDRICH HEGEL (1770–1831) was among the most important nineteenth-century philosophers, famous for his theory of dialectical change.

"I have but one lamp by which my feet are guided, and that is the lamp of experience. I know no way of judging of the future but by the past."

—EDWARD GIBBON

"History is more or less bunk. It's tradition. We don't want tradition. We want to live in the present and the only history that is worth a tinker's damn is the history we make today."

—HENRY FORD

"The past is always a rebuke to the present."

—ROBERT PENN WARREN

"If you would understand anything, observe its beginning and its development."

—ARISTOTLE

"One faces the future with one's past."

—PEARL S. BUCK (1892–1973) was a novelist who lived in China and was the first woman to be awarded the Nobel Prize, for her novel *The Good Earth*.

"History is merely a list of surprises. It can only prepare us to be surprised yet again."

—Kurt Vonnegut

P art of the confusion over the usefulness of studying the past arises from whether history represents actual events or if historians are simply making it up. In other words, is history real or is it myth? Are historians capable of objectivity? Or are they simply voicing their own collection of prejudices and preconceptions? If you want to enter this discussion, do so by quoting one of the following.

"Patriotism ruins history."
—Johann Wolfgang von Goethe

"History will be kind to me for I intend to write it."
—Winston Churchill

"History consists of a series of accumulated imaginative inventions."
—Voltaire

"Clio, the muse of history, is as thoroughly infected with lies as a street whore with syphilis."

—ARTHUR SCHOPENHAUER

(1788–1860)

was a German philosopher whose thought was generally pessimistic.

"The historian must not try to know what is truth, if he values his honesty; for if he cares for his truths, he is certain to falsify his facts."

—HENRY ADAMS

"History is the most dangerous product evolved from the chemistry of the intellect . . . . History will justify anything. It teaches precisely nothing, for it contains everything and furnishes examples of everything."

—PAUL VALÉRY

"Historian: an unsuccessful novelist."

—H. L. MENCKEN

"History is not history unless it is the truth."

—ABRAHAM LINCOLN

"Who does not know that the first law of historical writing is the truth."

—CICERO

So history is truth, rumor, falsehood, invented, objective, and infected with lies. Truly, as the Muslim historian Ibn Khaldun wrote, "It should be known that history is a discipline that has a great number of approaches." One thing many agree on, though, is that it tends to repeat itself. You can sound like a knowledgeable historian if you can quote a sentiment like these:

"Those who cannot learn from history are doomed to repeat it."
—GEORGE SANTAYANA
(1863–1952)
was a Spanish philosopher and poet, best remembered for the above quotation.

"People are trapped in history, and history is trapped in them."
—JAMES BALDWIN

"The great eventful Present hides the Past; but through the din/ Of its loud life hints and echoes from the life behind steal in."
—JOHN GREENLEAF WHITTIER

"History is a vast early warning system."
—NORMAN COUSINS

"History repeats itself, first as tragedy, second as farce."
—KARL MARX

"History does not repeat itself. The historians repeat one another."

—MAX BEERBOHM

"Whoever wishes to foresee the future must consult the past; for human events ever resemble those of preceding times. This arises from the fact that they are produced by men who ever have been, and ever shall be, animated by the same passions, and thus they necessarily have the same results."

—NICCOLÒ MACHIAVELLI

(1469–1527)

an Italian philosopher, is sometimes called the first modern political thinker because of his masterwork, *The Prince*

"The past does not repeat itself, but it rhymes."

—MARK TWAIN

"Each time history repeats itself, the price goes up."

—AUTHOR UNKNOWN

In Jane Austen's novel *Northanger Abbey*, Catherine Morland complains, "History, real solemn history, I cannot be interested in. . . . I read it a little as a duty; but it tells me nothing that does not either vex or weary me. The quarrels of popes and kings, with wars and pestilences in every page; the men all so good for nothing, and hardly any women at all—it is very tiresome." Sadly, this is the view of most people who have sat in a college history class on a warm summer's afternoon, listening to the professor drone on in a voice as gray and drab as himself. If the subject of history comes up and someone says, "Oh, I never was any good at history," quote one of the following.

"Few will have the greatness to bend history itself; but each of us can work to change a small portion of events, and in the total of all those acts will be written the history of this generation."

—ROBERT F. KENNEDY

"Historical awareness is a kind of resurrection."

—WILLIAM LEAST HEAT MOON

"History is a race between education and catastrophe."

—H. G. WELLS (1866–1946)
novelist, historian, political figure, was co-founder of the Fabian Society of socialists in England.

"Anybody can make history. Only a great man can write it."

—OSCAR WILDE

"Men make their own history, but they do not make it just as they please; they do not make it under circumstances chosen by themselves, but under circumstances directly found, given and transmitted from the past."

—KARL MARX (1818–1883)
the father of Communism, lived most of his life in London, where he researched his massive opus, *Capital.*

"History, despite its wrenching pain, cannot be unlived, but if faced with courage, need not be lived again."

—MAYA ANGELOU

"History does nothing; it does not possess immense riches, it does not fight battles. It is men, real, living, who do all this."

—KARL MARX

PART VI

PHILOSOPHY

"I love talking about nothing. It is the

only thing I know anything about."

—OSCAR WILDE

LOVE

"Love," as the writer George Jean Nathan observed, "is an emotion experienced by the many and enjoyed by the few." Perhaps its very elusiveness is what makes it so fascinating to us. Justice Potter Stewart once said of pornography, "I don't know how to define it, but I know what it is when I see it." Most of us could say the same thing about love: we don't have a succinct explanation of it, but we recognize it in others and in ourselves.

Intellectuals, who generally prefer to reduce emotions to definitions, have been as puzzled as everyone else over the years by the flitting spirit of love. You can emulate their approach to this complicated feeling by citing something like the following.

"Love must be as much a light as it is a flame."

—HENRY DAVID THOREAU

"The one thing we can never get enough of is love. And the one thing we never give enough of is love."

—HENRY MILLER (1891–1980) was an American novelist known for his sexually explicit stories that were to some degree autobiographically based.

"If love is the answer, could you rephrase the question?"

—LILY TOMLIN

"For one human being to love another: that is perhaps the most difficult of our tasks; the ultimate, the last test and proof, the work for which all other work is but preparation."

—RAINER MARIA RILKE (1875–1926) a German-Austrian poet, had a profound influence on twentieth-century European literature.

"Love makes your soul crawl out from its hiding place."

—ZORA NEALE HURSTON

"Have you ever been in love? Horrible, isn't it? It makes you so vulnerable. It opens your chest and it opens your heart and it means someone can get inside you and mess you up. You build up all these defenses. You build up this whole armor, for years, so nothing can hurt you, then one stupid person, no different from any other stupid person, wanders into your stupid life . . . ."

—NEIL GAIMAN

"Love is the poetry of the senses."

—HONORÉ DE BALZAC

"Love is a condition in which the happiness of another person is essential to your own."

—ROBERT HEINLEIN
(1907–1988)
was among the most important science fiction authors of the twentieth century. His most widely read book is *Stranger in a Strange Land*.

Love can be so confusing that sometimes it's best treated with humor. In fact, sometimes that's the only way to approach it. Thus intellectuals prefer their love spiced with generous portions of cynicism. If you speak to a friend of love and want to appear detached and Olympian, consider making use of one of the following:

"Nothing takes the taste out of peanut butter quite like unrequited love."

—CHARLES SCHULZ (1922–2000)
one of the great cartoon geniuses of American literature, created the comic strip *Peanuts* in 1950.

"Oh, life is a glorious cycle of song,

A medley of extemporanea;

And love is a thing that can never go wrong;

And I am Marie of Romania."

—DOROTHY PARKER

"Love is the triumph of imagination over intelligence."

—H. L. Mencken

"Love is the delightful interval between meeting a beautiful girl and discovering that she looks like a haddock."

—John Barrymore

"Before I met my husband, I'd never fallen in love, though I'd stepped in it a few times."

—Rita Rudner

"Gravitation is not responsible for people falling in love."

—Albert Einstein

S ince love is so ineffable a quality, it's often easier to talk about the end of love or the lack of love. Plenty of people have found things to say about the tragedy of an old love affair or a failing marriage. You can sound both experienced and intellectual by quoting them.

"I hold it true, whate'er befall;

I feel it, when I sorry most;

'Tis better to have loved and lost

Than never to have loved at all."

—Alfred, Lord Tennyson
(1809–1892)
was the English Poet Laureate
during Victoria's reign.

"Love never dies a natural death. It dies because we don't know how to replenish its source. It dies of blindness and errors and betrayals. It dies of illness and wounds; it dies of weariness, of witherings, of tarnishings."

—Anaïs Nin

"Love involves a peculiar unfathomable combination of understanding and misunderstanding."

—DIANE ARBUS (1923–1971) was a photographer whose works included *Identical Twins, Roselle, New Jersey, 1967*. She committed suicide at forty-eight.

"Friendship is the finest balm for the pangs of despised love."

—JANE AUSTEN

"You know you're in love when you don't want to fall asleep because reality is finally better than your dreams."

—THEODORE GEISEL (A.K.A. DR. SEUSS)

"Sometimes I wonder if men and women really suit each other. Perhaps they should live next door and just visit now and then."

—KATHARINE HEPBURN (1907–2003) was an American actress best known for her roles opposite Spencer Tracy in *Adam's Rib*, *Pat and Mike*, and others.

One of the peculiar features of love is that it doesn't just have to be between two people—though two is pretty much the minimum necessary. But love can be a transformative force in the world. If you want to say something lofty and socially conscious, employ something like these thoughts:

"Love is patient, love is kind. It does not envy, it does not boast, it is not proud. It is not rude, it is not self seeking. It is not easily angered, it keeps no record of wrongs. Love does not delight in evil but rejoices with the truth. It always protects, always trusts, always hopes, always perseveres. Love never fails."

—I CORINTHIANS 13:4–8

"Love is the only force capable of transforming an enemy into a friend."

—MARTIN LUTHER KING JR.

"Man has conquered whole nations, but all his armies could not conquer love. Man has chained and fettered the spirit, but he has been utterly helpless before love. . . Thus love has the magic power to make of a beggar a king. Yes, love is free; it can dwell in no other atmosphere."

—EMMA GOLDMAN (1869–1940) was an anarchist and political activist and advocate of birth control.

"Hatred ever kills, love never dies. Such is the vast difference between the two. What is obtained by love is retained for all time. What is obtained by hatred proves a burden in reality for it increases hatred."

—MOHANDAS GANDHI

"For there is one thing I can safely say: that those bound by love but obey each other if they are to keep company long. Love will not be constrained by master; when mastery comes, the God of love at once beats his wings and farewell he is gone."

—GEOFFREY CHAUCER

"Neither a lofty degree of intelligence nor imagination nor both together go to the making of genius. Love, love, love, that is the soul of genius."

—WOLFGANG AMADEUS MOZART

In the end, love is sitting with someone at the end of the day, watching the sun set, and knowing that even when neither of you is saying anything, the conversation between you will never end. That's the best kind of love. And here are some thoughts to help it along.

"I love you not only for what you are but for what I am when I am with you. I love you not only for what you have made of yourself but for what you are making of me. I love you for the part of me that you bring out."

—ELIZABETH BARRETT BROWNING (1806–1861) has been celebrated both for her poetry, such as *Sonnets from the Portuguese*, and for her marriage to the poet Robert Browning,

"That Love is all there is,

Is all we know of Love."

—EMILY DICKINSON

"He is not a lover who does not love forever."

—EURIPIDES

"Love at first sight is easy to understand; it's when two people have been looking at each other for a lifetime that it becomes a miracle."
—AMY BLOOM

"Love does not consist of gazing at each other, but in looking together in the same direction."
—ANTOINE DE SAINT-EXUPÉRY

"The first duty of love is to listen."
—PAUL TILLICH

"Love is a canvas furnished by Nature and embroidered by imagination."
—VOLTAIRE

"Those who love deeply never grow old; they may die of old age, but they die young."
—SIR ARTHUR PINERO
(1855–1944)
was an English actor and director. He was associated with Henry Irving's Lyceum Theater, as well as the Haymarket Theater in London.

"Keep love in your heart. A life without it is like a sunless garden when the flowers are dead. The consciousness of loving and being loved brings a warmth and richness to life that nothing else can bring."
—OSCAR WILDE

"Life is the flower for which love is the honey."

—VICTOR HUGO

MARRIAGE

Coming as it does after the lofty heights of love, marriage inevitably seems like a descent into something more mundane. Sometimes the decline is gentle and both participants have a chance to get used to breathing the thicker air in the lower altitudes of everyday life together. Sometimes it's more precipitate. And occasionally (the Paul McCartney-Heather Mills wedlock springs to mind), it's like falling off a cliff onto a bed of nails. Whatever the case, there's no lack of cynical comparisons between love and marriage. You can sound properly detached and disillusioned (two qualities essential to intellectualism) by quoting along the following lines:

"Getting married is a lot like getting into a tub of hot water. After you get used to it, it ain't so hot."

—MINNIE PEARL

"Marriage: A word which should be pronounced 'mirage.'"

—HERBERT SPENCER
(1820–1903)
English philosopher, is credited with the phrase "survival of the fittest" and with the creation of the philosophy of Social Darwinism.

"Bachelors know more about women than married men; if they didn't they'd be married too."

—H. L. MENCKEN

"The secret of a happy marriage remains a secret."

—HENNY YOUNGMAN

"Marriage, a market which has nothing free but the entrance."

—MICHEL DE MONTAIGNE

"Bride, n. A woman with a fine prospect of happiness behind her."

—AMBROSE BIERCE

"He that hath a wife and children hath given hostages to fortune."

—FRANCIS BACON

"It is not a lack of love, but a lack of friendship that makes unhappy marriages."

—FRIEDRICH NIETZSCHE

"If you want to sacrifice the admiration of many men for the criticism of one, go ahead, get married."

—KATHARINE HEPBURN

"When two people are under the influence of the most violent, most insane, most delusive, and most transient of passions, they are required to swear that they will remain in that excited, abnormal, and exhausting condition continuously until death do them part."

—GEORGE BERNARD SHAW

"Any intelligent woman who reads the marriage contract, and then goes into it, deserves all the consequences."

—ISADORA DUNCAN (1877–1927) dancer, was widely hailed for her innovative and sensual style, considered by many a precursor to modern dance.

"Marriage, n. The state or condition of a community consisting of a master, a mistress and two slaves, making in all, two."

—AMBROSE BIERCE

Marriage has often been compared to war. The American humorist James Thurber captured this in cartoons (*The War Between Men and Women*). Others have said much the same thing over the centuries. These days wars are fought with bombs, bullets, and IEDs. Sometimes it seems as if the modern marriage is fought with lawyers, prenups, and depositions. If you and your spouse are deep in a discussion of your marriage and things seem to be growing tense, defuse the situation with an apt quotation.

"Marriage is the only war in which you sleep with the enemy."

—FRANÇOIS DE LA ROCHEFOUCAULD

"Marriage must constantly fight against a monster which devours everything: routine."

—HONORÉ DE BALZAC

"Never go to bed mad. Stay up and fight."

—Phyllis Diller

"Though women are angels, yet wedlock's the devil."

—Lord Byron

"I have yet to hear a man ask for advice on how to combine marriage and a career."

—Gloria Steinem

"All married couples should learn the art of battle as they should learn the art of making love. Good battle is objective and honest—never vicious or cruel. Good battle is healthy and constructive, and brings to a marriage the principle of equal partnership."

—Ann Landers

"My husband and I have never considered divorce . . . murder sometimes, but never divorce."

—Dr. Joyce Brothers

"Marriage is the alliance of two people, one of whom never remembers birthdays and the other who never forgets."

—Ogden Nash

"Marriage is an alliance entered into by a man who can't sleep with the window shut, and a woman who can't sleep with the window open."

—George Bernard Shaw

"How can a woman be expected to be happy with a man who insists on treating her as if she were a perfectly normal human being?"

—Oscar Wilde

"Though marriage makes man and wife one flesh, it leaves 'em still two fools."

—William Congreve

"So heavy is the chain of wedlock that it needs two to carry it, and sometimes three."

—Alexandre Dumas, fils

"The problem with marriage is that it ends every night after making love, and it must be rebuilt every morning before breakfast."

—GABRIEL GARCÍA MÁRQUEZ

(1927–)

Colombian novelist, most well-known for his book, *One Hundred Years of Solitude.*

"It destroys one's nerves to be amiable every day to the same human being."

—BENJAMIN DISRAELI

"In the early years, you fight because you don't understand each other. In the later years, you fight because you do."

—JOAN DIDION

"Strike an average between what a woman thinks of her husband a month before she marries him and what she thinks of him a year afterward, and you will have the truth about him."

—H. L. MENCKEN

"Why does a woman work ten years to change a man's habits and then complain that he's not the man she married?"

—BARBRA STREISAND

"No man is regular in his attendance at the House of Commons until he is married."

—BENJAMIN DISRAELI

Marriage, as any number of people have observed, is something that needs work. If you're wondering the best way of arriving at a peaceful old age in the company of your spouse, you might want to consider this advice.

"I have learned that only two things are necessary to keep one's wife happy. First, let her think she's having her own way. And second, let her have it."

—LYNDON B. JOHNSON

"My mother said it was simple to keep a man. You must be a maid in the living room, a cook in the kitchen, and a whore in the bedroom. I said I'd hire the other two and take care of the bedroom bit."

—JERRY HALL

"Once a woman has forgiven her man, she must not reheat his sins for breakfast."

—MARLENE DIETRICH

"Never strike your wife—even with a flower."

—HINDU PROVERB

"My wife tells me she doesn't care what I do when I'm away, as long as I'm not enjoying it."

—LEE TREVINO

"To keep your marriage brimming,

With love in the loving cup,

Whenever you're wrong, admit it;

Whenever you're right, shut up."

—OGDEN NASH

S till, not everyone scoffs at marriage. For some, it's the highest, truest, and best expression of love. When you're looking for something to write on that twenty-fifth anniversary card—the one standing next to the dozen roses, the bottle of champagne, and the two tickets to Paris—try one of these sentiments.

"If ever two were one, then surely we. If ever man were loved by wife, then thee."

—ANNE BRADSTREET

"Marriage is not a noun; it's a verb. It isn't something you get. It's something you do. It's the way you love your partner every day."

—BARBARA DE ANGELIS

"An ideal wife is any woman who has an ideal husband."

—BOOTH TARKINGTON
(1869–1946)
author of a number of popular novels, is remembered for *The Magnificent Ambersons* and for his Penrod stories.

"A good marriage is that in which each appoints the other guardian of his solitude."

—RAINER MARIA RILKE

"I think men who have a pierced ear are better prepared for marriage. They've experienced pain and bought jewelry."

—RITA RUDNER

"Chains do not hold a marriage together. It is threads, hundreds of tiny threads which sew people together through the years. That is what makes a marriage last—more than passion or even sex!"

—SIMONE SIGNORET

"The sum which two married people owe to one another defies calculation. It is an infinite debt, which can only be discharged through eternity."

—JOHANN WOLFGANG VON
GOETHE

"No man or woman really knows what perfect love is until they have been married a quarter of a century."

—MARK TWAIN

"Here's to matrimony, the high sea for which no compass has yet been invented!"

—HEINRICH HEINE

"A happy marriage is a long conversation which always seems too short."

—André Maurois

"I love being married. It's so great to find that one special person you want to annoy for the rest of your life."

—Rita Rudner

"One of the good things that come of a true marriage is, that there is one face on which changes come without your seeing them; or rather there is one face which you can still see the same, through all the shadows which years have gathered upon it."

—George MacDonald
(1824–1905)
English author of fantasy novels, was a great influence on later authors such as J. R. R. Tolkien and C. S. Lewis.

"That quiet mutual gaze of a trusting husband and wife is like the first moment of rest or refuge from a great weariness or a great danger."

—George Eliot

"There is no more lovely, friendly and charming relationship, communion or company than a good marriage."

—Martin Luther

The most profound and succinct comment on marriage comes to us, as does so much wisdom, from ancient Rome:

"And when will there be an end of marrying? I suppose, when there is an end of living!"

—Tertullian

FRIENDSHIP

Ralph Waldo Emerson, the Sage of Concord, said, "The ornament of a house is the friends who frequent it." Like many men and women of culture, Emerson had a good deal to say about friends. In fact, from the beginnings of civilization people have tried to understand how to make friends, keep friends, and get rid of unwanted friends. Perhaps you're looking for something to write in a birthday card for one of your oldest friends. Consider one of these.

"Friendship makes prosperity more shining and lessens adversity by dividing and sharing it."

—CICERO

"What is a friend? A single soul dwelling in two bodies."

—ARISTOTLE

"True friendship consists not in the multitude of friends but in their worth and value."

—BEN JONSON (1572–1637) dramatist and actor, was a contemporary of William Shakespeare. His plays include *Vulpone* and *The Alchemist.*

"Friendship with oneself is all important because without it one cannot be friends with anybody else in the world."

—ELEANOR ROOSEVELT

"Perhaps the most delightful friendships are those in which there is much agreement, much disputation, and yet more personal liking."

—GEORGE ELIOT

"True friendship can afford true knowledge. It does not depend on darkness and ignorance."

—HENRY DAVID THOREAU

"Though friendship is not quick to burn,

It is explosive stuff."

—MAY SARTON (1912–1995) novelist, poet, and autobiographer whose writing was strongly influenced by her lesbian relationships.

"It is one of the blessings of old friends that you can afford to be stupid with them."

—RALPH WALDO EMERSON
(1803–1882)
a close friend of Thoreau, had a unifying effect on the New England-based movement that came to be known as Transcendentalism.

"We are all travelers in the wilderness of this world, and the best we can find in our travels is an honest friend."

—ROBERT LOUIS STEVENSON

"But friendship is precious, not only in the shade but in the sunshine of life; and thanks to a benevolent arrangement of things, the greater part of life is sunshine."

—THOMAS JEFFERSON

"It seems to me that trying to live without friends is like milking a bear to get cream for your morning coffee. It is a whole lot of trouble, and then not worth much after you get it."

—ZORA NEALE HURSTON
(1891–1960)
author and poet during the Harlem Renaissance, played a significant role in reviving African American folklore.

"Think where man's glory most begins and ends,

And say my glory was I had such friends."

—WILLIAM BUTLER YEATS

"Love is like the wild-rose briar;

Friendship is like the holly tree.

The holly is dark when the rose briar blooms,

But which will bloom most constantly?"

—EMILY BRONTË (1818–1848)
one of several highly talented members of the Yorkshire Brontë family, authored the Gothic classic *Wuthering Heights*.

A lot of time and effort has been expended on trying to find a surefire formula for making friends. No one's ever found a way that works every time, but it must be admitted that some people seem to be more successful at it than others. When the topic comes up during dinner table conversation, drop in something like this.

"You can make more friends in two months by becoming interested in other people than you can in two years by trying to get other people interested in you."

—DALE CARNEGIE

"Be courteous to all, but intimate with few, and let those few be well tried before you give them your confidence. True friendship is a plant of slow growth and must undergo and withstand the shocks of adversity before it is entitled to the appellation."

—GEORGE WASHINGTON

"We secure our friends not by accepting favors but by doing them."

—THUCYDIDES

"Friendship is born at that moment when one person says to another: 'What! You, too? Thought I was the only one.'"

—C. S. LEWIS

"The best time to make friends is before you need them."

—ETHEL BARRYMORE
(1879–1959)
member of the famous Barrymore acting family, won an Academy Award for Best Supporting Actress for *None but the Lonely Heart*.

"Choose your friends carefully. Your enemies will choose you."

—YASSIR ARAFAT

"It is in the thirties that we want friends. In the forties we know they won't save us any more than love did."

—F. SCOTT FITZGERALD

"The wicked can have only accomplices, the voluptuous have companions in debauchery, self-seekers have associates, the politic assemble the factions, the typical idler has connections, princes have courtiers. Only the virtuous have friends."

—VOLTAIRE

The truest test of friendship, of course, is how much your friends will tolerate you talking about yourself. Narcissism is probably the greatest enemy real friendship ever has. Still another test is your willingness to be honest with friends and their openness with you. If, however, you don't want to be open and wish to deflect the conversation, quote from one of these as a distraction from a deeper discussion of your feelings

"A man must eat a peck of salt with his friend before he knows him."

—Miguel de Cervantes

"Do not use a hatchet to remove a fly from your friend's forehead."

—Chinese proverb

"Only your real friends will tell you when your face is dirty."

—Sicilian proverb

"Men kick friendship around like a football, but it doesn't seem to crack. Women treat it like glass and it goes to pieces."

—Anne Morrow Lindbergh
(1906–2001)
the wife of aviator Charles Lindbergh, won fame in her own right as an author and early female aviator.

"Consult your friend on all things, especially on those which respect yourself. His counsel may then be useful where your own self-love might impair your judgment."

—Seneca

"The holy passion of friendship is so sweet and steady and loyal and enduring in nature that it will last through a whole lifetime, if not asked to lend money."

—Mark Twain

"True friendship can afford true knowledge. It does not depend on darkness and ignorance."

—Henry David Thoreau

"It is difficult to say who do you the most mischief: enemies with the worst intentions or friends with the best."

—Edward Bulwer-Lytton

"It is one of the severest tests of friendship to tell your friend his faults. So to love a man that you cannot bear to see a stain upon him and to speak painful truth through loving words, that is friendship."

—HENRY WARD BEECHER

(1813–1887)

associated with various radical causes of the Victorian era, including female suffrage, temperance, and evolution.

"The best way to destroy an enemy is to make him a friend."

—ABRAHAM LINCOLN

"Don't believe your friends when they ask you to be honest with them. All they really want is to be maintained in the good opinion they have of themselves."

—ALBERT CAMUS

"It's a lot like nature. You only have as many animals as the ecosystem can support and you only have as many friends as you can tolerate the bitching of."

—RANDY K. MILHOLLAND

"A true friend stabs you in the front."

—OSCAR WILDE

"Don't flatter yourself that friendship authorizes you to say disagreeable things to your intimates. The nearer you come into relation with a person, the more necessary do tact and courtesy become."

—OLIVER WENDELL HOLMES JR.

(1841–1935)

was a member of the United States Supreme Court for almost thirty years.

"Misfortune shows those who are not really friends."

—ARISTOTLE

"Between friends differences in taste or opinion are irritating in direct proportion to their triviality."

—W. H. AUDEN

"A good friend can tell you what is the matter with you in a minute. He may not seem such a good friend after telling."

—ARTHUR BRISBANE

"Prosperity makes friends, adversity tries them."

—PUBLILIUS SYRUS

(1ST CENTURY BCE)

is known for his epigrams, though his sole surviving work, *Sententiae*, may not even have been compiled by him.

A bove all, friends are those people who stand by you no matter what. As movie diva Marlene Dietrich said, "It's the friends you can call up at four A.M. that matter." How many of us have friends like that? Make a list and send them a note with something from the following:

"The friendship that can cease has never been real."

—SAINT JEROME

"Perhaps the most delightful friendships are those in which there is much agreement, much disputation, and yet more personal liking."

—GEORGE ELIOT

"Let us be grateful to people who make us happy; they are the charming gardeners who make our souls blossom."

—MARCEL PROUST

"Some people go to priests; others to poetry; I to my friends."

—VIRGINIA WOOLF

"But if the while I think on thee, dear friend,

All losses are restored and sorrows end."

—WILLIAM SHAKESPEARE

"We are all travelers in the wilderness of this world, and the best we can find in our travels is an honest friend."

—ROBERT LOUIS STEVENSON

"Friendship is the only cement that will ever hold the world together."

—WOODROW WILSON

"In everyone's life, at some time, our inner fire goes out. It is then burst into flame by an encounter with another human being. We should all be thankful for those people who rekindle the inner spirit."

—ALBERT SCHWEITZER

"Constant use will not wear ragged the fabric of friendship."

—DOROTHY PARKER
(1893–1967)
poet and short story writer, was part of the circle of writers, actors, and literary figures known as the Algonquin Round Table

"The bird a nest, the spider a web, man friendship."

—WILLIAM BLAKE

"Friendship is a sheltering tree."

—SAMUEL TAYLOR COLERIDGE

"The language of friendship is not words but meanings."

—HENRY DAVID THOREAU
(1817–1862)
best remembered for his book, *Walden*, an account of his life in a cabin by the shores of Walden Pond in Concord, Massachusetts.

"I am speaking now of the highest duty we owe our friends, the noblest, the most sacred—that of keeping their own nobleness, goodness, pure and incorrupt. If we let our friend become cold and selfish and exacting without a remonstrance, we are no true lover, no true friend."

—HARRIET BEECHER STOWE

"One friend in a lifetime is much; two are many; three are hardly possible."

—HENRY ADAMS

The Roman politician Cicero, who devoted an entire book to the subject of friendship, put it best:

"Life is nothing without friendship."

—CICERO

KNOWLEDGE

A little learning may be a dangerous thing, as the poet Alexander Pope observed, but the general consensus of intellectuals seems to be that too much learning can crush knowledge. Knowledge, as distinct from learning, is desirable, with wisdom being valued above either commodity. To appear wise as well as learned, feel free to use some of what follows in conversation.

"All men, by nature, desire knowledge."

—ARISTOTLE

"I am not young enough to know everything."

—OSCAR WILDE

"All wish to possess knowledge, but few, comparatively speaking, are willing to pay the price."

—JUVENAL (C. 60–C. 140)
a Roman poet, was the author of the *Satires*, a collection of poems that critiqued contemporary Roman society and customs.

"The good life is inspired by love and guided by knowledge."

—BERTRAND RUSSELL

"We can understand almost anything, but we can't understand how we understand."

—ALBERT EINSTEIN

"The beginning of knowledge is the discovery of something we do not understand."

—FRANK HERBERT

"Science is organized knowledge. Wisdom is organized life."

—IMMANUEL KANT

"If knowledge can create problems, it is not through ignorance that we can solve them."

—ISAAC ASIMOV

"Knowledge will forever govern ignorance; and a people who mean to be their own governors must arm themselves with the power which knowledge gives."

—JAMES MADISON (1751–1836)
the fourth president of the United States, also played a central role in shaping the new republic by his role in the Constitutional Convention.

"The improvement of understanding is for two ends: first, our own increase of knowledge; secondly, to enable us to deliver that knowledge to others."

—JOHN LOCKE

"Great are they who see that spiritual is stronger than any material force, that thoughts rule the world."

—RALPH WALDO EMERSON

"There is much pleasure to be gained from useless knowledge."

—BERTRAND RUSSELL

"If you have knowledge, let others light their candles at it."

—MARGARET FULLER
(1810–1850)
a journalist and critic, was a close associate of Emerson and Thoreau and the Concord circle of thinkers.

"Knowledge and timber shouldn't be much used till they are seasoned."

—OLIVER WENDELL HOLMES

"Knowledge is power."

—FRANCIS BACON

"It is no good to try to stop knowledge from going forward. Ignorance is never better than knowledge."

—ENRICO FERMI

"Knowledge is not simply another commodity. On the contrary. Knowledge is never used up. It increases by diffusion and grows by dispersion."

—DANIEL BOORSTIN
(1914–2004)
historian, author of several works of popular history, was Librarian of the U.S. Congress for more than a decade.

"The only good is knowledge, and the only evil is ignorance."

—SOCRATES

Socrates' sentiment is all well and good, but how does one set about gaining knowledge? The first step, most authorities agree, is to accept your own ignorance. Humility isn't something that comes easily to intellectuals, but you can at least show you understand the need for its appearance by eating these slices of humble pie.

"To be conscious that you are ignorant is a great step to knowledge."

—BENJAMIN DISRAELI

"The dumbest people I know are those who know it all."

—MALCOLM FORBES

"Trust yourself. You know more than you think you do."

—BENJAMIN SPOCK

"Nothing that is worth knowing can be taught."

—OSCAR WILDE

"A man's errors are his portals of discovery."

—JAMES JOYCE (1882–1941) in such novels as *Ulysses* initiated a new style of writing, sometimes dubbed "stream of consciousness."

"It is impossible for a man to learn what he thinks he already knows."

—EPICTETUS

"Whosoever wishes to know about the world must learn about it in its particular details. Knowledge is not intelligence. In searching for the truth be ready for the unexpected."

—HERACLITUS (535 BCE–475 BCE) believed that the universe was in a constant state of flux. He also suggested that Logos (or "reason") governs all things.

"The eye sees only what the mind is prepared to comprehend."

—HENRI BERGSON

"Trust your hunches. They're usually based on facts filed away just below the conscious level."

—DR. JOYCE BROTHERS

"Each excellent thing, once learned, serves for a measure of all other knowledge."

—PHILIP SIDNEY

"Anyone who conducts an argument by appealing to authority is not using his intelligence; he is just using his memory."

—LEONARDO DA VINCI

"A great many people think they are thinking when they are merely rearranging their prejudices."

—WILLIAM JAMES

"Expertise in one field does not carry over into other fields. But experts often think so. The narrower their field of knowledge the more likely they are to think so."

—ROBERT HEINLEIN

"Integrity without knowledge is weak and useless, and knowledge without integrity is dangerous and dreadful."

—SAMUEL JOHNSON

"The fact that some geniuses were laughed at does not imply that all who are laughed at are geniuses. They laughed at Columbus, they laughed at Fulton, they laughed at the Wright brothers. But they also laughed at Bozo the Clown."

—CARL SAGAN

"When a true genius appears in the world you may know him by this sign: that all the dunces are in confederacy against him."

—JONATHAN SWIFT (1667–1745) wrote *Gulliver's Travels*, a commentary on the state of society in his day, as well as other satiric works.

"To succeed in the world it is not enough to be stupid, you must also be well-mannered."

—VOLTAIRE

"Knowledge is of two kinds: we know a subject ourselves, or we know where we can find information upon it."

—SAMUEL JOHNSON

"It is a great nuisance that knowledge can only be acquired by hard work."

—W. SOMERSET MAUGHAM

Knowledge is just the beginning, though. Intellectuals strive for wisdom, which means, essentially, admitting that the more they know, the more they know that they don't know. Furthermore, knowledge and wisdom can't be compelled and can't be controlled. Should the conversation take a turn in this direction, make sure your dinner guests know where you stand on the issue.

"An ounce of love is worth a pound of knowledge."

—JOHN WESLEY

"If we value the pursuit of knowledge, we must be free to follow wherever that search may lead us. The free mind is not a barking dog, to be tethered on a ten-foot chain."

—ADLAI STEVENSON (1900–1965) twice the unsuccessful candidate of the Democratic Party for president, was beloved of liberals for his intellect and brilliant speeches.

"If you don't read the newspaper, you are uninformed; if you do read the newspaper, you are misinformed."

—MARK TWAIN

"Bodily exercise, when compulsory, does no harm to the body; but knowledge which is acquired under compulsion obtains no hold on the mind."

—PLATO

"Whoever undertakes to set himself up as a judge of Truth and Knowledge is shipwrecked by the laughter of the gods."

—ALBERT EINSTEIN

"There is no squabbling so violent as that between people who accepted an idea yesterday and those who will accept the same idea tomorrow."

—CHRISTOPHER MORLEY

"Perplexity is the beginning of knowledge."

—KAHLIL GIBRAN (1883–1931)
a Lebanese-American poet, is best remembered for *The Prophet*, a collection of essays that surged in popularity during the 1960s.

"Knowledge comes, but wisdom lingers."

—ALFRED, LORD TENNYSON

"Knowledge is of no value unless you put it into practice."

—ANTON CHEKOV

"Those that know, do. Those that understand, teach."

—ARISTOTLE

"Be wiser than other people if you can, but do not tell them so."

—LORD CHESTERFIELD

"Knowing others is wisdom; knowing yourself is Enlightenment."

—LAO TZU

"Let us be thankful for the fools. But for them the rest of us could not succeed."

—MARK TWAIN (1835–1910)
whose real name was Samuel L. Clemens, authored such classics as *Tom Sawyer* and *Huckleberry Finn*.

"The more I know,

the less tortured

I am."

—ALANIS MORISSETTE

POWER

Knowledge may be power, but it doesn't follow that the reverse is true. Power is often in the hands of the ignorant, something that causes intellectuals to sit up late at night drinking too much white wine, gobbling Brie, and worrying about the state of the world. It may be that you can offer some comfort with words of great thinkers. It may not make anyone feel more powerful, but it should at least make them feel as if wisdom is in their corner.

"No science is immune to the infection of politics and the corruption of power."

—JACOB BRONOWSKI

"Power tends to corrupt, and absolute power corrupts absolutely."

—LORD ACTON

"Power corrupts the few, while weakness corrupts the many."

—ERIC HOFFER

"The highest proof of virtue is to possess boundless power without abusing it."

—LORD MACAULAY

"Power has only one duty—to secure the social welfare of the People."

—BENJAMIN DISRAELI

"I hope our wisdom will grow with our power, and teach us, that the less we use our power the greater it will be."

—THOMAS JEFFERSON
(1743–1826)
author of the Declaration of Independence and founder of the University of Virginia, was the third president of the United States.

"We look forward to the time when the Power of Love will replace the Love of Power. Then will our world know the blessings of peace."

—WILLIAM GLADSTONE

"Concentrated power has always been the enemy of liberty."

—RONALD REAGAN

"Arbitrary power is most easily established on the ruins of liberty abused to licentiousness."

—GEORGE WASHINGTON

"There is no knowledge that is not power."

—RALPH WALDO EMERSON

"Who is wise? He that learns from everyone. Who is powerful? He that governs his passions. Who is rich? He who is content. Who is that? Nobody."

—BENJAMIN FRANKLIN
(1706–1790)
scientist and inventor, was a printer and a
writer, as well as a politician and diplomat.

"Justice without force is powerless; force without justice is tyrannical."

—BLAISE PASCAL

"There will be no end to the troubles of states, or of humanity itself, till philosophers become kings in this world, or till those we now call kings and rulers really and truly become philosophers, and political power and philosophy thus come into the same hands."

—PLATO

The chief power one can hold, so voices from the past tell us, is power over oneself. That may be comforting in a world in which the powerful are increasingly uncaring about the powerless. At least there's something we can accomplish.

"He is the most powerful who has power over himself."

—SENECA

"He who controls others may be powerful, but he who has mastered himself is mightier still."

—LAO TZU
(C. 604 BCE–C. 531 BCE)
is revered as a god in the Taoist religion,
which is largely based on his teachings
of self-discipline and mysticism.

"The power of man has grown in every sphere except over himself."

—WINSTON CHURCHILL

"The love of liberty is the love of others; the love of power is the love of ourselves."

—WILLIAM HAZLITT

"Nearly all men can stand adversity, but if you want to test a man's character, give him power."

—ABRAHAM LINCOLN

"To achieve, you need thought. You have to know what you are doing and that's real power."

—AYN RAND (1905–1982)
is known for her novels *The Fountainhead* and *Atlas Shrugged*, which expounded her philosophy of enlightened self-interest.

"The attempt to combine wisdom and power has only rarely been successful and then only for a short while."

—ALBERT EINSTEIN

P ower, according to most intellectuals' way of thinking, is exercised by the wise person over herself and by the ignorant over others (most notoriously in the world of the intellectual it is exercised by university administrators over professors). By its nature it is corrupting and evil. The advantage of this point of view is that it allows you to feel superior to those who are oppressing you. If that's the case, keep some of these sentiments handy.

"Power is given only to those who dare to lower themselves and pick it up."

—FYODOR DOSTOEVSKY

"Power, like a desolating pestilence,

Pollutes whate'er it touches."

—PERCY SHELLEY

"In order to obtain and hold power, a man must love it."

—LEO TOLSTOY

"Arbitrary power is like most other things which are very hard—very liable to be broken."

—ABIGAIL ADAMS

"What we call Man's power over Nature turns out to be a power exercised by some men over other men with Nature as its instrument."

—C. S. LEWIS (1898–1963) medievalist and the author of the *Narnia* children's fantasy series, was a powerful defender of Christian theology.

"Power is something of which I am convinced there is no innocence this side of the womb."

—NADINE GORDIMER

"Once you give a charlatan power over you, you almost never get it back."

—CARL SAGAN

"Never work just for money or for power. They won't save your soul or help you sleep at night."

—MARION WRIGHT EDELMAN

Power, as numerous thinkers have reminded us, doesn't give itself away. It has to be taken; often the seizure of power is by those on whose behalf it was supposedly being exercised. If you want to show yourself as a champion of the oppressed against their oppressors, launch one of these quotations into the conversation.

"Power concedes nothing without a demand. It never did, and it never will."

—FREDERICK DOUGLASS

"Power can be taken, but not given. The process of the taking is empowerment in itself."

—GLORIA STEINEM (1934–) founder of *Ms.* magazine. She led campaigns for abortion rights, culminating in the 1973 Supreme Court decision *Roe v. Wade*.

"Free election of masters does not abolish the masters or the slaves."

—HERBERT MARCUSE

"You can have power over people as long as you don't take everything away from them. But when you've robbed a man of everything, he's no longer in your power."

—ALEKSANDR SOLZHENITSYN

"Of all tyrannies, a tyranny exercised for the good of its victims may be the most oppressive."

—C. S. LEWIS

"Where justice is denied, where poverty is enforced, where ignorance prevails, and where any one class is made to feel that society is an organized conspiracy to oppress, rob, and degrade them, neither persons nor property will be safe."

—FREDERICK DOUGLASS

"The most common way people give up their power is by thinking they don't have any."

—ALICE WALKER

There's something very attractive about power. Even if we don't have it, we seem drawn to it. So perhaps the best thing is to admit we find it fascinating—after all, so many interesting people, for good or for ill, have had it.

"God is on everyone's side . . . and in the last analysis, he is on the side with plenty of money and large armies."

—JEAN ANOUILH (1910–1987)
French dramatist, is best known in the United States as the author of *Becket or The Honor of God*.

"All too often arrogance accompanies strength, and we must never assume that justice is on the side of the strong. The use of power must always be accompanied by moral choice."

—THEODORE BIKEL

"Power is when you have every justification to kill someone and then you don't."

—OSKAR SCHINDLER

"I am not interested in power for power's sake but I'm interested in power that is moral, that is right, and that is good."

—MARTIN LUTHER KING JR.

"Power is my mistress. I have worked too hard at her conquest to allow anyone to take her away from me."

—NAPOLEON BONAPARTE
(1769–1821)
rose from the rank of corporal in the French army to become emperor of France.

"The world itself is the will to power—and nothing else! And you yourself are the will to power—and nothing else!"

—FRIEDRICH NIETZSCHE

"Silence is the ultimate weapon of power."

—CHARLES DE GAULLE

"Being powerful is like being a lady. If you have to tell people you are, you aren't."

—MARGARET THATCHER

"You see what power is—holding someone else's fear in your hand and showing it to them!"

—AMY TAN (1952–)
has turned her experiences as a Chinese American into themes for such novels as *The Joy Luck Club* and *The Kitchen God's Wife.*

"The great secret of power is never to will to do more than you can accomplish."

—HENRIK IBSEN

"The problem of power is how to achieve its responsible use rather than its irresponsible and indulgent use—of how to get men of power to live for the public rather than off the public."

—ROBERT F. KENNEDY

"Power is the ultimate aphrodisiac."

—HENRY KISSINGER (1923–)
served in the Nixon administration, first as national security advisor, then as secretary of state.

"Power consists in one's capacity to link his will with the purpose of others, to lead by reason and a gift of cooperation."

—WOODROW WILSON

"I love power. But it is as an artist that I love it. I love it as a musician loves his violin, to draw out its sounds and chords and harmonies."

—NAPOLEON BONAPARTE

"Power in America today is control of the means of communication."

—THEODORE WHITE

"The first principle of a civilized state is that power is legitimate only when it is under contract."

—WALTER LIPPMANN

"The illegal we do immediately, the unconstitutional takes a little longer."

—HENRY KISSINGER

Old Age

The book of Ecclesiastes says, "Again I saw that under the sun the race is not to the swift, nor the battle to the strong, nor bread to the wise, nor riches to the intelligent, nor favor to those with knowledge, but time and chance happen to them all."

Time, indeed, comes to all of us. Our hair thins, our skin wrinkles, our steps grow slower, and we climb stairs at a gentler pace. Old age is to be celebrated as a time of wisdom and experience, or—particularly if you're under thirty—feared as the demon waiting hidden around the corner. Fortunately, as you grow older you acquire a rich stock of quotes with which to counter the protestations of the young.

"If you live to be one hundred, you've got it made. Very few people die past that age."

—George Burns

"The tragedy of old age is not that one is old but that one is young."

—Oscar Wilde

"No man loves life like him that's growing old."

—Socrates

"Forty is the old age of youth; fifty the youth of old age."

—Victor Hugo

"The old are in a second childhood."

—Aeschylus (525 BCE–426 BCE)
early Greek playwright, was noted for his tragedies, including *The Oresteia*, *Seven Against Thebes*, and *The Suppliants*.

"Grow old along with me!

The best is yet to be,

The last of life, for which the first was made."

—Robert Browning

"I think your whole life shows in your face and you should be proud of that."

—LAUREN BACALL

"Old age is like everything else. To make a success of it, you've got to start young."

—THEODORE ROOSEVELT

"I want to die young at a ripe old age."

—ASHLEY MONTAGU
(1905–1999)

anthropologist and humanist scholar, is the author of a number of works dealing with the need for racial tolerance.

"Age is something that doesn't matter, unless you are a cheese."

—BILLIE BURKE

"First you are young; then you are middle-aged; then you are old; then you are wonderful."

—LADY DIANA COOPER

"The great thing about getting older is that you don't lose all the other ages you've been."

—MADELEINE L'ENGLE

"Old age is the most unexpected of all the things that can happen to a man."

—LEON TROTSKY

One's attitude to old age depends largely on whether one accepts it or wrestles with it. On the whole, it's probably better to accept its inevitability, since it's a wrestling match you're sure to lose. There's plenty of wisdom on both sides of the question.

"To get back my youth I would do anything in the world, except take exercise, get up early, or be respectable."

—OSCAR WILDE

"I don't believe one grows older. I think that what happens early on in life is that at a certain age one stands still and stagnates."

—T. S. ELIOT (1888–1965)
was a poet whose works were influential in developing Modernism.

"How pleasant is the day when we give up striving to be young— or slender."

—WILLIAM JAMES

"It takes a long time to become young."

—PABLO PICASSO

"Age is an issue of mind over matter. If you don't mind, it doesn't matter."

—MARK TWAIN

"A man is not old until regrets take the place of dreams."

—JOHN BARRYMORE

"There is more felicity on the far side of baldness than young men can possibly imagine."

—LOGAN PEARSALL SMITH

"It's sad to grow old, but nice to ripen."

—BRIGITTE BARDOT

"Growing old is a bad habit which a busy man has no time to form."

—ANDRÉ MAUROIS

"When grace is joined with wrinkles, it is adorable. There is an unspeakable dawn in happy old age."

—VICTOR HUGO

"Old age adds to the respect due to virtue, but it takes nothing from the contempt inspired by vice; it whitens only the hair."

—IRA GERSHWIN (1896–1983) together with his brother George, wrote many acclaimed Broadway shows and movies, including *Porgy and Bess* and *An American in Paris.*

"A man's only as old as the woman he feels."

—GROUCHO MARX

"I don't plan to grow old gracefully. I plan to have face lifts until my ears meet."

—RITA RUDNER

Some people greet old age like a valued companion, while for others it's only a harbinger of inevitable and painful decay. For many, the onset of old age is accompanied by such stages as denial, bargaining, anger, and, finally, acceptance. Depending on which of those stages you're in will determine which of the following quotes you choose to unleash into a gathering of intellectuals who are trying to stare down middle age.

"As I give thought to the matter, I find four causes for the apparent misery of old age: first, it withdraws us from active accomplishments; second, it renders the body less powerful; third, it deprives us of almost all forms of enjoyment; fourth, it stands not far from death."

—CICERO

"A woman has the age she deserves."

—COCO CHANEL

"Every old man complains of the growing depravity of the world, of the petulance and insolence of the rising generation."

—SAMUEL JOHNSON

"There's no such thing as old age, there is only sorrow."

—EDITH WHARTON (1862–1937) prolific novelist and interior designer, wrote such important books as *Ethan Frome* and *The House of Mirth*.

"The older I grow, the more I distrust the familiar doctrine that age brings wisdom."

—H. L. MENCKEN

"What is the worst of woes that wait on age?

What stamps the wrinkle deeper on the brow?

To view each loved one blotted from life's page,

And be alone on earth, as I am now."

—LORD BYRON

"Age is a very high price to pay for maturity."

—TOM STOPPARD

"Whatever poet, orator, or sage may say of it, old age is still old age."

—SINCLAIR LEWIS

THE QUOTABLE INTELLECTUAL

Still, taken all around, there are certainly worse things than old age. And if someone you know has been complaining a lot about their aches and pains, comfort them with this.

"Old age isn't so bad when you consider the alternative."

—MAURICE CHEVALIER

"I'm very pleased to be here. Let's face it, at my age I'm very pleased to be anywhere."

—GEORGE BURNS (1896–1996) vaudeville, film, and television actor, continued working until the very end of his life at age 100.

"Sex at the age of eighty-four is a wonderful experience. Especially the one in the winter."

—MILTON BERLE

"The old begin to complain of the conduct of the young when they themselves are no longer able to set a bad example."

—FRANÇOIS DE LA ROCHEFOUCAULD

"The youth gets together his materials to build a bridge to the moon, or, perchance, a palace or temple on the earth, and, at length, the middle-aged man concludes to build a woodshed with them."

—HENRY DAVID THOREAU

"The great secret that all old people share is that you really haven't changed in seventy or eighty years. Your body changes, but you don't change at all. And that, of course, causes great confusion."

—DORIS LESSING (1919–) is the British author of such notable novels as *The Golden Notebook* and *The Good Terrorist*.

"I recently had my annual physical examination, which I get once every seven years, and when the nurse weighed me, I was shocked to discover how much stronger the Earth's gravitational pull has become since 1990."

—DAVE BARRY

"Regrets are the natural property of grey hairs."

—CHARLES DICKENS

"Life is a moderately good play with a badly written third act."

—TRUMAN CAPOTE

"An aged man is but a paltry thing,

A tattered coat upon a stick, unless

Soul clasp its hands and sing, and louder sing

For every tatter in its mortal dress."

—WILLIAM BUTLER YEATS

(1865–1939)

one of Ireland's most important twentieth-century poets, was deeply involved in the Irish literary revival at the beginning of the century.

"All diseases run into one—old age."

—RALPH WALDO EMERSON

"The first forty years of life give us the text; the next thirty supply the commentary on it."

—ARTHUR SCHOPENHAUER

"Life would be infinitely happier if we could only be born at the age of eighty and gradually approach eighteen."

—MARK TWAIN

"Advice in old age is foolish; for what can be more absurd than to increase our provisions for the road the nearer we approach to our journey's end."

—CICERO

"In old age we are like a batch of letters that someone has sent. We are no longer in the past, we have arrived."

—KNUT HAMSUN

MONEY

Money is something most intellectuals hold in contempt. This is because most of them don't have it, would like to have it, but don't want to admit wanting to have it. In fact, in the circles in which the true cognoscenti move, it is considered declassé to do anything for money. Instead there should be a "higher calling" of some kind—from God, society, the *New York Times* editorial page . . . whatever.

Intellectuals enjoy tossing off quotations about the absurdity of money— that it won't buy happiness, is the root of all evil, and so forth. It's best to do this in the presence of someone who has a great deal of money. For example, if you find yourself at a party in a Park Avenue apartment and the person next to you has taken a sip of Dom Pérignon from his cut-glass champagne flute while casually mentioning that he and his partner are wintering in the south of France this year on his yacht, you can let drop one of the following:

"The chief value of money lies in the fact that one lives in a world in which it is overestimated."

—H. L. MENCKEN

"Money often costs too much."

—RALPH WALDO EMERSON

"Endless money forms the sinews of war."

—CICERO (106 BCE–43 BCE) wrote Latin literature that is considered by many the apex of the Golden Age of Roman prose.

"Money is like manure, of very little use except to be spread."

—FRANCIS BACON

"Money is not required to buy one the necessity of the soul."

—HENRY DAVID THOREAU

"A wise man should have money in his head but not in his heart."

—JONATHAN SWIFT

"If money help a man to do good to others, it is of some value; but if not, it is simply a mass of evil, and the sooner it is got rid of, the better."

—SWAMI VIVEKENANDA

"It's the wretchedness of being rich that you have to live with rich people."

—LOGAN PEARSALL SMITH

"Too many of us look upon Americans as dollar chasers. This is a cruel libel, even if it is reiterated thoughtlessly by the Americans themselves."

—ALBERT EINSTEIN

"I choose the likely man in preference to the rich man. I want a man without money rather than money without a man."

—THEMISTOCLES (524 BCE–459 BCE)
played a major role in Athens' nascent democracy. He was a commander at the battle of Marathon in 490 BCE.

"If you want to know what God thinks of money, look at the people he gave it to."

—DOROTHY PARKER

O f course, when pushed on the point, intellectuals will admit that money is necessary. Not for them, of course, they hasten to add. But Ordinary People need it to get by. Thus, while idly turning the pages of the *New Yorker* or *The Nation* or flipping through channels to find the local PBS station, you can casually observe:

"Money isn't everything. But lack of money isn't anything."

—GEORGE S. KAUFMANN

"Money is like a sixth sense, and you can't make use of the other five without it."

—W. SOMERSET MAUGHAM

"Money can't buy friends, but it can get you a better class of enemy."

—SPIKE MILLIGAN (1918–2002)
was a comedian and creator of *The Goon Show*, a pioneering British comedy series of the 1940s and 1950s.

"He that is of the opinion money will do everything may well be suspected of doing everything for money."

—BENJAMIN FRANKLIN

"If you can count your money, you don't have a billion dollars."

—J. PAUL GETTY

"Be rich to yourself and poor to your friends."

—JUVENAL

"It is better to have a permanent income than to be fascinating."

—OSCAR WILDE

"I'd like to live as a poor man with lots of money."

—PABLO PICASSO

"A rich man is nothing but a poor man with money."

—W. C. FIELDS (1880–1946)
was one of the great comedians of early American film.

"Money is better than poverty, if only for financial reasons."

—WOODY ALLEN

"The only way not to think of money is to have a great deal of it."

—EDITH WHARTON

"You can be young without money. But you can't be old without it."

—TENNESSEE WILLIAMS

"Lack of money is the root of all evil."

—GEORGE BERNARD SHAW

In the recent past, money has been much in the news, particularly as invested in banks and the stock market. Banks and bankers are a bit like lawyers—always a good subject for snarky quotations. Try some of these on your friends in the financial industry.

"A banker is a fellow who lends you his umbrella when the sun is shining but wants it back the minute it begins to rain."
—MARK TWAIN

"The concerned investment banker is the one who blows the horn on his Mercedes as he drives through a red light."
—ANONYMOUS

"It is easier to rob by setting up a bank than by holding up a bank clerk."
—BERTOLT BRECHT (1898–1956)
German poet and playwright, is best known for his musical play (cowritten with Kurt Weil) *The Threepenny Opera*.

"Because bankers measure their self-worth in money, and pay themselves a lot of it, they think they're fine fellows and don't need to explain themselves."
—JOHN BUCHAN

"I believe that banking institutions are more dangerous to our liberties than standing armies."

—THOMAS JEFFERSON

Finally, of course, should the subject of your own income come up in conversation, it's best to turn it into a joke while at the same time making it clear that money is something you never think about, save in jest.

"My problem lies in reconciling my gross habits with my net income."

—ERROL FLYNN

"Money frees you from doing things you dislike. Since I dislike doing nearly everything, money is handy."

—GROUCHO MARX

"I have enough money to last me the rest of my life, unless I buy something."

—JACKIE MASON

SEX

Dorothy Parker once arrived at a Halloween party. "Come on in," the host said. "We're ducking for apples."

"Change one letter in that last sentence," muttered Mrs. Parker, "and you have the story of my life."

Intellectual attitudes toward sex are complicated. On the one hand, those who live the life of the mind have needs and drives like everyone else. On the other hand, they're rather embarrassed by them. For an intellectual, talking about sex is a bit like reaching for a well-thumbed copy of Marcus Aurelius's *Meditations* and discovering to his horror that he's picked up the *Sports Illustrated* swimsuit issue by mistake.

Therefore, the best way to approach the delicate topic of male-female relations in the bedroom is to make light of it, commenting over the wine and canapés with something along the following lines:

"Don't knock masturbation—it's sex with someone I love."

—WOODY ALLEN

"Sex. In America an obsession. In other parts of the world a fact."

—MARLENE DIETRICH

"Love is the answer, but while you are waiting for the answer, sex raises some pretty good questions."

—WOODY ALLEN

"Life without sex might be safer but it would be unbearably dull."

—H. L. MENCKEN

"Sex: the thing that takes up the least amount of time and causes the most amount of trouble."

—JOHN BARRYMORE
(1882–1942)

among the most charismatic and talented of the Barrymore family of actors, was noted for his portrayal of Richard III.

"Love ain't nothing but sex misspelled."

—HARLAN ELLISON

"When the authorities warn you of the dangers of having sex, there is an important lesson to be learned. Do not have sex with the authorities."

—MATT GROENING

"The tragedy is when you've got sex in the head instead of down where it belongs."

—D. H. LAWRENCE

"I believe that sex is a beautiful thing between two people. Between five, it's fantastic."

—WOODY ALLEN

"I think people should be free to engage in any sexual practices they choose; they should draw the line at goats, though."

—ELTON JOHN

"Nothing risqué, nothing gained."
—ALEXANDER WOOLLCOTT
(1887–1943)
was a leading New York theater critic.

"Sex is one of the most wholesome, beautiful, and natural experiences that money can buy."

—STEVE MARTIN

"Do you find it easy to get drunk on words," asks a character in Dorothy Sayers's novel *Gaudy Night*. "So much so," replies her companion, "that I am scarcely ever perfectly sober." Words can entice as easily as wine, and if conversation turns to the art of seduction, you can offer plenty of advice from the following.

"For women the best aphrodisiacs are words. The G-spot is in the ears. He who looks for it below there is wasting his time."

—ISABEL ALLENDE

"There are a number of mechanical devices which increase sexual arousal, particularly in women. Chief among these is the Mercedes-Benz 380SL convertible."

—P. J. O'ROURKE

"It's not true that I had nothing on. I had the radio on."

—MARILYN MONROE

"Christ died for our sins. Dare we make his martyrdom meaningless by not committing them?"

—JULES FEIFFER (1929–) is an American cartoonist and political activist, whose cartoons in the *Village Voice* won him a Pulitzer Prize.

"Graze on my lips; and if those hills be dry, stray lower, where the pleasant fountains lie."

—WILLIAM SHAKESPEARE

"Brevity is the soul of lingerie."

—DOROTHY PARKER

"Sex pleasure in woman is a kind of magic spell; it demands complete abandon; if words or movements oppose the magic of caresses, the spell is broken."

—SIMONE DE BEAUVOIR

"It's been so long since I made love I can't even remember who gets tied up."

—JOAN RIVERS

S ex is inextricably linked to two things far less romantic: marriage and children. If these come up, have something like the following handy:

"No matter how much cats fight, there always seem to be plenty of kittens."

—ABRAHAM LINCOLN

"Familiarity breeds contempt—and children."

—MARK TWAIN

"The reproduction of mankind is a great marvel and mystery. Had God consulted me in the matter, I should have advised him to continue the generation of the species by fashioning them out of clay."

—MARTIN LUTHER (1483–1546) was one of the originators of the Protestant Reformation and its most prominent spokesperson.

"The art of procreation and the members employed therein are so repulsive, that if it were not for the beauty of the faces and the adornments of the actors and the pent-up impulse, nature would lose the human species."

—LEONARDO DA VINCI

"You know, of course, that the Tasmanians, who never committed adultery, are now extinct."

—W. SOMERSET MAUGHAM

"I know nothing about sex because I was always married."

—ZSA ZSA GABOR

"The Love Bird is 100 percent faithful to his mate as long as they are locked in the same cage together."

—WILL CUPPY (1884–1949) was an American humorist whose best-known book is *The Decline and Fall of Practically Everybody*.

Should the subject of your own sex life come up, be prepared to pass it off lightly. There's nothing so boring to someone else than hearing about the great sex you're having with your boyfriend or girlfriend.

"If it wasn't for pickpockets and frisking at the airport, I'd have no sex life at all."

—RODNEY DANGERFIELD

"A terrible thing happened to me last night again—nothing."

—PHYLLIS DILLER

"Lead me not into temptation—I can find the way myself."

—RITA MAE BROWN

"Life is a sexually transmitted disease."

—R. D. LAING

"Sex," John Updike observed, "is like money; only too much is enough." It is perhaps not surprising that something necessary to the continuance of the human race preoccupies us so much. What is startling is the apparently excessive amount of time and effort it takes to get it right. In the following thoughts, you may find some helpful instruction—or at least something to show others that you know about the arts of love.

"When it comes to being a good lover, a guy has to ask a girl what she wants and be willing to give it to her."

—JENNA JAMESON

"Whoever called it necking was a poor judge of anatomy."

—GROUCHO MARX

"The difference between pornography and erotica is lighting."

—GLORIA LEONARD

"Sex is emotion in motion."

—MAE WEST (1893–1980)
one of film's earliest sex symbols, was wildly bawdy in an age that tried to greatly restrict such moments on the screen.

"We have reason to believe that man first walked upright to free his hands for masturbation."

—LILY TOMLIN

"Men reach their sexual peak at eighteen. Women reach theirs at thirty-five. Do you get the feeling that God is playing a practical joke?"

—RITA RUDNER

"Were kisses all the joys in bed

One woman would another wed."

—WILLIAM SHAKESPEARE

"Sexual intercourse is kicking death in the ass while singing."

—CHARLES BUKOWSKI
(1920–1994)
was an American poet and novelist. His works concentrated on ordinary citizens and the simple details of their lives.

JOHNNY AND FRANKIE WERE LOVERS.
OHO MY GOD..HOW THEY LOVED!
(OLD SONG)
JOHN HELD JR

"There is nothing safe about sex. There never will be."

—Norman Mailer

"One half of the world cannot understand the pleasures of the other."

—Jane Austen

"If sex is such a natural phenomenon, how come there are so many books on how to do it?"

—Bette Midler

"Sex is one of the nine reasons for reincarnation—the other eight are unimportant."

—Henry Miller

"Sexuality is the lyricism of the masses."

—Charles Baudelaire

"Sexual love is the most stupendous fact of the universe and the most magical mystery our poor blind senses know."

—Amy Lowell

"Sex and beauty are inseparable, like life and consciousness."

—D. H. Lawrence (1885–1930)
novelist and essayist, probed areas of human sexual relationships, defying many of the early publishing taboos on the subject.

"Sex lies at the root of life, and we can never learn to reverence life until we know how to understand sex."

—Henry Ellis

"Instruction in sex is as important as instruction in food; yet not only are our adolescents not taught the physiology of sex, but never warned that the strongest sexual attraction may exist between persons so incompatible in tastes and capacities that they could not endure living together for a week much less a lifetime."

—George Bernard Shaw

The point of sex—which sometimes people need to be reminded of—is to enjoy it. And there's nothing wrong with a laugh or two along the way. If things seem to be getting too serious in the bedroom, take out one of these and improve the mood.

"From the moment I was six, I felt sexy. And let me tell you, it was hell, sheer hell, waiting to do something about it."
—BETTE DAVIS

"I used to be Snow White, but I drifted."
—MAE WEST

"The ability to make love frivolously is the chief characteristic which distinguishes human beings from the beasts."
—HEYWOOD BROUN

"To err is human, but it feels divine."
—MAE WEST

"Some things are better than sex, and some are worse, but there's nothing exactly like it."

—W. C. FIELDS

"Sex appeal is 50 percent what you've got and 50 percent what people think you've got."

—Sophia Loren

"Sex is as important as eating or drinking and we ought to allow the one appetite to be satisfied with as little restraint or false modesty as the other."

—Marquis de Sade
(1740–1814)
whose name gave us Sadism, was a French aristocrat and author whose books dealt in detail with his sexual conquests.

"Sex contains all, bodies, souls,

Meanings, proofs, purities, delicacies, results, promulgations,

All hopes, benefactions, bestowals, all the passions, loves, beauties, delights of the earth,

All the governments, judges, gods."

—Walt Whitman

EDUCATION

Intellectuals, with a few exceptions, agree that education is important. However, most of them don't think that their schooling played a large role in educating them, and they're divided on whether schools should be improved or simply abolished. They admire teachers in general but seem to dislike those particular teachers who taught them, since they claim it takes years to undo the effects of poor instruction in the classroom. No matter what your educational background and experiences, be prepared to toss out something like these to show you recognize the inadequacy of formal education.

"A mind is a fire to be kindled, not a vessel to be filled."

—PLUTARCH

"It is, in fact, nothing short of a miracle that the modern methods of instruction have not entirely strangled the holy curiosity of inquiry."

—ALBERT EINSTEIN

"Nine tenths of education is encouragement."

—ANATOLE FRANCE

"Education is the transmission of civilization."

—WILL AND ARIEL DURANT

"Education is the best provision for old age."

—ARISTOTLE

"A well-informed mind is the best security against the contagion of folly and of vice."

—ANN RADCLIFFE (1764–1823)
author of early Gothic novels, is best known for *The Mysteries of Udolpho* and *The Italian*.

"Only the educated are free."

—EPICTETUS

"Perhaps the most valuable result of all education is the ability to make yourself do the thing you have to do, when it ought to be done, whether you like it or not."

—THOMAS HUXLEY

"The highest result of education is tolerance."

—HELEN KELLER

"Education's purpose is to replace an empty mind with an open one."

—Malcolm S. Forbes

There are also those who claim education is a harmful activity, tampering with a more virtuous ignorance or with knowledge derived from outside the confines of the classroom. "Ignorance," Oscar Wilde remarked, "is like a delicate exotic fruit; touch it and the bloom is gone." You can imply the uselessness of all educational systems while at the same time showing your own sophistication and erudition by casually lobbing a quotation such as the following into a conversation about learning.

"What does education often do? It makes a straight-cut ditch of a free, meandering brook."

—HENRY DAVID THOREAU

"Education: the inculcation of the incomprehensible into the indifferent by the incompetent."

—JOHN MAYNARD KEYNES

"Education is what remains when we have forgotten all that we have been taught."

—GEORGE SAVILE (1633–1695) was a leader of England's Glorious Revolution, which deposed James II and replaced him with William of Orange and his queen, Mary.

"Education . . . has produced a vast population able to read but unable to distinguish what is worth reading."

—G. M. TREVELYAN

"Thank goodness I was never sent to school. It would have rubbed off some of the originality."

—BEATRIX POTTER

"College isn't the place to go for ideas."

—HELEN KELLER

"A university is what a college becomes when the faculty loses interest in students."

—JOHN CIARDI

"Don't set your wit against a child."

—JONATHAN SWIFT

"In the first place God made idiots. This was for practice. Then He made School Boards."

—MARK TWAIN

"Fathers send their sons to college either because they went to college or because they didn't."

—L. L. HENDERSON

"The advantage of a classical education is that it enables you to despise the wealth that it prevents you from achieving."

—RUSSELL GREEN

"It is a thousand times better to have common sense without education than to have education without common sense.

—ROBERT G. INGERSOLL
(1833–1899)
was an outstanding freethinker, who defended the philosophic position of agnosticism.

"There is nothing so stupid as the educated man if you get him off the thing he was educated in."

—WILL ROGERS

"I have never let my schooling interfere with my education."

—MARK TWAIN

"I prefer the company of peasants because they have not been educated sufficiently to reason incorrectly."

—MICHEL DE MONTAIGNE

The purpose of education is to fill the empty vessel of the mind, to make students better, more productive members of society, to teach social responsibility, or to do all and none of these things. Any one of the following should be useful in the event that your friends start chatting about teachers and education.

"Everyone has a right to a university degree in America, even if it's in Hamburger Technology."

—CLIVE JAMES (1939–)
is a television personality in England and in Australia.

"The foundation of every state is the education of its youth."

—DIOGENES LAERTIUS

"The direction in which education starts a man will determine his future life."

—PLATO

"If you think education is expensive, try ignorance."

—DEREK CURTIS BOK

"Education is the ability to listen to almost anything without losing your temper or your self-confidence."

—ROBERT FROST

"Any genuine teaching will result, if successful, in someone's knowing how to bring about a better condition of things than existed earlier."

—JOHN DEWEY (1859–1952)
was the chief representative of pragmatic philosophy in America and a leader of the progressive education movement.

"Education is the transmission of civilization."

—WILL AND ARIEL DURANT

"That is what learning is. You suddenly understand something you've understood all your life, but in a new way."

—DORIS LESSING

"In a completely rational society, the best of us would aspire to be teachers and the rest of us would have to settle for something less, because passing civilization along from one generation to the next ought to be the highest honor and the highest responsibility anyone could have."

—LEE IACOCCA

"It must be remembered that the purpose of education is not to fill the minds of students with facts . . . it is to teach them to think, if that is possible, and always to think for themselves."

—ROBERT HUTCHINS

"The job of an educator is to teach students to see vitality in themselves."

—JOSEPH CAMPBELL

"Every time you stop a school, you will have to build a jail. What you gain at one end you lose at the other. It's like feeding a dog on his own tail. It won't fatten the dog."

—MARK TWAIN

"Learning is a treasure that will follow its owner everywhere."

—CHINESE PROVERB

"Education is not preparation for life; education is life itself."

—JOHN DEWEY

"The true teacher defends his pupils against his own personal influence."

—A. BRONSON ALCOTT

FAME

Fame is deplored largely by those who are famous, much as money is held in contempt by those who have a lot of it. We are living in a time when the definition of "famous" has extended from people who've actually done something to people who are famous for being underwear-challenged, such as Paris Hilton or Britney Spears. Probably the most quoted comment about fame is Andy Warhol's "In the future everyone will be world-famous for fifteen minutes." It's instructive to keep an eye on the tabloid pages to determine who's on their fourteenth minute.

Before the latter half of the twentieth century, fame was something people worked to acquire, though they often pretended not to. Today, when it seems everyone is striving to be on Reality TV, you can display your contempt for such vulgar ambitions by quoting something like this:

"Fame is the thirst of youth."

—LORD BYRON

"The strongest poison ever known came from Caesar's laurel crown."

—WILLIAM BLAKE (1757–1827) was a poet, painter, and printmaker, who unified all these talents to create a strange cycle of myth, poetry, and art.

"True glory takes root and even spreads; all false pretences, like flowers, fall to the ground; nor can any counterfeit last long."

—CICERO

"Worldly fame is but a breath of wind that blows now this way, and now that, and changes name as it changes direction."

—DANTE ALIGHIERI

"He that pursues fame with just claims, trusts his happiness to the winds; but he that endeavors after it by false merit, has to fear, not only the violence of the storm, but the leaks of his vessel."

—SAMUEL JOHNSON

"The fame of great men ought to be judged always by the means they used to acquire it."

—FRANÇOIS DE LA ROCHEFOUCAULD

"True glory consists in doing what deserves to be written; in writing what deserves to be read; and in so living as to make the world happier and better for our living in it."

—PLINY THE ELDER

"Fame has also this great drawback, that if we pursue it, we must direct our lives so as to please the fancy of men."

—BARUCH SPINOZA

"Fame is no plant that grows on mortal soil."

—JOHN MILTON (1608–1674) is considered by many to be England's greatest poet outside of Shakespeare. His masterwork is the epic poem *Paradise Lost*.

"Fame and power are the objects of all men. Even their partial fruition is gained by very few; and that, too, at the expense of social pleasure, health, conscience, life."

—BENJAMIN DISRAELI

"What is popularly called fame is nothing but an empty name and a legacy from paganism."

—DESIDERIUS ERASMUS

"All the fame you should look for in life is to have lived it quietly."

—MICHEL DE MONTAIGNE

"Fame is like a river, that beareth up things light and swollen, and drowns things weighty and solid."

—FRANCIS BACON

"All is ephemeral—fame and the famous as well."

—MARCUS AURELIUS

"Fame is a fickle food

Upon a shifting plate."

—EMILY DICKINSON

"Fame is the perfume of heroic deeds."

—SOCRATES

"Fame and tranquility can never be bedfellows."

—MICHEL DE MONTAIGNE (1533–1592) popularized the essay (from the French "to try") as a literary form.

Gradually, fame has come to be seen as an end in itself, something decried by thinkers of the past but hailed by some of today's entertainers. The following quotations should be pitched in tones of contempt, showing that although the foolish may be seduced by the bubble reputation, you are above such fleeting things.

"Don't confuse fame with success. Madonna is one; Helen Keller is the other."

—ERMA BOMBECK

"I won't be happy till I'm as famous as God."

—MADONNA

"I want to be famous everywhere."

—LUCIANO PAVAROTTI

"The professional celebrity, male and female, is the crowning result of the star system of a society that makes a fetish of competition. In America, this system is carried to the point where a man who can knock a small white ball into a series of holes in the ground with more efficiency than anyone else thereby gains social access to the president of the United States."

—C. WRIGHT MILLS

"Fame is fickle and I know it. It has its compensations, but it also has its drawbacks, and I've experienced them both."

—MARILYN MONROE
(1926–1962)
showed her comedic abilities in Billy Wilder's
Some Like It Hot. She was found dead in 1962,
an apparent victim of a drug overdose.

"I'm shy, paranoid, whatever word you want to use. I hate fame. I've done everything I can to avoid it."

—JOHNNY DEPP

"Fame hit me like a ton of bricks."

—EMINEM

"Sometimes I wish I weren't famous."

—TAMMY WYNETTE

You can show your contempt for worldly fame by gently disparaging it while at the same time implying that if you were to get your fifteen minutes it would be for something worthwhile, like curing cancer or stopping world hunger.

"I'm afraid of losing my obscurity. Genuineness only thrives in the dark. Like celery."
—ALDOUS HUXLEY

"It is a short walk from the hallelujah to the hoot."
—VLADIMIR NABOKOV

"A celebrity is one who is known to many persons he is glad he doesn't know."
—H. L. MENCKEN

"The highest form of vanity is a love of fame."
—GEORGE SANTAYANA

"He lives in fame that died in virtue's cause."
—WILLIAM SHAKESPEARE

"The fact that my fifteen minutes of fame has extended a little longer than fifteen minutes is somewhat surprising to me and completely baffling to my wife."
—BARACK OBAMA

"The fame you earn has a different taste from the fame that is forced upon you."
—GLORIA VANDERBILT (1924–)
American heiress and socialite, was the subject of a conflict between her guardians, who sought to control her trust fund.

"It is strange to be known so universally and yet to be so lonely."
—ALBERT EINSTEIN

"Fame is proof that people are gullible."
—RALPH WALDO EMERSON

"I do not like the man who squanders life for fame; give me the man who living makes a name."
—EMILY DICKINSON

"Even those who write against fame wish for the fame of having written well, and those who read their works desire the fame of having read them."
—BLAISE PASCAL

"If you modestly enjoy your fame you are not unworthy to rank with the holy."

—JOHANN WOLFGANG VON GOETHE (1749–1832) was a leader of the German Romantic movement in art and literature.

"The longer a man's fame is likely to last, the longer it will be in coming."

—ARTHUR SCHOPENHAUER

"Good fame is like fire; when you have kindled you may easily preserve it; but if you extinguish it, you will not easily kindle it again."

—FRANCIS BACON

"Fame usually comes to those who are thinking about something else."

—OLIVER WENDELL HOLMES

PART VII
NATURE

"Adopt the pace of nature.

Her secret is patience."

—RALPH WALDO EMERSON

NATURE

"Nature red in tooth and claw," wrote Alfred Lord Tennyson in the nineteenth century, citing the inexorable, merciless character of the natural world. Yet for centuries humans have respected and even worshipped nature. Today, many reject not only fur and sport hunting but renounce meat altogether in an effort to live at peace with plants and animals. It's not hard to see why: In a world filled with violence and horror, nature seems to offer a serene vista of harmony and peace. You too can draw and dispense inspiration from the words of those who adore nature as a friend and companion.

"The best remedy for those who are afraid, lonely or unhappy is to go outside, somewhere where they can be quiet, alone with the heavens, nature, and God. Because only then does one feel that all is as it should be and that God wishes to see people happy, amidst the simple beauty of nature."

—ANNE FRANK

"Nature is an infinite sphere of which the center is everywhere and the circumference nowhere."

—BLAISE PASCAL (1623–1662) wrote on subjects ranging from geometry and probability theory to physics.

"My best Acquaintances are those

With whom I spoke no Word—

The Stars that stated come to Town

Esteemed Me never rude

Although to their Celestial Call

I failed to make reply—

My constant—reverential Face

Sufficient Courtesy."

—EMILY DICKINSON

"Study nature, love nature, stay close to nature. It will never fail you."

—FRANK LLOYD WRIGHT

"Those who contemplate the beauty of the earth find reserves of strength that will endure as long as life lasts."

—RACHEL CARSON (1907–1964)
nature writer and marine biologist, exposed the damaging use of pesticides in her book *Silent Spring*.

"What humbugs we are, who pretend to live for Beauty, and never see the Dawn!"

—LOGAN PEARSALL SMITH

"When I go into the garden with a spade, and dig a bed, I feel such an exhilaration and health that I discover that I have been defrauding myself all this time in letting others do for me what I should have done with my own hands."

—RALPH WALDO EMERSON

"To see a world in a grain of sand,

And a heaven in a wild flower,

Hold infinity in the palm of your hand,

An eternity in an hour."

—WILLIAM BLAKE

"The goal of life is living in agreement with nature."

—ZENO

"To sit in the shade on a fine day and look upon verdure is the most perfect refreshment."

—JANE AUSTEN

"Look deep into nature, and then you will understand everything better."

—ALBERT EINSTEIN

"What would the world be, once bereft

Of wet and wildness? Let them be left,

O let them be left, wildness and wet,

Long live the weeds and the wildness yet."
— GERARD MANLEY HOPKINS
(1844–1889)
a leading Victorian poet, was much ahead of
his time in his use of imagery.

"I'll tell you how the sun rose a ribbon at a time."
— EMILY DICKINSON

"Breathless, we flung us on a windy hill,

Laughed in the sun, and kissed the lovely grass."
— RUPERT BROOKE

"I am in love with the green earth."
— CHARLES LAMB

"The world will never starve for wonder but only for want of wonder."
— G. K. CHESTERTON

"I think it annoys God if you walk by the color purple in a field and don't notice."

— ALICE WALKER

William Wordsworth, wandering lonely as a cloud, found his spirit renewed by a field of golden daffodils. He's by no means the first to discover beauty and wonder in flowers. If you send a bouquet to someone, accompany it with a sentiment.

"Flowers are heaven's masterpiece."
—DOROTHY PARKER

"The sun does not shine for a few trees and flowers but for the wide world's joy."
—HENRY WARD BEECHER

"The earth laughs in flowers."
—RALPH WALDO EMERSON

"Flowers are the sweetest things that God ever made and forgot to put a soul into."
—HENRY WADSWORTH LONG-
FELLOW (1807–1882)
wrote his poems on distinctively American themes, such as "Paul Revere's Ride" and "The Song of Hiawatha."

"A weed is no more than a flower in disguise."
—JAMES RUSSELL LOWELL

Nineteenth- and twentieth-century writers believed that nature was a guide to a higher purpose. It represented a divine order and beauty that can't be found in the works of Man. You can elevate the tone of any conversation about nature by quoting from the following.

"To me a lush carpet of pine needles or spongy grass is more welcome than the most luxurious Persian rug."
—HELEN KELLER

"Nature abhors a vacuum, and if I can only walk with sufficient carelessness I am sure to be filled."
—HENRY DAVID THOREAU

"I've made an odd discovery. Every time I talk to a savant I feel quite sure that happiness is no longer a possibility. Yet when I talk with my gardener, I'm convinced of the opposite."
—BERTRAND RUSSELL

"And how should a beautiful, ignorant stream of water know it heads for an early release—out across the desert, running toward the Gulf, below sea level, to murmur its lullaby, and see the Imperial Valley rise out of burning sand with cotton blossoms, wheat, watermelons, roses, how should it know?"

—CARL SANDBURG

"I will be the gladdest thing under the sun.

I will touch a hundred flowers and not pick one."

—EDNA ST. VINCENT MILLAY
(1892–1950)
was a poet and part of the Greenwich Village artistic scene in the 1930s and 1940s.

"People with a planet without flowers would think we must be mad with joy the whole time to have such things about us."

—IRIS MURDOCH

"I believe a leaf of grass is no less than the journey-work of the stars."

—WALT WHITMAN

"If a man walks in the woods for love of them half of each day, he is in danger of being regarded as a loafer. But if he spends his days as a speculator, shearing off those woods and making the earth bald before her time, he is deemed an industrious and enterprising citizen."

—HENRY DAVID THOREAU

"I love to think of nature as an unlimited broadcasting station, through which God speaks to us every hour, if we will only tune in."

—GEORGE WASHINGTON CARVER

THE QUOTABLE INTELLECTUAL

Nature can be unforgiving as well as beautiful, and not all thoughts about her are benevolent. If you want to resist a close friend's suggestion that a brisk walk of ten miles through muddy fields in a driving rainstorm would be just the thing to get the blood circulating, try quoting from the following:

"Nature has no mercy at all. Nature says, 'I'm going to snow. If you have on a bikini and no snowshoes, that's tough. I am going to snow anyway.'"

—MAYA ANGELOU

"In nature there are neither rewards nor punishments. There are consequences."

—ROBERT G. INGERSOLL

"If people think nature is their friend, then they sure don't need an enemy."

—KURT VONNEGUT

"Adapt or perish, now as was ever, is nature's inexorable imperative."

—H. G. WELLS

Many have noted the close connection between Nature and Art. Indeed, for much of the nineteenth century artists and poets believed that true Art derived from Nature. Although nowadays intellectuals reject this as naïve and simplistic, you can still stir cocktail conversation with something along these lines:

"The poetry of the earth is never dead."

—JOHN KEATS (1795–1821) had significant influence after his early death, though his poetry is more notable for what it might have become than for what it is.

"Keep your love of nature, for that is the true way to understand art more and more."

—VINCENT VAN GOGH

"Nature is a revelation of God; art is a revelation of man."

—HENRY WADSWORTH LONGELLOW

"To the artist there is never anything ugly in nature."

—August Rodin

"If nature were not beautiful, it would not be worth knowing, and if nature were not worth knowing, life would not be worth living."

—Henri Poincaré

"Nature is beneficent. I praise her and all her works. She is silent and wise. She is cunning but for good ends. She has brought me here and will also lead me away."

—Johann Wolfgang von Goethe

A bove all, you can quote the wisdom of the past and present to impress upon your listeners the need to respect Nature and her close friendship with humans. If we don't destroy her, she has wonderful revelations for us.

"Man has been endowed with reason, with the power to create, so that he can add to what he's been given. But up to now he hasn't been a creator, only a destroyer. Forests keep disappearing, rivers dry up, wild life's become extinct, the climate's ruined and the land grows poorer and uglier every day."

—Anton Chekhov

"We cannot command nature except by obeying her."

—Francis Bacon

"God writes the gospel not in the Bible alone, but on trees and flowers and clouds and stars."

—Martin Luther

"The sun, with all those plants revolving around it and dependent upon it, can still ripen a bunch of grapes as if it had nothing else in the universe to do."

—GALILEO GALILEI
(1564–1642)

was a scientist and a strong supporter of Copernicus's theory of a sun-centered planetary system.

"Forget not that the earth delights to feel your bare feet and the winds long to play with your hair."

—KAHLIL GIBRAN

"If one way be better than another, that you may be sure is Nature's way."

—ARISTOTLE

"There is not a sprig of grass that shoots uninteresting to me."

—THOMAS JEFFERSON

"Maybe nature is fundamentally ugly, chaotic, and complicated. But if it's like that, then I want out."

—STEVEN WEINBERG

"The day, water, sun, moon, night—I do not have to purchase these things with money."

—PLAUTUS

"The fog comes in on little cat feet. It sits looking over the harbor and city on silent haunches and then moves on."

—CARL SANDBURG

"Nature reserves the right to inflict upon her children the most terrifying jests."

—THORNTON WILDER

"Let us permit nature to have her way. She understands her business better than we do."

—MICHEL DE MONTAIGNE

Animals

Mohandas Gandhi, among the great figures of twentieth-century national movements, once remarked, "The greatness of a nation and its moral progress can be judged by the way its animals are treated."

Humans love animals. They are affectionate, loyal, uncomplaining (mostly), and reliable. Yet throughout history, they've been mistreated, abused, and killed with no good reason. Animals serve to ground us and remind us of our place in the scheme of things. These words can do the same.

"I like pigs. Dogs look up to us. Cats look down on us. Pigs treat us as equals."

—Winston Churchill

"Animals are such agreeable friends—they ask no questions, they pass no criticisms."

—George Eliot

"Horse sense is the thing a horse has that keeps it from betting on people."

—W. C. Fields

"The bee is more honored than other animals, not because she labors but because she labors for others."

—St. John Chrysostom (347–407)

an early father of the church, is honored as a saint by the Eastern Orthodox faith.

"Don't approach a goat from the front, a horse from the back, or a fool from any side."

—Yiddish proverb

"Animals generally return the love you lavish on them by a swift bite in passing—not unlike friends and wives."

—Gerald Durrell

"Life is as dear to a mute creature as it is to man. Just as one wants happiness and fears pain, just as one wants to live and not die, so do other creatures."

—DALAI LAMA

"Mankind's true moral test, its fundamental test (which lies deeply buried from view), consists of its attitude towards those who are at its mercy: animals. And in this respect mankind has suffered a fundamental debacle, a debacle so fundamental that all others stem from it."

—MILAN KUNDERA

"I don't believe in the concept of hell, but if I did I would think of it as filled with people who were cruel to animals."

—GARY LARSON

"A Robin Redbreast in a cage

Puts all Heaven in a Rage."

—WILLIAM BLAKE

"The indifference, callousness and contempt that so many people exhibit toward animals is evil first because it results in great suffering in animals, and second because it results in an incalculably great impoverishment of the human spirit."

—ASHLEY MONTAGU

"If you have men who will exclude any of God's creatures from the shelter of compassion and pity, you will have men who will deal likewise with their fellow men."

—ST. FRANCIS OF ASSISI
(1181–1226)
founder of the Franciscan order, dedicated his life to poverty and charity. He is the patron saint of animals.

"He who is cruel to animals becomes hard also in his dealings with men. We can judge the heart of a man by his treatment of animals."

—IMMANUEL KANT

"An animal's eyes have the power to speak a great language."

—MARTIN BUBER

Humans by and large tend to separate into two great groups: cat people and dog people. Depending on which group you fall into, you can use the following thoughts to propel conversation.

"Dogs come when they're called; cats take a message and get back to you later."

—MARY BLY

"A black cat crossing your path signifies that the animal is going somewhere."

—GROUCHO MARX

"The problem with cats is that they get the same exact look whether they see a moth or an ax murderer."

—PAULA POUNDSTONE

"Cats are connoisseurs of comfort."

—JAMES HERRIOTT (1916–1995) pen name of Alf Wight, a Yorkshire veterinarian whose memoir was published in the United States as *All Creatures Great and Small*.

"Never wear anything that panics the cat."

—P. J. O'ROURKE

"The great pleasure of a dog is that you may make a fool of yourself with him and not only will he not scold you, but he will make a fool of himself too."

—SAMUEL BUTLER

"Time spent with cats is never wasted."

—SIGMUND FREUD

"Dogs are getting bigger, according to a leading dog manufacturer."

—LEO ROSTEN

"The dog has got more fun out of Man than Man has got out of the dog, for the clearly demonstrable reason that Man is the more laughable of the two animals."

—JAMES THURBER

"You enter into a certain amount of madness when you marry a person with pets."

—NORA EPHRON (1941–) author and film director, has created a number of hit movies, including *Sleepless in Seattle*, *Julie and Julia*, and *When Harry Met Sally*.

The most basic point about animals and intellectuals is that the latter, except under extreme provocation, don't shoot or eat the former. Instead, intellectuals can be counted on to respect animals, sometimes to extremes. Quote something like this to them to make them feel better.

"Animals are my friends, and I don't eat my friends."

—GEORGE BERNARD SHAW

"Until one has loved an animal, a part of one's soul remains unawakened."

—ANATOLE FRANCE

"Any glimpse into the life of an animal quickens our own and makes it so much the larger and better in every way."

—JOHN MUIR

"Animals have these advantages over man: They have no theologians to instruct them, their funerals cost them nothing, and no one starts lawsuits over their wills."

—VOLTAIRE

"The animals of the world exist for their own reasons. They were not made for humans any more than black people were made for white, or women created for men."

—ALICE WALKER (1944–)
is an American author, best known for her novel *The Color Purple*, which was made into a hit film and for which she won a Pulitzer Prize.

"The best thing about animals is that they don't talk much."

—THORNTON WILDER

"Animals give me more pleasure through the viewfinder of a camera than they ever did in the crosshairs of a gunsight. And after I've finished 'shooting,' my unharmed victims are still around for others to enjoy. I have developed a deep respect for animals. I consider them fellow living creatures with certain rights that should not be violated any more than those of humans."

—JIMMY STEWART

"The squirrel that you kill in jest, dies in earnest."

—HENRY DAVID THOREAU

"I ask people why they have deer heads on their walls. They always say because it's such a beautiful animal. There you go. I think my mother is attractive, but I have photographs of her."

—ELLEN DeGENERES

"When a man wantonly destroys one of the works of man we call him a vandal. When he destroys one of the works of God we call him a sportsman."

—JOSEPH WOOD KRUTCH

"The fascination of shooting as a sport depends almost wholly on whether you are at the right or wrong end of a gun."

—P. G. WODEHOUSE (1881–1975) is best known as the creator of the comic duo Bertie Wooster and his valet Jeeves.

"A growing and increasingly influential movement of philosophers, ethicists, law professors, and activists are convinced that the great moral struggle of our time will be for the rights of animals."

—MICHAEL POLLAN

"To a man whose mind is free there is something even more intolerable in the sufferings of animals than in the sufferings of man. For with the latter it is at least admitted that suffering is evil and that the man who causes it is a criminal. But thousands of animals are uselessly butchered every day without a shadow of remorse. If any man were to refer to it, he would be thought ridiculous. And that is the unpardonable crime."

—ROMAIN ROLLAND

"All animals are equal, but some animals are more equal than others."

—GEORGE ORWELL

"If having a soul means being able to feel love and loyalty and gratitude, then animals are better off than a lot of humans."

—JAMES HERRIOTT

"It is just like man's vanity and impertinence to call an animal dumb because it is dumb to his dull perceptions."

—MARK TWAIN

"All of the animals except for man know that the principle business of life is to enjoy it."

—SAMUEL BUTLER

PART VIII

WORK

"A business exists to

create a customer."

—PETER DRUCKER

BUSINESS

President Calvin Coolidge remarked in the 1920s, "The business of America is business." Of course, since then we've had the Great Depression, one or two world wars, a couple of smaller wars, an extended economic boom, and the Great Recession, not to mention 9/11, disco, and the advent of reality TV. So it's possible that the business of America is a bit more complicated than Coolidge made it out to be.

Whatever the case, business has always been at the heart of American life and culture. If you want to sound informed, let off a quote from one of these.

"Whenever you see a successful business, someone once made a courageous decision."

—PETER DRUCKER

"The goal of war is peace, of business, leisure."

—ARISTOTLE

"No nation was ever ruined by trade."

—BENJAMIN FRANKLIN

"Business is a combination of war and sport."

—ANDRÉ MAUROIS

"Business, more than any other occupation, is a continual dealing with the future; it is a continual calculation, an instinctive exercise in foresight."

—HENRY R. LUCE (1898–1967)
founder of *Time* magazine and a powerful figure in the Republican Party and conservative politics.

"Every young man would do well to remember that all successful business stands on the foundation of morality."

—HENRY WARD BEECHER

"Hell, there are no rules here—we're trying to accomplish something."

—THOMAS EDISON

Americans admire ambition and energy in business. Business people aren't slow about letting others known How They Did It. In fact, with all the business advice available, it's surprising that all businesses aren't wildly successful. If someone complains to you about their struggling enterprise, quote them these words of wisdom.

"Good business leaders create a vision, articulate the vision, passionately own the vision, and relentlessly drive it to completion."

—JACK WELCH

"The success combination in business is: Do what you do better . . . and do more of what you do."

—DAVID JOSEPH SCHWARTZ

"Failure is simply the opportunity to begin again, this time more intelligently."

—HENRY FORD (1863–1947) founder of the Ford Motor Company, epitomized the early twentieth-century American industrialist.

"In the end, all business operations can be reduced to three words: people, product, and profits. Unless you've got a good team, you can't do much with the other two."

—LEE IACOCCA

"To succeed in business it is necessary to make others see things as you see them."

—JOHN H. PATTERSON

"Executive ability is deciding quickly and getting somebody else to do the work."

—EARL NIGHTINGALE

"The most successful businessman is the man who holds onto the old just as long as it is good and grabs the new just as soon as it is better."

—LEE IACOCCA

"A cardinal principle of Total Quality escapes too many managers: you cannot continuously improve interdependent systems and processes until you progressively perfect interdependent, interpersonal relationships."

—STEPHEN COVEY

"The final test of a leader is that he leaves behind him in other men the conviction and the will to carry on."

—WALTER LIPPMANN

"It is not the employer who pays the wages. He only handles the money. It is the product that pays the wages."

—HENRY FORD

"Effective leadership is putting first things first. Effective management is discipline, carrying it out."

—STEPHEN COVEY

"Obstacles are those frightful things you see when you take your eyes off your goal."

—HENRY FORD

"The buck stops with the guy who signs the checks."

—RUPERT MURDOCH

"Almost all quality improvement comes via simplification of design, manufacturing . . . layout, processes, and procedures."

—TOM PETERS (1942–)
is a well-known business writer and speaker. His book *In Search of Excellence* is today considered a business classic.

There are some who are a good deal more cynical about business and executives than others. If an MBA of your acquaintance gets a swelled head, bring her or him down to earth with one of these.

"In college, Yuppies major in business administration. If to meet certain requirements they have to take a liberal arts course, they take Business Poetry."

—DAVE BARRY

"Competition brings out the best in products and the worst in people."

—DAVID SARNOFF (1891–1971)
was a pioneer of early television and founder of the National Broadcasting Company.

"About the time we can make the ends meet, somebody moves the ends."

—HERBERT HOOVER

"Informed decision-making comes from a long tradition of guessing and then blaming others for inadequate results."

—SCOTT ADAMS

"An advertising agency is 85 percent confusion and 15 percent commission."

—FRED ALLEN

"Corporation, n. An ingenious device for obtaining individual profit without individual responsibility."

—AMBROSE BIERCE

"I find it rather easy to portray a businessman. Being bland, rather cruel, and incompetent comes naturally to me."

—JOHN CLEESE

"Remind people that profit is the difference between revenue and expense. This makes you look smart."

—SCOTT ADAMS (1957–)
from the vantage point of his daily comic strip *Dilbert* chronicles the insanities of cubicle life.

"Give a man a fish and he will eat for a day. Teach a man to fish and he will eat for a lifetime. Teach a man to create an artificial shortage of fish and he will eat steak."

—JAY LENO

In the end we rely on innovation and know-how to get us through any business crisis, led by executives who are strong, smart, capable, and—we hope—ethical. To keep yourself grounded, and to remind others of the importance of honesty in business, quote from this selection of thoughts.

"To open a shop is easy; to keep it open is an art."

—CHINESE PROVERB

"It is difficult but not impossible to conduct strictly honest business."

—MOHANDAS GANDHI

"In the business world, the rearview mirror is always clearer than the windshield."

—WARREN BUFFETT (1930–)
is America's foremost investor and one of the richest men in the world.

"I buy when other people are selling."

—JOHN PAUL GETTY

"Government 'help' to business is just as disastrous as government persecution . . . . The only way a government can be of service to national prosperity is by keeping its hands off."

—AYN RAND

"Economic depression cannot be cured by legislative action or executive pronouncement. Economic wounds must be healed by the action of the cells of the economic body—the producers and consumers themselves."

—HERBERT HOOVER

"And while the law of competition may be sometimes hard for the individual, it is best for the race, because it ensures the survival of the fittest in every department."

—ANDREW CARNEGIE

"It is not from the benevolence of the butcher, the brewer, or the baker that we expect our dinner, but from their regard to their own interest."

—ADAM SMITH (1723–1790)
was a Scottish economist whose book
The Wealth of Nations set out the basic elements of the capitalist system.

"If you owe the bank $100 that's your problem. If you owe the bank $100 million, that's the bank's problem."

—John Paul Getty

"A business that makes nothing but money is a poor business."

—Henry Ford

"Drive thy business, let not that drive thee."

—Benjamin Franklin

"Sometimes when you innovate, you make mistakes. It is best to admit them quickly, and get on with improving your other innovations."

—Steve Jobs

"The first rule of any technology used in a business is that automation applied to an efficient operation will magnify the efficiency. The second is that automation applied to an inefficient operation will magnify the inefficiency."

—Bill Gates

"If you cannot work with love but only with distaste, it is better that you should leave your work."

—Kahlil Gibran

"I want to put a ding in the universe."

—Steve Jobs (1955–)
founder and CEO of Apple Computers, is considered to be on the cutting edge of innovation in information technology.

"I understand small business growth. I was one."

—George W. Bush

TECHNOLOGY

Ever since cavemen began to bang rocks together, humans have been fascinated and repelled by technology. Even then, there were probably other cavemen who complained that rock banging would lead to Bad Things and that the noise kept them up at night after a hard day of hunting sabertooth tigers. On the other hand, others were busy developing Banging Rocks 2.0—Now with Special Sabertooth Tiger Stunning App. Since then, the debate has only intensified as we've felt ourselves more and more at the mercy of our inventions. If you find yourself standing with a group of R&D engineers, all of them pontificating about the revolutionary features of their new software system, use one of these quotations to remind them of the triviality of their work.

"All of the biggest technological inventions created by man—the airplane, the automobile, the computer—says little about his intelligence, but speaks volumes about his laziness."

—MARK KENNEDY

"Inventor, n. A person who makes an ingenious arrangement of wheels, levers and springs, and believes it civilization."

—AMBROSE BIERCE

"It has become appallingly obvious that our technology has exceeded our humanity."

—ALBERT EINSTEIN

"If it keeps up, man will atrophy all his limbs but the push-button finger."

—FRANK LLOYD WRIGHT

"Soon silence will have passed into legend. Man has turned his back on silence. Day after day he invents machines and devices that increase noise and distract humanity from the essence of life, contemplation, meditation . . . tooting, howling, screeching, booming, crashing, whistling, grinding, and trilling bolster his ego. His anxiety subsides. His inhuman void spreads monstrously like a gray vegetation."

—JEAN ARP

"Technological progress has merely provided us with more efficient means for going backwards."

—ALDOUS HUXLEY

"The drive toward complex technical achievement offers a clue to why the U.S. is good at space gadgetry and bad at slum problems."

—JOHN KENNETH GALBRAITH

"Once upon a time we were just plain people. But that was before we began having relationships with mechanical systems. Get involved with a machine and sooner or later you are reduced to a factor."

—ELLEN GOODMAN (1941–)
is an American journalist and columnist. She retired from writing her syndicated column in 2010.

"It is questionable if all the mechanical inventions yet made have lightened the day's toil of any human being."

—JOHN STUART MILL

"We are becoming the servants in thought, as in action, of the machine we have created to serve us."

—JOHN KENNETH GALBRAITH

Of all our inventions, computers scare us the most. Whether it's Hal in *2001: A Space Odyssey* taking over the space ship and trying to kill the astronauts ... or the supercomputer in *WarGames* trying to start a war with the Soviet Union ... or Arnold Schwarzenegger, back from the future to destroy the hope of the human race .... Computers seem to be something that could easily get out of control. Lest computer programmers in your vicinity wax too enthusiastic about the newest products of Microsoft and Apple, have one of the following quotations ready to take the wind out of their sails.

"The real danger is not that computers will begin to think like men, but that men will begin to think like computers."

—SYDNEY J. HARRIS

"One day soon the Gillette company will announce the development of a razor that, thanks to a computer microchip, can actually travel ahead in time and shave beard hairs that don't even exist yet."

—DAVE BARRY

"A computer is like an Old Testament god, with a lot of rules and no mercy."

—JOSEPH CAMPBELL

"Where is all the knowledge we lost with information?"

—T. S. ELIOT

"Computers make it easier to do a lot of things, but most of the things they make it easier to do don't need to be done."

—ANDY ROONEY

"Computers are useless. They can only give you answers."

—PABLO PICASSO

"Computer dating is fine if you're a computer."

—RITA MAE BROWN (1944–)
is a novelist whose early novel, *Rubyfruit Jungle,* was one of the first to bring lesbianism into mainstream literature.

"To err is human, but to really foul things up, you need a computer."

—PAUL ERLICH

Naturally, there are people who are much more optimistic about computers and their role in society. Not too surprisingly, a lot of these people work in the information technology industry. But it's worthwhile to have some of their comments handy on your laptop.

"The number one benefit of information technology is that it empowers people to do what they want to do. It lets people be creative. It lets people be productive. It lets people learn things they didn't think they could learn before, and so in a sense it is all about potential."

—STEVE BALLMER

"It's a fact that more people watch television and get their information that way than read books. I find new technology and new ways of communication very exciting and would like to do more in this field."

—STEPHEN COVEY

"Information technology and business are becoming inextricably interwoven. I don't think anybody can talk meaningfully about one without the talking about the other."

—BILL GATES

"The Internet is the Viagra of big business."

—JACK WELCH (1935–)
was CEO of General Electric
for almost two decades.

"There might be new technology, but technological progress itself was nothing new—and over the years it had not destroyed jobs, but created them."

—MARGARET THATCHER

"Technology is a gift of God. After the gift of life, it is perhaps the greatest of God's gifts. It is the mother of civilizations, of arts, and of sciences."

—FREEMAN DYSON

"If GM had kept up with technology like the computer industry has, we would all be driving $25 cars that got 1,000 MPG."

—BILL GATES

"The science of today is the technology of tomorrow."

—EDWARD TELLER

"The technologies which have had the most profound effects on human life are usually simple."

—Freeman Dyson

Still, after all is said and done and despite our technological advancements and inclinations, we face the future with a certain nervousness. If you want to sound appropriately anxious about the future of the planet and of humanity, remember these thoughts.

"For a successful technology, reality must take precedence over public relations, for Nature cannot be fooled."

—Richard P. Feynman

"Technology . . . is a queer thing. It brings you great gifts with one hand, and it stabs you in the back with the other."

—C. P. Snow

"The system of nature, of which man is a part, tends to be self-balancing, self-adjusting, self-cleansing. Not so with technology."

—E. F. Schumacher

"I am sorry to say that there is too much point to the wisecrack that life is extinct on other planets because their scientists were more advanced than ours."

—JOHN F. KENNEDY

"Humanity is acquiring all the right technology for all the wrong reasons."

—R. BUCKMINSTER FULLER

"The greatest task before civilization at present is to make machines what they ought to be, the slaves, instead of the masters of men."

—HAVELOCK ELLIS (1859–1939)
British sex theorist and activist, was one of the first to believe that homosexuality was not a disease.

"You cannot endow even the best machine with initiative; the jolliest steam-roller will not plant flowers."

—WALTER LIPPMANN

"We live in a society exquisitely dependent on science and technology, in which hardly anyone knows anything about science and technology."

—CARL SAGAN

"If we continue to develop our technology without wisdom or prudence, our servant may prove to be our executioner."

—OMAR BRADLEY

"The real problem is not whether machines think but whether men do."

—B. F. SKINNER

"There are three roads to ruin: women, gambling, and technicians. The most pleasant is with women, the quickest is with gambling, but the surest is with technicians."

—GEORGES POMPIDOU

"Lo! Men have become the tools of their tools."

—HENRY DAVID THOREAU

"God never made his work for man to mend."

—JOHN DRYDEN

"Technology. No place for wimps."

—SCOTT ADAMS

PART IX

RELIGION

"Religion is what an individual does
with his solitariness."

—ALFRED NORTH WHITEHEAD

RELIGION

Religion is one subject that can be counted upon to start arguments, break up friendships, and occasionally to begin wars. This isn't surprising; it deals with deeply held beliefs that affect the most basic ways in which we live. When the discussion around the dinner table turns to religion and voices begin to rise or chairs are pushed back, have some calming quotations ready to throw into the mix so that tempers can cool.

"True religion is real living; living with all one's soul, with all one's goodness and righteousness."

—ALBERT EINSTEIN

"The highest knowledge is to know that we are surrounded by mystery. Neither knowledge nor hope for the future can be the pivot of our life or determine its direction. It is intended to be solely determined by our allowing ourselves to be gripped by the ethical God, who reveals Himself in us, and by our yielding our will to His."

—ALBERT SCHWEITZER

"I have an everyday religion that works for me. Love yourself first, and everything else falls into line."

—LUCILLE BALL

"The true meaning of religion is thus not simply morality, but morality touched by emotion."

—MATTHEW ARNOLD

(1822–1888)

poet and critic, was widely regarded both for his writings and for his pleasant character.

"Being religious means asking passionately the question of the meaning of our existence and being willing to receive answers, even if the answers hurt."

—PAUL TILLICH

"As to the gods, I have no means of knowing either that they exist or do not exist."

—PROTAGORAS

"Religion without humanity is very poor human stuff."

—SOJOURNER TRUTH

"God made so many different kinds of people. Why would he allow only one way to serve him?"

—Martin Buber

"This is my simple religion. There is no need for temples; no need for complicated philosophy. Our own brain, our own heart is our temple; the philosophy is kindness."

—Dalai Lama

Intellectuals, on the whole, have tended to distrust religion, especially during the past century. If you're looking for something snippy to say about religious beliefs—though not necessarily about one particular religion—consider one of the following.

"But who prays for Satan? Who, in eighteen centuries, has had the common humanity to pray for the one sinner that needed it most?"

—Mark Twain

"Scriptures, n. The sacred books of our holy religion, as distinguished from the false and profane writings on which all other faiths are based."

—Ambrose Bierce

"Religion is a monumental chapter in the history of human egotism."

—William James (1842–1910) psychologist and philosopher, was the brother of the novelist Henry James.

"If God has created us in His image, we have more than returned the compliment."

—VOLTAIRE

"Lighthouses are more helpful than churches."

—BENJAMIN FRANKLIN

"Men never do evil so completely and cheerfully as when they do it from religious conviction."

—BLAISE PASCAL

"A deist is someone who has not lived long enough to become an atheist."

—DENIS DIDEROT

"If the concept of God has any validity or any use, it can only be to make us larger, freer, and more loving. If God cannot do this, then it is time we got rid of Him."

—JAMES BALDWIN (1924–1987) was an African American novelist, playwright, political activist, and author of *Go Tell It on the Mountain* and *Another Country*.

"We have just enough religion to make us hate, but not enough to make us love."

—JONATHAN SWIFT

"In religion and politics people's beliefs and convictions are in almost every case gotten at second-hand, and without examination, from authorities who have not themselves examined the questions at issue but have taken them at second-hand from other non-examiners, whose opinions about them were not worth a brass farthing."

—MARK TWAIN

"If God did not exist it would be necessary for us to invent Him."

—VOLTAIRE

"It is wonderful how much time good people spend fighting the devil. If they would only expend the same amount of energy loving their fellow men, the devil would die in his own tracks of ennui."

—HELEN KELLER

"All religions, with their gods, their demi-gods, and their prophets, their messiahs and their saints, were created by the prejudiced fancy of men who had not attained the full development and full possession of their faculties."

—MIKHAIL BAKUNIN

"The religion of one age is the literary entertainment of the next."

—RALPH WALDO EMERSON

Karl Marx's famous comment that religion is the opiate of the people is sometimes interpreted as a slur against Christianity. In point of fact, Marx was actually talking about religion in general. (If you consider that opium makes its users feel better, at least in the short run, Marx's comments could also be interpreted as a positive sentiment about religion.) But plenty of others have criticized the lack of Christian spirit among Christians. If you find yourself in a room full of True Believers, all fulminating about the sinfulness of mainstream Christians, stop them by quoting from the following:

"Christianity might be a good thing if anyone ever tried it."

—George Bernard Shaw

"Religious suffering is at one and the same time the expression of real suffering and a protest against real suffering. Religion is the sigh of the oppressed creature, the heart of a heartless world and the soul of soulless conditions. It is the opiate of the people."

—KARL MARX

"Puritanism: the haunting fear that someone, somewhere, may be happy."

—H. L. MENCKEN

"The secret of a good sermon is to have a good beginning and a good ending, then having the two as close together as possible."

—GEORGE BURNS

"A cult is a religion with no political power."

—TOM WOLFE (1931–)
is an American writer and journalist known for such nonfiction books of reportage as *The Right Stuff* and for novels such as *Bonfire of the Vanities*.

D espite opposition over the years, a good number of people have found positive things to say about both religion and the need for a religion that doesn't tell its followers to hate someone else. You can close out a discussion of religion by giving your listeners something to think about.

"I always like a dog so long as he isn't spelled backward."

—G. K. CHESTERTON

"Although he's regularly asked to do so, God does not take sides in American politics."

—GEORGE MITCHELL

"Did St. Francis really preach to the birds? Whatever for? If he really liked birds he would have done better to preach to the cats."

—REBECCA WEST

"Doubt is part of all religion. All the religious thinkers were doubters."

—Isaac Bashevis Singer

"Religion either makes men wise and virtuous, or it makes them set up false pretenses to both."

—William Hazlitt

"If I were personally to define religion, I would say that it is a bandage that man has invented to protect a soul made bloody by circumstances."

—Theodore Dreiser

(1871–1945)

was an American novelist whose works created searing psychological portraits of the protagonists.

"Aim at heaven and you will get earth thrown in. Aim at earth and you get neither."

—C. S. Lewis

"I would rather live my life as if there is a God and die to find out there isn't, than live my life as if there isn't and die to find out there is."

—Albert Camus

"Religion is essentially the art and the theory of the remaking of man. Man is not a finished creation."

—Edmund Burke

"A man's ethical behavior should be based effectually on sympathy, education, and social ties and needs; no religious basis is necessary. Man would indeed be in a poor way if he had to be restrained by fear of punishment and hope of reward after death."

—Albert Einstein

"I am determined that my children shall be brought up in their father's religion if they can find out what it is."

—Charles Lamb

"It is in our lives and not our words that our religion must be read."

—Thomas Jefferson

"Everyone ought to worship God according to his own inclinations and not to be constrained by force."

—FLAVIUS JOSEPHUS (37–100) was a historian of the early Roman Empire.

"To die for a religion is easier than to live it absolutely."

—JORGE LUIS BORGES

"The point is, could God pass an examination in Theology?"

—MALCOLM MUGGERIDGE

"Religion is what keeps the poor from murdering the rich."

—NAPOLEON BONAPARTE

"When men destroy their old gods they will find new ones to take their place."

—PEARL S. BUCK

Perhaps the poet Kahlil Gibran said it best:

"I love you when you bow in your mosque, kneel in your temple, pray in your church. For you and I are sons of one religion, and it is the spirit."

—KAHLIL GIBRAN

DEATH

"In this world, nothing can be said to be certain but death and taxes." This quote, which is doubtfully attributed to Benjamin Franklin, encapsulates the dilemma of the human condition: no matter how ingenious we are, no matter how much money we make, no matter how good or bad a life we lead, no matter how we ring ourselves round with the miracles of medicine and religion, death comes for us all.

Thus we—as expressed in the following quotes—confront death by defying it, laughing at it, or rationalizing it . . . or sometimes all three at once.

"Death? Why this fuss about death. Use your imagination, try to visualize a world without death! . . . Death is the essential condition of life, not an evil."

—CHARLOTTE PERKINS GILMAN
(1860–1935)

wrote "The Yellow Wallpaper," a classic short story of madness, which later became a key feminist document.

"Down, down, down into the darkness of the grave

Gently they go, the beautiful, the tender, the kind;

Quietly they go, the intelligent, the witty, the brave.

I know. But I do not approve. And I am not resigned."

—EDNA ST. VINCENT MILLAY

"Destroying is a necessary function in life. Everything has its season, and all things eventually lose their effectiveness and die."

—MARGARET J. WHEATLEY

"Do not go gentle into that good night,

Old age should burn and rave at close of day;

Rage, rage against the dying of the light."

—DYLAN THOMAS

"When the gods created man they allotted to him death, but life they retained in their own keeping."

—THE EPIC OF GILGAMESH

"I went to the woods because I wished to live deliberately, to front only the essential facts of life, and see if I could not learn what it had to teach, and not, when I came to die, discover that I have not lived."

—HENRY DAVID THOREAU

"Thus that which is the most awful of evils, death, is nothing to us, since when we exist there is no death, and when there is death we do not exist."

—EPICURUS

"The goal of all life is death."

—SIGMUND FREUD (1856–1939) is regarded as a seminal figure in the development of Modernist culture, although many of his scientific theories have been discredited.

"Oh, for the time when I shall sleep

Without identity."

—EMILY BRONTË

"For death is no more than a turning of us over from time to eternity."

—WILLIAM PENN

"I think we should look forward to death more than we do. Of course everybody hates to go to bed or miss anything but dying is really the only chance we'll get to rest."

—FLORENCE KENNEDY

"Life does not cease to be funny when people die any more than it ceases to be serious when people laugh."

—GEORGE BERNARD SHAW

"There is no cure for birth and death save to enjoy the interval."

—GEORGE SANTAYANA

"Pale Death with impartial tread beats at the poor man's cottage door and at the palaces of kings."

—HORACE (65 BCE–8 BCE) was a Roman lyric poet. His odes are considered one of the literary high points of Rome's Augustan age.

"Death can sneak up on you like a silent kitten, surprising you with its touch and you have a right to act surprised. Other times death stomps in the front door, unwanted and unannounced, and makes its noisy way to your seat on the sofa."

—HUGH ELLIOTT

The worst thing about death, paradoxically, is knowing that we're going to die. A being without awareness beyond the immediate moment of its existence—a frog, say, or a garden slug or Kim Kardashian—is probably pretty content without the knowledge of death to blight its existence. We, on the other hand, have to come to terms with it.

"The fear of death follows from the fear of life. A man who lives fully is prepared to die at any time."

—MARK TWAIN

"The idea of death, the fear of it, haunts the human animal like nothing else; it is a mainspring of human activity—designed largely to avoid the fatality of death, to overcome it by denying in some way that it is the final destiny of man."

—ERNEST BECKER

"Because I could not stop for Death,

He kindly stopped for me.

The Carriage held but just ourselves

And Immortality."

—EMILY DICKINSON

"Life is better than death, I believe, if only because it is less boring and because it has fresh peaches in it."

—ALICE WALKER

"Think not disdainfully of death, but look on it with favor; for even death is one of the things Nature wills."

—MARCUS AURELIUS (121–180) sometimes called the Philosopher Emperor, wrote *Meditations*, reflecting on human duty and accomplishment.

"Dying is a very dull, dreary affair. And my advice to you is to have nothing whatever to do with it."

—W. SOMERSET MAUGHAM

"Death, the sable smoke where vanishes the flame."

—LORD BYRON

P robably the best approach to death is to enjoy living, because this is about the only chance we're going to get at it. Thus, to someone who's sunk in morbidity, you can always fish out a piece of wisdom the brighten their day and jerk them out of their dark mood.

"Do not fear death so much, but rather the inadequate life."

—BERTOLT BRECHT

"For certain is death for the born

And certain is birth for the dead;

Therefore over the inevitable

Thou shouldst not grieve."

—BHAGAVAD GITA

"I'm not afraid of death. It's the stake one puts up in order to play the game of life."

—JEAN GIRAUDOUX

"Death is a delightful hiding place for weary men."

—HERODOTUS

"There are so many little dyings, it doesn't matter which of them is death."

—KENNETH PATCHEN
(1911–1972)
a poet and novelist, wrote works that reflected Modernist trends on the American scene

"Death may be the greatest of all human blessings."

—SOCRATES

"From my rotting body, flowers shall grow, and I am in them and that is eternity."

—EDVARD MUNCH

"Death is for many of us the gate of hell; but we are inside on the way out, not outside on the way in."

—GEORGE BERNARD SHAW

"Death is a debt we all must pay."

—EURIPIDES

Despite Euripides' comforting words, there's no denying that death can cast a damper on the liveliest of parties. If the conversation around you turns to death and everyone is gloomy and hanging on the edge of their cocktails, silently planning their next visit to an estate planner, cheer things up by saying something such as:

"Religion is the human response to being alive and having to die."

—F. FORRESTER CHURCH

"If my doctor told me I had only six minutes to live, I wouldn't brood. I'd type a little faster."

—ISAAC ASIMOV

"There are worse things in life than death. Have you ever spent an evening with an insurance salesman?"

—WOODY ALLEN

"A man's dying is more the survivors' affair than his own."

—THOMAS MANN

"Let children walk with Nature, let them see the beautiful blendings and communions of death and life, their joyous inseparable unity, as taught in woods and meadows, plains and mountains and streams of our blessed star, and they will learn that death is stingless indeed and as beautiful as life."

—JOHN MUIR (1838–1914) naturalist and cocreator of the Sierra Club, is the founding figure of the American environmental movement.

"I am ready to meet my Maker. Whether my Maker is prepared for the ordeal of meeting me is another matter."

—WINSTON CHURCHILL

"Of all the wonders that I yet have heard,

It seems to me most strange that men should fear;

Seeing that death, a necessary end,

Will come when it will come."

—WILLIAM SHAKESPEARE

"Biography lends to death a new terror."

—OSCAR WILDE

"For what is it to die but to stand in the sun and melt into the wind? And when the Earth has claimed our limbs, then we shall truly dance."

—KAHLIL GIBRAN

"I shall not die of a cold. I shall die of having lived."

—WILLA CATHER (1873–1947)
an American author whose novels depict the harsh life on the frontier., was awarded the Pulitzer Prize for *One of Ours*.

"Our brains are seventy-year clocks. The Angel of Life winds them up once for all, then closes the case and gives the key into the hand of the Angel of Resurrection."

—OLIVER WENDELL HOLMES

"Tomorrow and tomorrow and tomorrow,

Creeps in this petty pace from day to day

Unto the last syllable of recorded time.

And all our yesterdays have lighted fools the way to dusty death."

—WILLIAM SHAKESPEARE

"Fear not death, for the sooner we die the longer we shall be immortal."

—BENJAMIN FRANKLIN

IMMORTALITY

And what comes after death? Is there something more? Intellectuals (and a lot of other people) have been batting this question around for the past two or three thousand years without arriving at any definitive answer. That hasn't, of course, stopped anyone from having strong opinions on the subject. Remind your listeners that death comes for each of us by dropping one of the following pearls of wisdom.

"Immortality is not a gift.

Immortality is an achievement.

And only those who strive mightily

Shall achieve it."

—EDGAR LEE MASTERS

"Surely God would not have created such a being as man, with an ability to grasp the infinite, to exist only for a day! No, no, man was made for immortality."

—ABRAHAM LINCOLN

"That man has reached immortality who is disturbed by nothing material."

—SWAMI VIVEKANANDA

"The day which we fear as our last is but the birthday of eternity."

—SENECA

"All men's souls are immortal, but the souls of the righteous are immortal and divine."

—SOCRATES

"I intend to live forever. So far, so good."

—STEVEN WRIGHT

Immortality, many agree, is achieved by what you leave behind: books, good works, children, and so forth. Some people may find it comforting to confront the hereafter if you quote them something like this.

"I don't want to achieve immortality through my work. I want to achieve it through not dying."

—WOODY ALLEN

"For Love is immortality."

—EMILY DICKINSON

(1830–1886)

remained in Amherst, Massachusetts, for most of her life, writing poetry and shunning human contact.

"Children are the only form of immortality that we can be sure of."

—PETER USTINOV

"Poets have said that the reason to have children is to give yourself immortality. Immortality? Now that I have five children, my only hope is that they are all out of the house before I die."

—BILL COSBY

"I don't believe in personal immortality; the only way I expect to have some version of such a thing is through my books."

—ISAAC ASIMOV

"I've put in so many enigmas and puzzles [in my books] that it will keep the professors busy for centuries arguing over what I meant, and that's the only way of insuring one's immortality."

—JAMES JOYCE

"If I have any beliefs about immortality, it is that certain dogs I have known will go to heaven, and very, very few persons."

—JAMES THURBER

"If all else fails, immortality can always be assured by spectacular error."

—JOHN KENNETH GALBRAITH

"If your contribution has been vital there will always be somebody to pick up where you left off, and that will be your claim to immortality."

—WALTER GROPIUS

"What a man does for others, not what they do for him, gives him immortality."

—Daniel Webster

(1782–1852)

was a politician and leader of the Whig Party before its destruction in the years leading up to the Civil War.

"He ne'er is crowned with immortality

Who fears to follow where airy voices lead."

—John Keats

"When a noble life has prepared old age, it is not decline that it reveals but the first days of immortality."

—Muriel Spark

"I shall tell you a great secret, my friend. Do not wait for the last judgment. It takes place every day."

—Albert Camus

"The key to immortality is first living a life worth remembering."

—Brandon Lee

S ome authorities are not even sure that immortality is really all that it's cracked up to be. You can show proper cynicism about the prospect of living eternally by quoting along these lines:

"The average man, who does not know what to do with his life, wants another one which will last forever."

—Anatole France (1844–1924)

French novelist and poet, was a champion of political and artistic liberty.

"Do not try to live for ever. You will not succeed."

—George Bernard Shaw

"Millions long for immortality who don't know what to do with themselves on a rainy Sunday afternoon."

—Susan Ertz

"Immortality—a fate worse than death."

—Edgar A. Shoaff

"A healthy nature needs no God or immortality."

—Friedrich von Schiller

"To desire immortality is to desire the eternal perpetuation of a great mistake."

—ARTHUR SCHOPENHAUER

If we're sure of anything, it's that the best way to ensure immortality is not to recognize our own death. After all, what do dead people know? If you want to scoff in the face of death and show that you're not intimidated by the Grim Reaper, after your fourth or fifth cocktail hurl one of these quotes into the conversation, laughing carelessly as you say it.

"To be immortal is commonplace; except for man, all creatures are immortal, for they are ignorant of death."
—JORGE LUIS BORGES

"A man has only one way of being immortal on earth; he has to forget he is a mortal."
—JEAN GIRAUDOUX (1882–1944)
French novelist and playwright, wrote primarily active between World War I and World War II.

"Immortality is the condition of a dead man who doesn't believe he is dead."
—H. L. MENCKEN

Some great thinkers have suggested that the afterlife is just a continuation of our present life. Thus we can go on forever, just as we are now. And to some, that may be a comforting thought. Encourage your listeners that there may be hope for immortality by citing something like these thoughts.

"One of the strange things about living in the world is that it is only now and then one is quite sure one is going to live forever and ever and ever. One knows it sometimes when one gets up at the tender solemn dawn-time and goes out and stands alone and throws one's head far back and looks up and up and watches the pale sky slowly changing and flushing and marvelous unknown things happening until the East almost makes one cry out and one's heart stands still at the strange unchanging majesty of the rising of the sun—which has been happening every morning for thousands and thousands and thousands of years. One knows it then for a moment or so . . . ."

—FRANCES BURNETT

"A graceful and honorable old age is the childhood of immortality."

—PINDAR

"Life is the childhood of our immortality."

—JOHANN WOLFGANG VON GOETHE

"The union of the Word and the Mind produces that mystery which is called Life . . . . Learn deeply of the Mind and its mystery, for therein lies the secret of immortality."

—JOSEPH ADDISON

"People always live forever when there is an annuity to be paid them."

—JANE AUSTEN

"I am like a falling star who has finally found her place next to another in a lovely constellation, where we will sparkle in the heavens forever."

—AMY TAN

Happiness

"Happiness," said Aristotle, "is the meaning and the purpose of life, the whole aim and the end of human existence."

By and large, most people would agree with this statement. The problem comes in trying to figure out what we each mean by "happiness." Is it big or small, selfish or altruistic, fleeting or permanent? There are as many opinions on the subject as there've been people to have them. You can show your listeners that you've meditated long and vigorously on the subject by murmuring a few words from one of the great thinkers here cited.

"Happiness is not being pained in body or troubled in mind."
—THOMAS JEFFERSON

"Happiness belongs to the self-sufficient."
—ARISTOTLE

"That man is richest whose pleasures are cheapest."
—HENRY DAVID THOREAU

"The truest greatness lies in being kind, the truest wisdom in a happy mind."
—ELLA WHEELER WILCOX
(1850–1919)
American poet.

"There is only one happiness in life, to love and be loved."
—GEORGE SAND

"Happiness is having a large, loving, caring, close-knit family in another city."
—GEORGE BURNS

"Happiness? That's nothing more than health and a poor memory."
—ALBERT SCHWEITZER

"Happiness is not a goal; it is a by-product."
—ELEANOR ROOSEVELT

"Happiness is a butterfly which, when pursued, is always just beyond your grasp but which, if you will sit down quietly, may alight upon you."
—NATHANIEL HAWTHORNE

"Happiness is your dentist telling you it won't hurt and then having him catch his hand in the drill."

—Johnny Carson

So how can you get happiness? Intellectuals agree it doesn't come from money or material possessions—which should be comforting to those who lack either—but they're divided on what creates happiness. They're not even united on whether one should strive to be happy. Since conversations often wind their way to this dilemma, have a quotation handy on the subject to round out the discussion and bring it to a more or less successful conclusion.

"If you want to live a happy life, tie it to a goal, not to people or things."

—ALBERT EINSTEIN

"There is only one way to happiness, and that is to cease worrying about things which are beyond the power of our will."

—EPICTETUS

"The greatest happiness you can have is knowing that you do not necessarily require happiness."

—WILLIAM SAROYAN
(1908–1981)
novelist and playwright, wrote stories about the immigrant experience, including the charming *My Name is Aram*.

"Eden is that old-fashioned house we dwell in every day

Without suspecting our abode until we drive away."

—EMILY DICKINSON

"It is not easy to find happiness in ourselves, and it is not possible to find it elsewhere."

—AGNES REPPLIER

"The secret of happiness is freedom. The secret of freedom is courage."

—THUCYDIDES

"If one advances confidently in the direction of one's dreams, and endeavors to live the life which one has imagined, one will meet with a success unexpected in common hours."

—HENRY DAVID THOREAU

"Sanity and happiness are an impossible combination."

—MARK TWAIN

"Life is made up of small pleasures. Happiness is made up of those tiny successes. The big ones come too infrequently. And if you don't collect all these tiny successes, the big ones don't really mean anything."

—NORMAN LEAR (1922–)
television producer, was responsible for such beloved classics as *All in the Family, The Jeffersons, Good Times,* and *Sanford and Son.*

"The Constitution only guarantees the American people the right to pursue happiness. You have to catch it yourself."

—BENJAMIN FRANKLIN

"The pursuit of happiness is a most ridiculous phrase: if you pursue happiness you'll never find it."

—C. P. SNOW

"The best way to cheer yourself up is to try to cheer somebody else up."

—MARK TWAIN

"If only we'd stop trying to be happy we could have a pretty good time."

—EDITH WHARTON

"To be happy, we must not be too concerned with others."

—ALBERT CAMUS (1913–1960)
received the Nobel Prize for literature in
1957. His novels include *The Stranger* and
The Plague.

"Happiness is when what you think, what you say, and what you do are in harmony."

—MOHANDAS GANDHI

"Happiness: We rarely feel it.

I would buy it, beg it, steal it,

Pay in coins of dripping blood

For this one transcendent good."

—AMY LOWELL

"If you want to be happy, be."

—LEO TOLSTOY

"Now and then it's good to pause in our pursuit of happiness and just be happy."

—GUILLAUME APOLLINAIRE

"Nothing can bring you to happiness but yourself."

—RALPH WALDO EMERSON

"My advice to you is not to inquire why or whither, but just enjoy your ice cream while it's on your plate."

—THORNTON WILDER

O ther people can contribute to our happiness—either by their presence or absence. Show your appreciation by quoting the likes of Proust, Frost, and Buddha.

"Let us be grateful to people who make us happy, they are the charming gardeners who make our souls blossom."

—MARCEL PROUST (1871–1922) was the author of *Remembrance of Things Past*, a rambling novel in seven books, more referred to than read.

"Happiness makes up in height for what it lacks in length."

—ROBERT FROST

"Thousands of candles can be lighted from a single candle, and the life of the candle will not be shortened. Happiness never decreases by being shared."

—BUDDHA

"Some cause happiness wherever they go; others whenever they go."

—OSCAR WILDE

The art of being happy, you may conclude, lies in understanding what makes you happy and then doing it. That seems simpler in theory than it is in practice, but you may be able to derive some satisfaction in contemplating these thoughts about happiness.

"The moments of happiness we enjoy take us by surprise. It is not that we seize them but that they seize us."

—Ashley Montagu

"A happy person is not a person in a certain set of circumstances but rather a person with a certain set of attitudes."

—Hugh Downs

"When one door of happiness closes, another opens; but often we look so long at the closed door that we do not see the one which has been opened for us."

—Helen Keller

"Man is fond of counting his troubles, but he does not count his joys. If he counted them up as he ought to, he would see that every lot has enough happiness provided for it."

—Fyodor Dostoevsky
(1821–1881)
a Russian novelist, is considered second to only Leo Tolstoy as Russia's greatest writer.

"Can anything be so elegant as to have few wants, and to serve them one's self?"

—Ralph Waldo Emerson

"Pleasure is spread through the earth

In stray gifts to be claimed by whoever shall find."

—William Wordsworth

"Just as a cautious businessman avoids investing all his capital in one concern, so wisdom would probably admonish us also not to anticipate all our happiness from one quarter alone."

—Sigmund Freud

"There are some days when I think I'm going to die from an overdose of satisfaction."

—Salvador Dali

"We are no longer happy so soon as we wish to be happier."

—Walter Savage Landor

"One should be either sad or joyful. Contentment is a warm sty for eaters and sleepers."

—Eugene O'Neill

"Happiness always looks small while you hold it in your hands, but let it go, and you learn at once how big and precious it is."

—Maxim Gorky (1868–1936) was a Russian author whose personal and literary reputation was compromised by his association with Stalin's regime

"The essence of philosophy is that a man should so live that his happiness shall depend as little as possible on external things."

—Epictetus

"Happiness is a matter of one's most ordinary and everyday mode of consciousness being busy and lively and unconcerned with self."

—Iris Murdoch

"What a wonderful life I've had! I only wish I'd realized it sooner."

—Colette

AFTERWORD

" A witty saying," Voltaire remarked sourly, "proves nothing." And he may be right. Wit is an inadequate substitute for wisdom—although these days both seem to be in short supply. However, dear reader, as you have browsed through this collection I hope you have realized that there is beauty in a well-turned phrase and wisdom in a happy epigram.

It may be that you yourself will, in time, become one of the notable quotables included herewith (it used to be a sign of intellectual eminence to be listed in *Bartlett's Quotations*. Alas, now the Internet has made that less of a distinction, since there are so many places where one's bon mots can appear).

As to using quotations to sound like an intellectual, remember that quoting is an art. Benjamin Disraeli—politician, novelist, and social butterfly—remarked aptly, "The art of quotation requires more delicacy in the practice than those conceive who can see nothing more in a quotation than an extract." To quote like an intellectual requires more than blundering into a conversation, bristling with funny sayings from Oscar Wilde or pungent comments made by Plutarch. There is an exquisite daintiness in precisely choosing the right moment to casually remark, "As Alan Bennett says, 'Life is like a tin of sardines; we're all of us looking for the key.'"

Here's hoping that within this distilled collection of the wisdom of the ages you've found the key—to sounding smart.

INDEX

THE QUOTABLE INTELLECTUAL

About the Author

Peter Archer is an editor with Adams Media. At various points in his life he has been a college teacher, a factory worker, a political activist, a convenience store clerk, and once had a job cleaning the cages of 100,000 laboratory mice. He is the author of six novels and a dozen short stories. Having graduated from the University of St. Andrews with an M.Litt. in Medieval History, he subscribes to the *New Yorker*, the *New York Review of Books*, and the *Economist*. He keeps a copy of *Dante's Divine Comedy* on his nightstand and reads the *New York Times* every morning. Which makes him as much of a pseudointellectual as he needed to be to write this book.